THE LIFE
AND
SCIENTIFIC AND MEDICAL CAREER
OF
BENJAMIN WATERHOUSE

This is a volume in the Arno Press collection

THREE CENTURIES
OF
SCIENCE IN AMERICA

Advisory Editor
I. Bernard Cohen

Editorial Board
Anderson Hunter Dupree
Donald H. Fleming
Brooke Hindle

See last pages of this volume for a complete list of titles

THE LIFE
AND
SCIENTIFIC AND MEDICAL CAREER
OF
BENJAMIN WATERHOUSE:

With Some Account of the Introduction
of Vaccination in America

I. Bernard Cohen, editor

Vol. II

ARNO PRESS

A New York Times Company
New York • 1980

Publisher's Note: This book has been reproduced from the best available copy.

Editorial Supervision: Steve Bedney

Reprint Edition 1980 by Arno Press Inc.

Copyright © 1980 by Arno Press Inc.

THREE CENTURIES OF SCIENCE IN AMERICA
ISBN for complete set: 0-405-12525-9
See last pages of this volume for titles
Manufactured in the United States of America

Library of Congress Cataloging in Publication Data

Main entry under title:

The Life and scientific and medical career of
   Benjamin Waterhouse.

   (Three centuries of science in America)
   1. Waterhouse, Benjamin, 1754-1846--Addresses,
essays, lectures. 2. Physicians--Massachusetts--
Biography--Addresses, essays, lectures.
3. Smallpox--United States--Preventive inoculation--
History--19th century--Addresses, essays, lectures.
4. Smallpox--Preventive inoculation--Addresses, essays,
lectures. I. Cohen, I. Bernard, 1914-   II. Series.
R154.W29L5   610'.92'4 [B]   79-8004
ISBN 0-405-12591-7

ACKNOWLEDGEMENTS

"An Episode in the History of Smallpox Vaccination in New Hampshire," by Morris C. Leikind, has been reprinted from the *Bulletin of the History of Medicine*, vol. 7, 1939, pp. 671-686. "Something Curious in the Medical Line," by Reginald Fitz, has been reprinted from the *Bulletin*, vol. 11, 1942, pp. 239-264. These articles have been reprinted by permission of the Johns Hopkins University Press.

"A Journal of a Young Man of Massachusetts...," by Henry R. Viets, has been reprinted from the *Yale Journal of Biology and Medicine*, vol. 12, 1940, by permission of the managing editor.

"Edward Jenner and Harvard University," by I. Bernard Cohen, has been reprinted from the *Harvard Library Bulletin*, vol. 3, Autumn, 1949, by permission of the editor.

"Edward Jenner, Benjamin Waterhouse, and the Introduction of Vaccination into the United States," by E. Ashworth Underwood, has been reprinted from *Nature*, vol. 163, 1949, by permission of Macmillan Journals Ltd.

"Benjamin Waterhouse and the Introduction of Vaccination," by John B. Blake, has been reprinted by permission of the University of Pennsylvania Press.

"The First Natural History Lectures at Brown University, 1786, by Benjamin Waterhouse," by J. Walter Wilson, has been reprinted from *Annals of Medical History*, Third Series, vol. 4, 1942, by permission of the Medical Department of Harper & Row, Publishers.

"Benjamin Waterhouse, Harvard's First Professor of Physic," by John B. Blake, has been reprinted from the *Journal of Medical Education*, vol. 33, 1958, by permission of the editor.

"Oratio Inauguralis," by George Gifford, has been reprinted from the Harvard Medical Alumni Bulletin, vol. 44, no. 5, May/June, 1970, by permission of the managing editor.

CONTENTS

Volume II

Wilson, J. Walter
The First Natural History Lectures at Brown University, 1786, by Dr. Benjamin Waterhouse (Reprinted from *Annals of Medical History,* vol. 4), New York, 1942

Cohen, I. Bernard
Edward Jenner and Harvard University (Reprinted from *Harvard Library Bulletin,* vol. 3), 1949

Underwood, E. Ashworth
Edward Jenner, Benjamin Waterhouse, and the Introduction of Vaccination into the United States (Reprinted from *Nature,* vol. 163, no. 4152), London, May 28, 1949

Blake, John B.
Benjamin Waterhouse and the Introduction of Vaccination: A Reappraisal. Philadelphia, 1957

Blake, John B.
Benjamin Waterhouse, Harvard's First Professor of Physic (Reprinted from *Journal of Medical Education,* vol. 33), Washington, D.C., 1958

Gifford, George
Oratio Inauguralis (Reprinted from *Harvard Medical Alumni Bulletin,* vol. 44, no. 5), Boston, May/June, 1970

THE HARVARD MEDICAL SCHOOL

Thomas F. Harrington

REV. JOSEPH WILLARD. ST.D.
Pres^t of Harvard College.
from Dec 1781 to Sep 1804.
Born Dec.1738. Died Sep.1804.

THE

Harvard Medical School

A HISTORY, NARRATIVE AND DOCUMENTARY

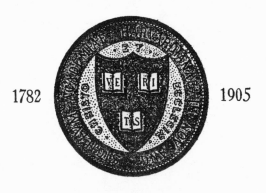

1782 1905

BY

THOMAS FRANCIS HARRINGTON, M. D.

Class of 1888

EDITED BY

JAMES GREGORY MUMFORD, M. D.

Class of 1888

VOLUME I

ILLUSTRATED

NEW YORK : : CHICAGO

LEWIS PUBLISHING COMPANY

1905

THE FOUNDING

The most important event, from an historical point of view at least (in the life of Waterhouse), was his connection with the introduction of vaccination into this country. In 1799 he received from Lettsom a copy of Jenner's " Inquiry Into Cause and Effect of Variolar Vaccine, or Cow Pox," published in June the year previous .

On March 12th, 1799, Waterhouse published in the " Columbian Sentinel " a treatise on vaccination, entitled " Something Curious in the Medical Line. A short account of the *New Inoculation.*" * This essay was received variously,— some few accepted and applauded, some doubted and kept quiet; the majority, especially the physicians, criticised and ridiculed. Those last apparently were justified because Waterhouse, as well as Woodville in London, had committed the error of vaccinating first, and in from three to five days inoculating the same patient with variolus matter, thus producing a cow pox infection and a small-pox inoculation at the same time. Waterhouse received some vaccine virus from Haggarth, of Bath, England, in June, 1800. With this (on July 8th, 1800) he vaccinated his five year old son. The case

---

* See " Johns Hopkins Bulletin," Jan., 1904, page 24, in reference to the claims of John Crawford, of Baltimore.

showed a typical reaction, the scar being described thus, " A piece of true skin was fairly taken out of the arm by the *virus* the part appearing as if eaten out by a caustic, *a never failing sign of thorough affection of the system in the inoculated small-pox.*" That was the first case of vaccination in this country.

Waterhouse, remembering no doubt the experience of Boylston under similar circumstances, wrote to Aspinwall, then in charge of the Small-Pox Hospital at Brookline: " I have collected everything that has been printed, and all the information I could procure from my correspondents, respecting this distemper (cow-pox), and have been so thoroughly convinced of its importance to humanity that I have procured some of the vaccine matter, and therewith inoculated seven of my family. The inoculation has proceeded in six of them exactly as described by Woodville and Jenner,* but my desire is to confirm the doctrine by having some of them inoculated by you. * * * I can obtain variolus matter and inoculate them privately, but I wish to do it in the most open and public way possible. As *I have imported a new distemper,* I conceive that the public has a right to know exactly every step I take in it. I write this, therefore, to enquire whether you will, on philanthropic principles, try the experiment of inoculating some of my children who have already undergone the cow-pox. If you accede to my proposal, I shall consider it as an experiment in which we have co-operated for the good of our fellow citizens, and relate it as such in the pamphlet I mean to publish on the subject."

In this letter there is nothing to support the satirical thrusts

---

* There was however no eruption on the children such as Woodville had observed in his cases. A single typical vaccine vesicle was all that was seen.

by Holmes, or the allegations of the newspaper articles directed against Waterhouse, in which he is styled an *old drone* enjoying the sweets of the beehive (the new medical school) without assisting in the labor, or even paying for the privilege of humming and buzzing in it. Whatever recompense came to Waterhouse for his labors at the Medical School and from other sources must have been small, for in 1810 he petitioned the legislature to reimburse him. This request was refused. In 1812, when he resigned from the School, he said that " during the last fifteen years of service he did not receive one farthing as salary, and that in no year did it amount to $400.00." From the years 1813 to 1820 he was supported by appointments received through Jefferson and President Madison, both of whom he had greatly interested in the vaccination question. No doubt some of this recognition was honestly earned by Waterhouse from his political writings, in which work he was active and in which he excelled to a marked degree. He was held in honor by scientific societies both at home and abroad, and it is said that the London Medical Society unanimously voted him the title " The Jenner of America." He died on October 2, 1846, at the age of ninety-two years.

Edward Jenner received the LL. D. from Harvard University in 1803. His death occurred on January 26th, 1823.

It is unnecessary to recite here the results of Jenner's great gift to humanity. Its application was immediately undertaken by leaders of medical thought, and it is our privilege to be able to record with propriety in these pages the conspicuous and honorable distinction our Alma Mater occupies in this great blessing. As early as March 16th, 1799, Benjamin Waterhouse published in the " Columbian Centinel," Boston, the first account given in this country of Jenner's recent discovery. It is called

" SOMETHING CURIOUS IN THE MEDICAL LINE.

" Every body has heard of those distempers accompanied with pocks or pustules, *called* the *Small pox*, the *chicken pox* or if you like the term better, the *cow-small pox:* or to express it in technical language, the *variola vaccinae.* There is, however, such a disease which has been noticed here and there in several parts of *England,* more particularly in *Gloucestershire,* for fifty or sixty years past, but has never been an object of medical inquiry until very lately. As we are too often misled by`. names,* it is not amiss to premise that there is nothing in the origen, nature or symptoms of this disorder anyhow resembling that incident to the human race, denominated *lues.*

" This *Variola vaccinae* or *cow pox,* is very readily communicated to those who milk cows infected with it. This malady appears first on the teats of the cow in the form of irregular pustules or pock. They are commonly of a palish blue, somewhat approaching to livid, and surrounded by an erysipelatious inflammation, resembling the St. Anthony's fire. These pustules, unless timely remedied, degenerate into those ragged ulcers known by the surgeons under the name of phagedenic. The cows soon become sick, and the secretion of milk lessened, but I never heard of one dying of it. Those who milk cows thus affected, seldom or never fail catching the distemper, *if there be cracks, wounds or abrasions in the hands.* When infected, there appear on different parts of the hands and wrists, inflamed spots, having the appearance of blisters, produced by

burns. These run quickly on to suppuration. These superficial suppurations have a circular form with their edges more elevated than their
centres, very much resembling a certain stage of small pox. These depressed pustules or pocks, are of a color approaching to blue. Absorption now takes place, and a soreness and sometimes a tumor appear in
the arm-pits. Then the arterial system becomes affected, the pulse is
quickened, and shivering with a general lassitude and pains in the back
and limbs supervene, and these symptoms are not unfrequently accompanied with vomiting. There is, too, a pain in the head and in some
people a dilirium. These symptoms varying in their degrees and violence,
generally continue from one day to three or four, leaving ulcerated sores
about the hands resembling those on the cow's teats, from whence they
spring. The lips, nostrils and eyelids are sometimes affected with
force, but these evidently arise from their being rubbed or scratched with
the patient's infected fingers. This is the common course of the disease
with the human species. *No person was ever known to die of this distemper.* But what makes this newly-discovered disease so very curious,
and so extremely important, is that every person thus affected, is Ever
After Secured From The Ordinary Small Pox, *let him be ever so much
exposed to the effluvium of it, or let ever so much ripe matter be inserted
into the skin by inoculation.* In other words,—a person who has undergone the local disease and *specific fever* occasioned by the Cow pox infection, is *thereby rendered ever after unsusceptable of the small pox.*
It is worthy remark that the infection of the Cow pox can be conveyed
to the human species by the ordinary mode of inoculation. And it is
observed, that there is no difference in the effects of the matter taken
from the cow, or from the matter generated successively in the second,
third, fourth or fifth human creature.

" Such are the outlines of a mild disease, the knowledge of which may
lead to consequences of the utmost importance to the whole human race,
no less indeed than that of superceding if not extinguishing that terrible
scourge, the Small Pox.

" Dr. Edward Jenner is the physician in *England* who has collected and
arranged a series of facts and experiments respecting the disease called
there the cow pox——His short work is commented on by Dr. George
Pearson, physician to St. George hospital, *London.*

" This imperfect sketch is thrown into the news-paper at this time
with a view of exciting the attention of our dairy farmers to such a distemper among their cows. It may also be gratifying to some of the
faculty of medicine who, it is presumed, are not yet generally informed of
an epizootic disease, capable of being communicated from the brute to
the human kind, and which, when communicated, is *a certain security
against the small pox.* The public anxiety has been roused of late to
search after the cause of a destructive *fever.* Their attention has been
directed merely to *effuvia, vapoures* or *gasses,* while they may here see a

disease, the *nearest a-kin* to the small pox of any yet known, which is never communicated by effluvia or medium of the air. It is highly probable that some of the most distressing distempers which affect mankind have an *animal* origin, and time may prove that the small pox, whooping cough, and one kind of quinsy, have like the hyrophobia, a similar source.

"B. W."

"Cambridge, March 12, 1799."

The first vaccination in America was performed in Boston, on July 8th, 1800, by Waterhouse. He vaccinated seven members of his household and six of these proved successful cases. Shortly afterwards three of the children were sent to the smallpox hospital, and one was inoculated with smallpox. None of them contracted the disease. The details of this heroic act have been fully given in previous pages of this book.

In September, 1800, James Jackson (H. U. 1796) returned to Boston after completing his medical course in Europe, and immediately became identified with the vaccination movement which he had studied under Woodville in London. The vaccine matter which Jackson brought with him from London had lost its effectiveness, a misfortune for Jackson, which was met by Manning of Ipswich, who supplied him with some fresh virus. Young Jackson was keenly alive to the advantages likely to result from prominence in a public movement destined to become popular. So, writing to his friend and companion, John C. Warren, then in London, for a fresh supply of vaccine matter, he set about taking advantage of the opportunities offered, and soon became one of the physicians most prominently identified with the introduction of vaccination. Thus it was that, in one of the greatest blessings to mankind, two physicians intimately associated with the history of the Harvard Medical School stand out prominently.

The honor and renown which the older of these two men brought to our Alma Mater by the introduction and advocacy of this new discovery was further increased and extended by the younger in his long, useful and notable career.

The vaccination " craze " spread rapidly in Massachusetts. as well as throughout Virginia, Pennsylvania and New York. Special hospitals were established for vaccinating purposes. The town of Milton, Massachusetts, offered the benefits of vaccination to its people; the first town in the country to act as a corporate body in the matter. Soon after the General Court* authorized the respective towns in the State to appoint committees to superintend and to raise money to defray the expenses of vaccination.

The new discovery had its enemies—many and venomous. The system was opposed by many physicians, and was denounced from many pulpits with great bitterness, as an attempt to bestialize the race. An epidemic of smallpox at Marblehead about this time caused much excitement. A variolus patient being mistaken for a vaccine patient was the cause of the outbreak. A committee from the Massachusetts Medical Society was appointed to visit that place and investigate the facts. On account of a misunderstanding between Waterhouse, who was one of the committee, and the Society, the controversy was carried into the public press. There were no medical journals at that date. In June, 1801, Jackson endeavored to have the Board of Health of Boston undertake a series of experiments to prove the efficacy of cowpox as a preventive against smallpox, but public opinion was not yet

---

* See Act, March 10th, 1810.

sufficiently crystallized to endorse any measure of that nature. In the following year, however, Waterhouse repeated the application made by Jackson, and accompanied it with a history of the disease, as well as the evidence of its efficacy which had been accumulated by medical societies in Massachusetts, New York and elsewhere. This memorial is well worth the reading:

"The Memorial of Benjamin Waterhouse, M. D. Professor of the Theory and Practice of Physic in the University of Cambridge,
"To The Board of Health in Boston.
"Gentlemen,
"No one can doubt the propriety of my addressing you on the subject of *the new inoculation,* who considers, that you are placed by law, as so many guardians of our lives, health, and safety. The authority, which has made it your duty to put in force the laws and rules, best calculated against the introduction of infection from abroad; and to obviate the causes of contagion at home, has made it my duty to investigate and teach the principles, on which such laws are founded. Under this idea, it is probable, your board, or the individuals of it, applied for my opinion, and made use of it, when the quarantine law was before the Legislature, From recollection of that circumstance, I am induced, at this time, to address you, not as a private practitioner, but as *the public teacher of the practice of physic in this Commonwealth;* and am willing to annex to the assertions in this memorial the implied responsibility of my official station; for it has been, agreeably to an early declaration,* under a serious impression of the duty imposed on me by the medical institution of this University, that I have laboured incessantly, for four years past, in the investigation and diffusion of the most important medical discovery, ever made since the world began; it being no less than that of exterminating the most loathsome and widely wasting pestilance, that Providence ever permitted to afflict the human race.
"Being made acquainted, at a very early period, with this extraordinary discovery, I felt it my duty, as a teacher of medicine, to collect all the facts for the information of those who attended my public lectures. Having imported the disease itself into America, I feel, if possible a still stronger obligation to acquaint the public with every step I took in diffusing it, even before it passed the limits of my own family. I therefore

---

* See page 18 of a pamphlet entitled "A prospect of exterminating the Small-pox."

published all my proceedings from time to time in the news-paper, in a style so simple as to require no other preparation, than common sense and an unprejudiced mind. But as they have never yet been collected together in one book, it may be of some use, on this particular occasion, to throw together the leading particulars, and lay them in order before the public, through the respectable medium of the *Boston Board of Health.* For really, gentlemen, (seeing vaccination is marching triumphantly over the globe, and PRESIDENTS, EMPERORS, KINGS, CONSULS, and PARLIAMENTS,* are giving it public countenance and support) it is time for BOSTON, distinguished as '*the headquarters of good principles,*' to consider whether they will choose to be the last in adopting a practice, which has been followed by France, Italy, Spain, Germany, Prussia, and Constantinople, and even received with warmth in the cold regions of Russia and Norway?

"It has been to me a humiliating reflection that the very plans I have offered for a *Vaccine Institution* in Boston, for inoculating the poor *gratis,* and which have been received with a chilling apathy, and a repellant suspicion, have, on being transmitted to some of the middle and southern states, been adopted with alacrity. From these places I am continually receiving letters, replete with the most grateful expressions for transmitting them the matter, and directions for carrying on this new inoculation.

"I pass from these prefatory remarks to

"A Concise History of the Kine-Pock Inoculation.

"THERE is a mild distemper, which has been noticed here and there among the herds of kine, in several parts of England, time immemorial. This disorder appears first on the teats and udder of the cows, in the form of irregular pustules, or pocks, of a palish blue colour; and those who milk them, when thus affected, seldom fail of catching the disease.

"This distemper has existed so long in Ireland, as to be known there by a *Celtic* name, viz. '*Shinnaugh,*' which word is found, on dissection to mean *a cow's teat.* This carries the knowledge of this epizootic disorder back full 500 years.

"There are innumerable instances of persons in Britain and Ireland, who caught the malady by milking cows in their youth, and who have passed through a long life, and have been repeatedly exposed to the contagion of the small-pox without being infected; so with a knowledge of this disease, has ever been connected an opinion, that a person once affected with it, is ever after secure from the small-pox.†

---

* The Parliament of England has given Dr. Jenner thirty thousand pounds sterling for the discovery.

† The absurd doctrine that the smallpox would secure a person only a short time, was urged *eighty* years ago to prevent Dr. Boylston from advancing with his inoculation in Boston.

" EDWARD JENNER of Berkeley, a town in the vale of Gloucestershire in England, a learned, skilful, and accomplished physician, was the first who took this knowledge, so long floating on the breath of the vulgar, and impressed upon it the stable form of science. He it was, that with a Franklinian sagacity first transferred it from the mild, healthy, and invaluable animal, the cow, to the human species; and by a series of experiments, demonstrated, that it is *a perfect security against that loathsome disease, which has destroyed more than* FORTY MILLIONS *of people every century;* whereby he has been the means of preserving more lives than ever fell to the lot of any other human being. This extraordinary fact came forth from his hands in so finished a form, that were all the other writings on the cow or kine-pock, but Jenner's destroyed, posterity might have a clear and perfect idea of this benign remedy, and its salutiferous consequences. For Dr. Jenner has demonstrated,

" I   That the cows are liable to a pustular disease, which was popularly called in England the *cow-pox.*

"II.   That the human species might be inoculated with the *limpid* fluid produced in the pustules of this cow-pox.

" III.   That, in consequence of such inoculation, an action commences, which makes such a change in the constitution, of the inoculated persons, as to render it impossible for them to be ever infected with the small-pox.

" IV.   That the disease, induced by inoculation with the cow-pox, is of a slight kind, wholly free from danger, seldom attended with fever, and never with suppurating eruptions, like those of the small-pox.

" V.   That if, by any accident, too much general disturbance is excited in the constitution by inoculating for the cow-pox, it is easy, by a proper application to the inoculated part, to regulate, or suppress such disturbance.

" VI.   That one child in a family might be inoculated for the cow-pox, without the hazard of infecting any other person in the family; the cowpox not being a contagious disease. And none of the facts or observations, published by Dr. Jenner, have been disproved, or refuted.*

" This vicarious disease retains in England its vulgar name of *Cow pox.* It is called *la vaccine* in France; *vajuolo vaccino* in Italy; *vaccina* in Spain, Germany, and the Northern Nations; and in the United States of America, the Kine-Pock.†

" That I produced the *same* diseases in America, is confirmed by virus taken from my patients here, and sent to England, producing the *same* disease there. We have, besides, demonstrated the *identity* of the dis-

---

* Dr. Denman.

† Instead of the plural pox, because it has but *one* pustule. In some parts of America cowpock is synonymous with *spurious*-pock; while by *kine-pock* they mean the *genuine* infection. Hence the Importance of adhering to the term Kine-Pock.

temper to the *eye* by means of pictures of the kine-pock in all its stages, printed in England under the direction of Jenner himself, which exquisite representations ascertain the *identity* of the local disease beyond the faintest shade of ambiguity. In like manner, the depicted *spurious* pustule is an exact description of the impostor that pestered us in the autumn of 1800.

"That this cow or kine-pox will secure the human constitution from the contagion of the small-pox as certainly, as rods of iron will secure a building from the effects of lightning, no one, *who has paid due attention to the subject,* now doubts in America. But as *lightning rods* may be so *injudiciously* placed, as not to protect the building from injury, so the kine-pock inoculation may be so *unskillfully* conducted, as not to secure the person from the contagion of the small-pox.

"When a building, guarded by rods of iron, is struck with lightning. we conclude they were not adjusted according to the rules laid down by *Franklin;* they being founded on a *law of nature* relative to the electric fluid and a metallic rod. And when we hear of a person having the small pox, after being supposed to have had the kine-pock, we are as certain that the inoculation was not conducted according to the rules laid down by *Jenner;* they being, in like manner, founded on a *law of nature* respecting the vaccine virus and the human subject. Whenever, therefore, we meet with adverse accidents in applying the *Franklinian,* or the *Jennerian* discovery to practice, we must look for the cause in *erring man,* and not in UNERRING NATURE. It is the business, then, of the philosopher and the physician, to enquire into the causes of these aberrations.

"Assuming it then, as a fact (and the learned of all nations have admitted it), that Dr. Jenner has demonstrated *a new law of nature,* respecting the prophylactic, or preventive power of the kine-pock in the human system; we presume that every one, who dreads the small-pox, would gladly shelter himself behind the *Aegis* of Jenner, from its too fatal effects, *had he but a cloudless view of the whole business;* and the ultimate object of this address, gentlemen, is a PLAN to help your fellow citizens to such a view of it: and thus to relieve them from their present state of doubt and uncertainty, respecting a matter of more importance to your commercial town, than any that ever exercised its deliberations, since our venerable forefathers first landed on your renowned peninsula.

"In the present unsettled state of this practice, the inhabitants of Boston know not what to adopt, or what to reject. Although I hold up to you. with *confidence,* a sure, safe, and effectual method of forever securing your offspring from the worst of maladies, yet I wish not that you should patronize, much less adopt it, without A PUBLIC EXPERIMENT PERFORMED UNDER YOUR OWN INSPECTION.

"The only question now remaining on the minds of those who are well wishers to the new inoculation is, *why has this operation ever failed? Why have not the true prophylactic effects followed every application of the vaccine virus to the abraded skin?* The full discussion of these questions is reserved for another place. Suffice it to say for the present, that I very early warned the public against *spurious* cases, or an appearance on the arm not possessing the characteristic marks of the genuine pustule, and cautioned my readers against certain occurrences, which, if not critically attended to, would bring the inoculation of this recently imported distemper into a *temporary* disrepute. But my warnings were misconceived, and misrepresented; so that at length, I ceased from any further expressions of caution, and endeavored to content myself with predicting the consequences, that would ensue from aiming to walk straight, in an unfrequented path, blindfold.

"A public experiment by some learned body, or association of physicians, or some regularly constituted body, as the board of health, is requisite to infuse confidence into the minds of the people. For an individual, however warmly disposed to promote the good of his fellow creatures, can do but little in such a peculiar business. This induced me to address the *Boston Board of Health*—to request them to take this new mode of preventing the small-pox infection into their serious consideration, as a matter of great importance to the community, and coming with peculiar propriety under their cognizance.

"The writer of this has, for more than three years, devoted his undivided attention to maturing, and bringing forward this mode of exterminating an horrid disease. He has, by suggesting, but not obtruding on the public, held up to their view A MILD AND EASY SUBSTITUTE. In the same spirit he would now propose to the *Board of Health,* as a principal means of effecting this end, that they would take some step towards forming a committee, to inquire, 1st, *Whether there be sufficient evidence of the efficacy of the kine-pock to justify the expense of a public experiment;* and ample documents are here transmitted to assist you in this inquiry. If this is found to be the case, to establish, 2dly, a COMMITTEE OF PHYSICIANS *to conduct the experiment.* To ensure universal satisfaction, it is suggested, that the committee should consist of *six of the oldest physicians* of Boston; men, who from their age and character, are rather retiring from extensive business, than candidates for it; and that to these should be invited the physician of the small-pox hospital at Brookline. I would further ask leave to propose, that to these medical characters should be associated as many *clergymen,* whose information, habits of inquiry, and benevolent views, would complete a committee, every way adequate to the important task, of forming, and laying, in conjunction with the board of health before the public, a correct and unbiassed report of facts.

"On this occasion, may I not be allowed to make a remark or two for the consideration of those, who from their daily occupations, cannot be supposed to have been in the habit of closely contemplating the works and operations of nature?* Such are apt to imbibe erronious opinions concerning what they denominate the *mean* and the *noble*, the *great* and the *small*, the *trivial* and the *magnificent*, which he, who is in the habit of closely contemplating the GREAT FRAME OF NATURE, the mutual connection, combination, affinity, and harmony of parts, as well as the never ceasing circulation of causes and effects, cannot admit. Such do not consider, that, however essential the distinction of bodies into *great* and *small* may be to *us*, they are not so in the view of the SOVEREIGN ARCHITECT, with whom an *atom* is a world, and a world and *atom!* Who then can stigmatize any work, or operation of nature, by the epithets of *mean* and *trivial?* I have been led to these remarks on hearing some declare, that they never could have faith in an operation, or process, that had so mean and trivial an origin as this, now offered to the public, as their greatest benefit, and as the most valuable discovery ever made in medicine. The fact is, gentlemen, the *greatest* benefits now enjoyed by man, both in *art* and *nature*, sprung from what is called *mean* and *trivial* origins. A few instances may illustrate my meaning.

"Two or three people, cast away in ancient times, on the coast of the Mediterranean, made a fire to cook their victuals and repair their boat. In this operation, they happened to burn the plant *Kali*, which mixing with some sand, or coarse gravel. and all melting together, first produced *glass;* by means of which we can not only bring distant objects as if within our touch, but open an intercourse with the Heavens. Nay further, by the help of two or three pieces of glass fixed in a triangle of wood, the seaman can tell to a mile where he is, south or north of the equator. But shall we despise the *telescope* and the *quadrant* because they had so mean an origin?

"Some other persons playing with a little *red stone*, found that it attracted iron; and at length that a needle touched with it, would always point towards the north-pole. Some lucky mortal, like Jenner, took the hint, and with it formed the *mariner's compass*, by means of which the sailor traverses the trackless ocean, in the darkest night, with perfect safety.

"If we turn from these instances in *art* to those in *nature*, and consider the causes of the wealth and power of nations, do we not see similar

---

*Local opinions and prejudices rendered these illustrations necessary. A considerable proportion of the board of health were unbelievers in the efficacy of the kine-pock at the time this memorial was presented.

instances, full as striking? Is not a *peppercorn* the foundation of the power, glory, and riches of India? as is the *acorn* of that renowned nation whence we of New England sprang.* 'A truth, constantly found,' says Bruce, 'in the disposition of all things in the universe, is, that God makes us of the *smallest* means and causes, to operate the *greatest* and most powerful effects.'

"Let us then no longer be told of the *contemptible origin* of that benign remedy, which PROVIDENCE has destined for the preservation of our offspring from a loathsome and destructive plague. The earth maintaines not a more clean, placid, healthy, and useful animal than the Cow. She is peculiarly the poor man's riches and support. From her is drawn, night and morning, the food for his ruddy children; while the more concentrated part of her healthy juices is sold to the rich, in the form of cream, butter, and cheese. It would indeed be uncomfortable to live without this animal, as she supplies man with more conveniences, and at a less expense, than any other quadruped in the creation. When we have exhausted her by age, her flesh serves for our nourishment, while every part of her has its particular uses in commerce and medicine. On these accounts she is an useful, though invisible wheel in the great machine of state.† Hence we cease to wonder that this useful domestic animal was consecrated among ancient nations, as an object of worship.

"You will readily see, gentlemen, that this memorial, though meant to carry every mark of respect, is not made in the style of cringing solicitation, like a man exclusively interested in the event, and actuated by personal motives merely; but of a man conscious of his duty, and zealous in promoting a public benefit every way worthy your patronage: a benefit of more real value to the town of BOSTON, *than all the riches contained within its limits.* You will also remember, that the main object of this address is not to persuade you blindly to patronize the new inoculation, *but to induce you to cause a rigid inquiry to be made into the truth of my assertions, and to have them subjected to the test of a* PUBLIC EX-

---

* The Board of Health was then composed principally of commercial men and sea captins retired from business. Hence the reason for selecting instances in the commercial and nautical line. The president at this time was Benjamin Russell, editor of the "Centinel," in whose paper Dr. Waterhouse's first publication on the kine-pock appeared. The cause of vaccination owes much to Mr. Russell, whose zeal in its promotion has never slackened.

† The word *wealth* was derived from this species of animals, viz. *pecuniary,* from pecus. Hence it was that the first money ever coined in the world had a *cow* stamped upon it, as a portable representative of riches.

PERIMENT *by a set of men, whose knowledge, age, and virtues, will create confidence, and inspire satisfaction.**

"BENJAMIN WATERHOUSE.

"Cambridge, May 31, 1802."

Waterhouse succeeded in convincing the Board of Health of the wisdom of some such action and the result is set forth in the following report, taken from a photographic reproduction in the "Boston Medical and Surgical Journal, October 17, 1901:

REPORT OF THE BOARD OF HEALTH.

The Board of Health for the town of *Boston*, are happy to have it in their power, this day, to announce to their fellow-citizens the result of one of the most complete experiments which perhaps has ever been made, to prove the efficacy of the *Cow-Pox*, as a preventive against the *Small-Pox*; and while they take the liberty to congratulate the public on this important discovery, they do earnestly recommend its introduction generally, and are confident that it will be the means of preserving the lives and adding to the happiness of millions.

The utmost care has been taken, during the experiments; and a detailed statement of facts are subjoined, for the gratification of every enquirer.

In June, 1801, Dr. JACKSON addressed a letter to the Board of Health, requesting their countenance in certain experiments which he contemplated making, to prove the efficacy of the Cow-Pox, as a preventive against the Small-Pox; to which application the avocations of the Board would not permit that attention which the plan proposed by Dr. JACKSON required.

In June, 1802, Dr. WATERHOUSE made a similar application, accompanied with a very minute history of that disorder, from himself, and also various documents in proof of its utility, from Societies in *New York* and elsewhere, who had associated for the purpose of making experiments similar to those proposed to be made by Dr. W. by which it appeared, that the public in those places, were deriving incalculable benefits by a pretty general inoculation. About this time the Small-Pox was raging in the family of Mr. HOLDEN, *Fifth-Street* and three persons out of five, under the care of the Board of Health, had died.—The Cow-pox had obtained much credit.

---

* That is a committee of six of the oldest physicians, and six of the oldest clergymen in Boston, together with Dr. Aspinwall.

The Board of Health, deeply affected with the fatal ravages of the Small-pox, in the family before mentioned, and viewing their Institution as founded, under God, for the preservation of the health of their fellow-citizens; and believing, as they did, that this mild and safe disorder, "*the Cow-Pox*," might be substituted for that fatal and distressing one, the Small-pox, so that if generally adopted, completely to annihilate and blot it from the catalogue of human woes;—determined, under the influence of these considerations, to prove by experiments, to be made under their immediate observation, whether their faith in the efficacy of the Cow-pox was well founded or not.

With this view, the plan of the experiments proposed were published in the newspapers, for the consideration of their fellow citizens. The Secretary of the Board was also directed, in their name, to desire the assistance of Doctors Lloyd, Danforth, Rand, Jeffries, Warren, Jarvis, and Waterhouse, who, agreeably to the invitation of the Board, met them at the Health-Office.—Various impediments presented themselves in carrying into effect the plan as published. It was alleged that the distance of *Rainsford's-Island* from town, would prevent the attendance of the gentlemen concerned, as often as would be requisite; and to make them in town, it would be necessary to have the permission of the town, in town-meeting, it being contrary to law to inoculate with the Small-pox without it. It was therefore determined to apply for this privilege; and the town being assembled for that purpose, it was objected to, on the grounds that it would alarm the country, and injure the trade of the town.—After much debate, it was voted by the town—"That the Board have power to make the experiments proposed, without the limits of the town; and to take up suitable buildings, &c. for that purpose." It was with much difficulty a place could be obtained, comporting with the vote of the town. But started in the pursuit, the object, the happiness of mankind, the Board was determined that no difficulties which perseverance could surmount, should divert them from their purpose.

At length Mr. Williams gave permission to erect a small building on *Noddle's Island*, and to make the proposed experiments there. Thus provided, on the 16th day of August, nineteen children, viz.

Daniel Scott, *Chambers-Street.*
Almarin Clarke, *Cornhill.*
John Silsby, *Prince-Street.*
Ozias Goodwin,
Geo. Goodwin,
Samuel Watts,   *Charter-Street.*
Samuel Richie,
Robert Williams,
Henry Williams,   *Cole Lane.*
Reuben Loring, *Willson's Lane.*

THOMAS TRUMAN, ⎫
E. L. TRUMAN, ⎬ *Dogget's Alley.*
JOHN WYER, ⎭

SETH KING, ⎫
GEORGE FOBES, ⎬ *Market-Square.*

WILLIAM AUSTIN, ⎫
JOHN HARRIS, ⎬ *Fifth-Street.*

THOMAS SPEAR, *Friends-Street.*

WM. GREENE, *Hanover-Street,*

Were inoculated with the Cow-pox, at the Health-Office, in presence of the Board, and of a number of gentlemen invited. The physicians who attended were Drs. *Lloyd, Rand, Jeffries, Warren, Waterhouse, Welsh, J. C. Howard,* and *T. Danforth;* and the children went through the disorder to the satisfaction of the gentlemen physicians, and of this Board.

Fresh Small-pox matter being obtained, through the politeness of Dr. WEEKS, the proprietor of the Small-pox Hospital at *Falmouth*—on the 9th of November, twelve of the children before named, together with *George Bartlett,* son of Dr. *Bartlett,* of *Charlestown,* who had the Cowpox two years since, were inoculated at the Hospital erected on *Noddle's Island,* with the Small-pox, from the matter obtained from Dr. *Weeks*— and at the same time two children of Mr. *Christopher Clark,* of *Hinchman's Lane,* viz. *Thomas* and *John,* who had never had either the Cowpox or Small-pox, were also inoculated with the latter; and in the proper time the arms (of the two *Clarks*) became inflamed—the symptomatic fever, and usual appearances attending the Small-pox, appeared—and finally pustules to the amount of about 500 on one, and 150 on the other, put forth and matterated, as has been invariably the case in all instances of the small-pox within our knowledge. From these two children, thus affected with the Small-pox, fresh matter was taken, and the thirteen children before named, who were totally unaffected with the first inoculation with Small-pox, were again inoculated on the 21st day of November; and the other seven children, who had the Cow-pox as first mentioned, were also inoculated with fresh matter from the *Clarks;* and the whole remained together in the same house, in the same room, and often in the same beds, without producing the least appearance of the Smallpox, either by uncommon soreness of the arm, head-ach, the least degree of fever or pustules—and this we certify to the public, having daily visited the Hospital ourselves, and made the most critical observations and inquiries, which are confirmed by the report of the physicians who attended the experiments (hereto annexed) and therefore are confident in affirming, That the Cow-pox is a complete preventive against all the effects of the Small-pox upon the human system.

THE PHYSICIANS' REPORT.

WITH a view of ascertaining the efficacy of the Cow-pox in preventing the Small-pox, and of diffusing through this country the knowledge of such facts as might be established by a course of experiments instituted for the purpose, and thereby removing any prejudices, which might possess the public mind on the subject, the Board of Health of the town of *Boston,* in the course of the last Summer, came to a determination to invite a number of Physicians to cooperate with them on this important design; and with a liberality becoming enlightened citizens, erected a Hospital on *Noddle's Island,* for carrying it into execution.—Accordingly, on the 16th of August last, nineteen boys, whose names are subjoined, were inoculated for the Cow pox at the office, and in presence of the above-mentioned Board, with fresh, transparent Cow-pox matter, taken from the arms of a number of patients then under this disease. These all received and passed through the disease to the complete satisfaction of every person present, conversant with the disease.

On the 9th of November, twelve of the above children, together with one other, GEORGE BARTLETT by name, who had passed through the Cow-pox two years before, were inoculated for the Small-Pox on *Noddle's-Island,* with matter taken from a Small-pox patient in the most infectious stage of that disease. The arms of these lads became inflamed at the incisions, in proportion to the various irritability of their habits, but not to a degree greater than what any other foreign, virulent matter would have produced. The Small-pox matter excited no general indisposition whatever, through the whole progress of the experiments, though the children took no medicines, but were indulged in their usual modes of living and exercise; and were all lodged promiscuously in one room.

At the same time and place, in order to prove the activity of the Small-pox matter, which had been used, two lads, who had never had either the Small-pox or Cow-pox, were inoculated from the same matter. At the usual time, the arms of these two patients exhibited the true appearance of the Small-pox. A severe eruptive fever ensued, and produced a plenteous crop of Small-pox pustules, amounting by estimation, to more than five hundred in one, and two hundred in the other.

When these pustules were at the highest state of infection, the thirteen children before mentioned were inoculated a second time, with recent matter, taken from the pustules, which said matter was likewise inserted into the arms of the seven other children, who were absent at the first inoculation.——They were all exposed, most of them for twenty days, to infection, by being in the same room with the two boys, who had the Small-pox, so that, if susceptible of this disease, they must inevitably have received it, if not by inoculation, in the natural way.

Each of the children was examined by the Subscribers, who were individually convinced from the inspection of their arms, their perfect state of health and exemption from every kind of eruption on their bodies, that the Cow-pox prevented their taking the Small-pox, and they do therefore consider the result of the experiment as satisfactory evidence, that the *Cow-pox is a complete security against the Small-pox.*

JAMES LLOYD.
SAMUEL DANFORTH.
ISAAC RAND.
JOHN JEFFRIES.
JOHN WARREN.
THOMAS WELSH.
BENJAMIN WATERHOUSE.
JOSIAH BARTLETT.
JOHN FLEET, JUN.
JOHN C. HOWARD.
THOMAS DANFORTH.

Charlestown, December 15, 1802.

This may certify, that my son, GEORGE BARTLETT, at the age of eight years, was inoculated for the Cow-pox, on the 11th day of November, 1800; that the appearance of his arm, and the symptoms, so fully corresponded with the plates and publications I had then seen, as to convince me, and others of my medical friends, that he had the *disease.*

JOSIAH BARTLETT,
Fellow of the Mass. Med. Society.

To the President and Members of the Board of Health, Boston.

Boston, Dec. 8th, 1802.

We, SUSANNA TRUMAN and LUCY LEARNED, nurses attending on the experiments corroboratnig the efficacy of the Cow-pox—do certify that there was not the least sickness or appearance of Small-pox among any of the children who were subjects of the same, during their stay at *Noddle's-Island,* excepting the two boys, THOMAS and JOHN CLARKE, who had never had the Cow-pox, and were inoculated for the Small-pox, with a view to render the experiment more complete.

SUSANNA TRUMAN.
LUCY LEARNED.

Health-Office, Boston, Dec. 16, 1802.
Published by order of the Board of Health.
ISAIAH DOANE, *President.*
R. GARDNER, *Secretary.*

DR. BENJAMIN WATERHOUSE
AND
HARVARD UNIVERSITY

William Coolidge Lane

PROCEEDINGS

OF

THE CAMBRIDGE HISTORICAL SOCIETY

THE FOURTEENTH MEETING

THE FOURTEENTH MEETING of THE CAMBRIDGE HISTORICAL SOCIETY was held the twenty-sixth day of January, nineteen hundred and nine, at a quarter before eight o'clock in the evening, in the building of the Cambridge Latin School, Trowbridge Street, Cambridge, Massachusetts.

In the absence of the President and of the Vice-Presidents, HOLLIS RUSSELL BAILEY, ESQUIRE, was elected Chairman pro tempore.

The minutes of the last meeting were read and approved.

The second Vice-President, ANDREW MCFARLAND DAVIS, then being present, took the chair.

Upon the subject for the meeting — Dr. Benjamin Waterhouse — WILLIAM COOLIDGE LANE read the following paper:

DR. BENJAMIN WATERHOUSE AND HARVARD UNIVERSITY

MR. CHAIRMAN, LADIES AND GENTLEMEN: To follow up all the details of Dr. Waterhouse's connection with the College would take us far afield, and would acquaint us with a series of more or less acrimonious discussions which have left their traces in the records and the papers of the Corporation, but are not worth reviving at the present day; yet the main facts of his service here are both interesting and important, for he was closely associated with much that now occupies a large place in the intellectual life of the University.

In 1783, he and two other physicians became the incumbents of the three newly established medical professorships — the first formal provision for public instruction in medicine in Massachusetts. Dr. John Warren, the first to be appointed, was Professor of Anatomy and Surgery; Dr. Waterhouse's appointment as Professor of the Theory and Practice of Physic followed in the course of a month; and that of Dr. Aaron Dexter as Professor of Chemistry and Materia Medica came shortly after. The first two were publicly inducted into their offices October 7, 1783.[1] Dr. Waterhouse, at this time, had just returned from his European studies, having graduated from the University of Leyden in 1780. "Without doubt he was the young man of learning then available for the place, just the man to quicken students with a love for science and a desire for general knowledge."[2] Though the proper subject of his professorship was the theory and practice of physic, he began, in 1788, the year after he removed to Cambridge, to give annual courses of lectures in the College on natural history in general and on mineralogy and botany in particular. These lectures, delivered first (1786 and 1787) in Brown University (or Rhode Island College, as it was then called) and afterwards for over twenty years in Cambridge, appear to have been the first ever given in America on these subjects, and so mark the beginning of the study here of natural science, a study which has since developed into such a highly organized and extensive province of university instruction. His correspondence with scientists abroad led to the acquisition of minerals and the formation of a mineral cabinet, from which has grown one of the great departments of the University Museum. During the greater part of his term of office, Dr. Waterhouse was keeper of the mineral cabinet, and as such received the modest sum of $40 a year. The nature of his duties as keeper of the cabinet is characteristically described in a letter from him to President Willard, dated March 8, 1801:[3]

[1] Dr. Waterhouse's Oratio Inauguralis was printed many years afterward, in 1829.

[2] The Harvard Medical School, 1782–1906, p. 117.

[3] Harvard College Papers, vol. iv. no. 83.

REVEREND SIR   suggestion

Agreeably to your intimation, "that the Corporation wished for some general information respecting the time consumed, and attention exercised in fulfilling their directions as expressed in their vote dated May 20ᵗʰ 1795 and a subsequent one dated   I take this method to acquaint them, that in consequence of a very general circulation of the printed letter which accompanies this, a pretty numerous & pretty constant application to view the cabinet ensued. By pretty constant I mean seldom a week without some visitants. These are people who are engaged in the study of minerals, or in some interested mineralogical pursuits, and who come to take a close & critical view of the specimens; and in this they differ from the ordinary visitants to the Library & Museum. They never stay less than 3, or 4 hours; very often all day, and in some instances *three*, and my house is most commonly their quarters. I have attended six visitants within these ten days. The person principally concerned in the *Jodin-hill* mine used to call on me at least twice a week for two or three months often to view the specimens, but oftener to converse on the subject of mineralogy. When some of these visitants appeared embarrassed by the trouble they gave me, I have told them that the Governors of the University allowed me a compensation for it.

Agreeably to the wish of the Corporation I have kept up my correspondence abroad and extended it at home on the subject of minerals. Whenever I have found in the course of my mineralogical studies, a deficiency in the collection, I have immediately written to some of my correspondents in England for them, and when received have placed them in the Cabinet without saying a word to any one. This was the case with a collection of Salts from a friend at Chester, and of a box of minerals & petrefactions from Birmingham. It was two or three years before I could obtain a specimen of *Platina*. I have now sent for specimens of english *Marles*, when they arrive, I shall place them in the Cabinet without saying a word to any one, because it is too much like my own donation to wish for either notice or thanks. Thus, I have, do, and shall continue to contribute to the encrease of the collection.

Since I received an annual grant, I have never presented, nor mean to present any charge for any freight, custom-house fees or the like, altho' a week has not elapsed since I paid about three dollars for a book sent from England for the Library which had remained from the month of October in the Supervisor's office at New-York, as well as a trifling sum for the porterage of a box containing an artificial curiosity for the Museum. Ought I, or ought I not to add that the superb volume containing specimens of the recently discovered *Stamps*, was sent by Dᵉ

Lettsom in consequence of my writing expressly to him to send a copy of that eligant work for our University-library? He having sent me a similar copy the year before. May I add, that I wrote three or four years ago to the same gentleman for a *prepared* Quadruped and a Bird, by way of *sample,* and he sent me eighteen. I then, wrote to him, that they were injured in the passage for want of being properly packed when he sent me twice that number finely preserved. Whether they were sent to me personally, or to the University was equivocal. I therefore construed it the safest way and presented them as from him. Now every gentleman must suppose that I could not be the receiver, much less the solicitor of these valuable articles without exerting myself to make some return in the products of this country. I have never done so much as I could wish, but have done as much as I could, being convinced that in this, as well as in all other cases, "he that will reap, must sow."

I never have, nor ever shall keep an account of such expences. Indeed, my habits of life, & literary pursuits are adverse to anything like merchantile calculations. I can only say with precision, that for what I sent to an individual correspondent the last year I paid nearer 50, than 40 dollars. This I will venture to specify to some one of the corporation as a private gentleman, but delicacy would forbid me to do it to him, or them, in their official station, more especially when a proportion of the books are sent to me personally; and the corporation may be assured, that I mention these things with no small reluctance, and that I apprehend they come within, or rather among the objects of their inquiry. I give the information which I think is needed, but ask for nothing.

Were I a *Professor* of Nat[l] History, and had of course a salary, these articles committed to my charge as well as the exhibition & explanation of them to strangers would be, like that of the Professor of Exp[l] Philosophy, part of my duty. But the case is far otherwise with me. *I have created this branch of instruction, and carried it on for more than twelve years at my own expence* without attaching any charge to the University, and it is only within one year or two that the lectures have been profitable; for more than 8 years, they yielded not so much as the annual income of a college-sweeper, and nothing but the constant encouragement of that most excellent friend to the College the late D[r] *Wigglesworth,* and his prophetic assurances, that by perseverance, these lectures on Nat[l] History would one day grow into a permanent establishment, have preserved them to this period of existence.

If from this general view of facts and circumstances the corporation should think it just, or generous to continue the annual grant for taking charge of the cabinet, corresponding, &c &c, I think I may assure them that it will be, as it always has been, quite, or nearly absorbed in the expences of a correspondence, which they have encouraged and I hesitate not to assure them, that if from any accident, sickness or un- usual occurrence my expences or attention, should be little or nothing, they will be informed of it, but I wish hereafter to be excused from giving in, from year to year any thing like an estimate, because it is somehow or other, very repugnant to the current of my feelings, and what I do with extreme reluctance.

BENJAMIN WATERHOUSE.

Revd President Willard.

For many years, he gave his natural history lectures in the Philosophy Chamber, as the room in Harvard Hall adjoining the Library was called. In this room was kept the philosophical apparatus, and here the Hollis Professor of Mathematics and Natu- ral Philosophy, Samuel Webber, afterward President, gave his lec- tures. The latter not unnaturally objected to the presence of the mineral cabinet, the stuffed birds, and the other impedimenta of the lecturer on natural history. But Dr. Waterhouse strenuously objected to being moved, and was never willing to occupy one of the rooms in Holden Chapel which had been devoted to the use of the Medical Professors.

On May 19, 1800, he writes to the President as follows:[1]

REV^D SIR

Last autumn I received a line from you expressing the opinion of the Corporation respecting my continuing to lecture in the philosophy chamber, which induces me to address you on that subject.

I gave my lectures in that room for a series of years on the invitation of Mr Smith, the then Librarian, and did not *at that time* know that it was necessary to ask leave of higher authority. During the seven years I gave my lectures there, no complaint had ever been made of soiling, deranging, or any way defacing the room; on the contrary the room has acquired an additional beauty in consequence of those lectures, for neither Birds, nor minerals would have been there had these lectures on Natural History never been given.

My application is for permission to continue my lectures in that room, and my reasons for it, are I presume strong enough to obtain it. In

[1] Harvard College Papers, vol. iv. no. 59.

the course of my lecturing it is necessary to have displayed a great number of minerals, and many of the specimens are so delicate & fragile that they cannot be removed up & down stairs without risking their destruction. Besides these minerals, delicate drawings, & costly books as well as valuable productions of nature must be exhibited in a room where the lecturer can *instantly turn the key* and *lock them up*, should he be called suddenly out in the course of his practice. On no occasion do I ever leave the students in the room. For my rule has ever been to go in first & come out last. I have been so carefull to keep the carpet neat & clean, that I always turn it up round the seats, & never give a lecture in rainy weather. The bordering of the paper, that has been picked off in some places was certainly never done by any of my audience. Their quiet, orderly & very proper behaviour are known & talked of — and if it be found that my pupils never did injure the room the presumption is they never will, unless I should break my rule of leaving them in it without me.

As I confess I felt a little hurt in being turned out of that room without a hearing, I cannot avoid wishing to inform the corporation that during the 18 years that I have been a Professor of the Theory & Practice of physic in this University, I never have been accomodated with a lecturing-room, but have been obliged repeatedly to quit my chair & dismiss my pupils in the middle of a lecture to give place to the stated teachers. I gave one whole course in a Tutor's room. In one, or two instances, I have been compelled to the derogatory step of giving my *medical lectures* in the room of an undergraduate; and for these three years past, I have been forced to give my *medical lectures* at my own house, altho' very inconvenient on account of the smallness of our rooms & the largeness of my family.

I will, however, cheerfully submit to this inconvenience, great as it is, provided the corporation will give me their permission to make use of the philosophy chamber, during *eighteen hours* in *twelve months*, pledging myself at the same time that every thing shall be preserved free from dirt, destruction or defacement. It has been suggested that I could give my lectures on N. History in the chapel, or dining hall, *both are absolutely unfit;* besides I wish to be indulged with a room, out of which I may not be turned by any Professor, Tutor, the Librarian or cook.

If you would be so good as to lay this request before the corporation, it would add to the kindnesses already conferred on

your very humble serv^t

BENJⁿ WATERHOUSE

Revd President Willard.

In 1805, various friends of the College subscribed to the foundation of a professorship of natural history, the first incumbent of which was to be elected by the subscribers. This proposal was bitterly opposed by Dr. Waterhouse, who felt that this department of instruction had been fostered and developed during many years by himself alone, and that another should not be allowed to displace him. He submitted a Memorial to the Corporation March 1, 1805, the first portion of which is worth quoting, since it states the results of his labors up to that time:[1]

"The Memorial of Benjamin Waterhouse, Teacher of Natural History in the University at Cambridge to the Honb¹. & Rev^d. the Corporation, most respectfully sheweth,

"That your memorialist was 17 years ago appointed to deliver annually a course of Lectures on Natural history in this college, as expressed by a vote of the Corporation here annexed, which vote was confirmed by the board of Overseers the May following.

"Thus constituted a teacher of Nat¹. History, your memorialist prepared a set of Lectures on that extensive subject. In executing this task he carefully selected such objects as would most forcibly impress the minds of youth with the harmony of the Universe, or unity of design throughout the great Temple of creation; the end & aim of the whole being to lead them ' to look through Nature up to Nature's God.'

"During the greatest part of the space above mentioned, your memorialist struggled with such difficulties, impediments, and discouragements as would have entirely checked anyone who was not animated with the ambitious sentiment of being considered hereafter the Founder of Nat¹. History in the first University in America.

"As Nat. History was an entirely new study in this College, your memorialist was compelled to exercise some address at its introduction. The College library was nearly barren of books on this subject; and what few there were appeared never to have been perused. Your Memorialist had first to excite a curiosity and then to gratify it. He had to prepare the ground, sow the seed & wait their produce. In this infantile state of things he had often to treat important subjects superficially, and to grow more particular as attention & taste increased.

"Your memorialist commenced the business in the autumn of 1788 by giving his first course gratis. The 2^d year he opened his course with five pupils at a guinea a piece. The 3^d year he had seven. The

---

[1] Harvard College Papers, vol. iv. no. 220.

4th year he allowed each to subscribe whatever he chose; then he had about thirty, some subscribed three guineas, some two, and some half a guinea; others clubb'd together and divided the half guinea & the lectures between them, one attending one half the course, the other the remaining part. The President disapproving this mode, as deviating from the fee established by the Corporation, it never was again pursued. It was an effort in discouragement; for as yet your memorialist had never received a farthing of salary as a medical professor. Once, in a day of greater difficulty and perplexity than he ever before experienced, he sunk under the discouragement, and felt entirely disposed to relinquish a *second time* all connexion with Harvard College. This would have been effected had it not been for the encouragement of the venerable D^r. *Wigglesworth.* ' *Persevere, said he, and you will find a reward. Pursue your plan of Natural history, BOTANY especially, which will not fail to raise up friends and supporters. On this subject I will venture to prophecy; it will grow into an establishment.'* On this gleam of encouragement he resumed his task with a degree of alacrity, and on the former plan of a guinea each pupil, his numbers were, if he remember right, ten. The 6th year the numbers were about the same. The 8th year they were nineteen. The 9th year forty one; the 10th year about the same number; and the 11th year I had *sixty six,* including some indigent youth, who pay nothing.

" At this period difficulties were raised through the medium of the late Librarian, respecting giving lectures on Nat^l History in the philosophy chamber, when your memorialist was ejected from it *without a hearing.* This ejectment materially effected the profits of his course of lectures, by altering the time of his lecturing from autumn to the busy season of spring; and has in every succeeding year reduced the number of his pupils one half. Your memorialist has never been indulged with any opportunity of representing this matter to the Corporation. This with some other matters connected with it, have been sources whence continually flowed uneasiness & discontent. Your memorialist was considered by some as an adventitious Lecturer without rights, rank, or privileges.

" Your memorialist begs leave to remark that he was the originator of the CABINET OF MINERALS; and has been for more than *thirteen* years the principal agent in collecting the specimens therein contained; which for number and value surpass anything of the kind in the United States. By the help of this collection a competent naturalist may illustrate *one of the three Kingdoms of Nature.* This rich collection is not like that of books, or plants perishable by time, but will remain unimpaired for ages.

" Your memorialist has likewise collected some curious and valuable articles in other branches of Nat! History, which he gratuitously transferred from his own private musæum to that of the College; the particulars of which he has detailed to that member of the Corporation who resides in Cambridge.

" Beside mineralogy your memorialist has sedulously cultivated 'philosophical Botany'; or the anatomy and physiology of vegetables, together with the elements of agriculture and vegetation; and this he presumes he has carried as far as his slender pecuniary means & other requisites could reasonably be expected. As his plan differs from that of any hitherto made public, he has chosen to submit it to the severity of public criticism. Your memorialist has collected no small number of indigenous plants & made & procured not a few drawings illustrative of the *Linnæan System*. In a word he has strove beyond his strength to introduce and build up the science of Nat! History in general in the University at Cambridge; but finding his strength failing, discouragements multiplying, and innovations approaching, he naturally turns to his constituents for protection & encouragement."

He goes on to beg the Corporation not to allow his work to be interfered with by the establishment of the proposed Professorship, of which he has only learned by hearsay, and the statutes governing which have never been submitted to him.

At about the same time, he wrote to Judge Davis, a member of the Corporation (February 15, 1805):[1]

" I feel free to say that this affair is a very important one to me. 'Tis a crisis, or turning point in my life, influencing my domestic plans & future prospects; as on the termination of this design, the education of my four sons, or in other words my connexion with Harvard College depends; since I had determined, if this hitherto concealed scheme, when develloped, should be found to interfere with my reputation or interest, to publish in a pamphlet a narrative of all my exertions, in founding, maturing & bringing forward, Natural history in general, & *Botany* in particular, then to quit the ground, go into Boston there to give my lectures & to attempt practice, in which idea I have been encouraged by characters of no small influence in society.

" I disavow any design or desire to marr or impede any beneficial plan. I explicitly declare that envy has no place in my composition;

[1] Harvard College Papers, vol. iv. no. 218.

but I should be divested of the ordinary feelings of humanity, nay I should be 'worse than a heathen,' were I totally insensible to some past and present transactions, in which my character & interest are concerned. After labouring seventeen years in establishing a new branch of science in this place, and having ALONE, and UNASSISTED brought it to a degree of maturity, then to have another person brought forward to take the most conspicuous & captivating part of it, with the title of Professor, while I remain with the humble title of Lecturer, giving lectures to boys at 25 cents each lecture, is what a man of Judge Davis knowledge of men & things can never suppose I will submit to. My friends would dispise me if I did, and they ought to."

When the Corporation submitted to him the statutes of the professorship, and assured him it was to be a professorship specifically of botany and entomology, he withdrew his objections, but although this title was in fact used in several votes of the Corporation, it was soon displaced by the original and more comprehensive designation.

One of the objects of the new fund was to found a Botanic Garden, and in this Dr. Waterhouse was actively interested. Indeed, his own lectures on Botany, repeated from year to year, doubtless had had their part in exciting a general interest in the project, so that we may truly say that the establishment of the Botanic Garden was, in part, due to Dr. Waterhouse.[1]

For four years Dr. Waterhouse continued his lectures on natural history, but on April 27, 1809, we find this vote in the Records of the Corporation:

" Whereas when there was no Professor of Natural History in Harvard College to instruct the Pupils in any branch of Natural History the Corporation on the 29. April 1788 authorized Dʳ. Waterhouse to deliver annually a course of Lectures upon Natural History to such of the students as should obtain permission under the hands of their Parents or guardians to attend, since that time a Professorship of Natural History has been founded at Cambridge & Professor elected & introduced into that office capable of reading Lectures in every branch of Natural History who has already been directed to read Lectures on

---

[1] See the " Advertisement " of his book, " The Botanist," published in 1811.

Botany, Entomology & Zoology and who may read Lectures in such other branches of Natural History as may be directed agreeably to the foundation, as it is inconvenient & improper that Lectures in the Natural History be read by two distinct professors, therefore it is

" Voted that hereafter no Lectures in Natural History be read in the College or to any of the Students but by the Professor of Natural History. But as the Corporation has learnt that D^r. Waterhouse has already began his annual course of Lectures for the present year it is further voted that he may finish the said course agreeably to the terms of the said vote passed in 1788, and that after his present course is finished to wit from & after the last Wednesday in August next the said vote be rescinded and made null & void."

A characteristic letter from Dr. Waterhouse to his friend, John Quincy Adams, for whom he entertained a sincere regard and who was shortly after to be installed as the first Boylston Professor of Rhetoric and Oratory, is found among the papers of Professor Pearson, now in the possession of Phillips Academy, Andover. It is dated March 30, 1806, just after the election of Samuel Webber as president and before his inauguration. Professor Pearson had been for twenty years Hancock Professor of Hebrew, six years a member of the Corporation, and after President Willard's death, September 25, 1804, for more than a year, Acting President. A theologian of the old school, he gave up all hope of saving the College from the advancing tide of Unitarianism when Henry Ware was elected Professor of Theology, and retired to Andover, where he soon after was instrumental in founding the Andover Theological Seminary as a protest against the defection of Harvard.

The letter is as follows:

CAMBRIDGE, March 30th, 1806.
DEAR SIR, —

In the last letter which I wrote to you, I was pleasing myself that we should have a President, that would break the scum, the thick scum which has covered our collegiate pool. Although Mr. Ames is not so profound a scholar nor so truly scientific as some others of the sons of Harvard, yet I hoped & believed that his brilliant talents would give science a more pleasing countenance than she has lately borne here. His declining set us once more afloat. All of us on the ground would have been well contented with Dr. Pearson, but, our Rulers in

Boston, not to say *Essex*, uttered their *veto;* and to give it due force they talked him down; and talked their man, Dr. K—— up; but the Corporation were disobedient & would not chuse him. What did they do next? They chose a man, whom no one ever thought of; a sort of negative character; a man without friends or enemies; a man as ignorant of the world as if he had never been born into it; a mere mathematician; to which branch of science he is a bigot; a man who thinks that all the rest of the world are busy about trifles, mathematicians excepted! The Corporation have been censured not a little for this choice; and their excuse is, that in these times of innovation, it is best to keep the College ship in Dock, and not suffer her to venture near an enemy; that they studied safety rather than risk a voyage of discovery: If these reasons be admitted why did they chuse Fisher Ames? The truth of the matter is, they did as has been done more than once in the Roman conclave, disappoint all the fierce contending princes & intriguing courts by chusing a good but obscure monk, who had neither power or inclination to do good or harm. What has been the consequence of this surprising election? The consequence has been the banishment of Dr. Pearson. He retires to a small house in Andover with very little to live on, after being 18 years in the service of college. It avails him nothing that he has enriched the college treasury, as it is said, 30,000 dollars. He is suffered to go off with as little feelings of compassion as some people turn off an old, sick decrepit cart-horse. Dr. P. had his notions, and labored to fortify them, yet was he a respectable man, a good scholar, and a faithful teacher. They accuse him of being at times passionate & cross. I never knew a good & faithful officer but what was. Who can have much to do with men, and with mens children, especially in controuling and correcting them and preserve a placid temper? But the man placed at the head of this great school, for it is but a school, never was known to be out of temper, say his advocates; — if so, say others, he will never make a good & energetic officer. Such is the state of things at this time, in this place, and such are the feelings of all I have yet conversed with in the college instruction & government, one person excepted, who says nothing.

Under these circumstances I have taken the resolution to stay at home & say nothing; but follow my medical & natural history lectures, & attend, as much as I can to the education of my children myself. I could not however keep my silence towards you, because I know that you feel a particular interest in the present & future state of this seminary, and because I supposed that you would like to know how we stood affected in this place, under our new arrangement; and I knew that what I said to you would never be mentioned to the injury of any mans feelings. With the highest degree of respect and esteem I remain your steady friend

BENJ. WATERHOUSE.

The later years of Dr. Waterhouse's professorship were stormy ones and attended with many mortifying experiences in his relations with the College. In 1807, the Corporation, becoming dissatisfied with his care of the mineral cabinet, appointed the President and Judge Davis a Committee to examine it and report whether all the specimens were to be found and in order. The Committee professed to be unable to find many of the specimens, and demanded them of the Professor, who replied with indignation. In 1809, he was "discharged from any further care of the Cabinet." He had never been on good terms with his fellow professors on the Medical Faculty, yet complained that they did not consult him in regard to measures contemplated relating to the school. In 1810, the lectures were moved from Cambridge to Boston, and Dr. Waterhouse was obliged, much against his will, to take up his residence in Boston, though he seems never to have given up his Cambridge house. March 29, 1811, he writes to President Kirkland, who had then been president just four months:[1]

DEAR SIR,

I receiv'd your letter with pleasure & read it with satisfaction, because I thought I perceived in it something inducing me to believe that you and I could do business together harmoniously. Nay I deem it impossible that any thing like that acrimony which broke out between me & some of the college legislators can arise between us; for I never can charge you with personal ingratitude.

Instead of twelve Lectures, I should like to give 18, or 20. I must as you intimated adapt them to my audience, which will cost me some labour. I wish however to give at least four this term. Perhaps two in a week, and if you can so arrange it, at 9, or 10 o'clock. Thirty or thirty five minutes each time would be all I wish for. Circumstances do not, at present allow of it. Perhaps your removal from Boston to Cambridge, may give you some idea of the state of my mind in removing from Cambridge to Boston. It is like two opposite streams that forms a whirlpool in which nothing advances. My sleep, my perspira-

[1] Harvard College Papers, vol. vi. p. 80.

tion & my appetite are deranged and every day or two I am afflicted with a dismal sick headache, by which that day is wasted; and this will continue, I expect more or less until I get fixed in Boston.

I find it is expected of me that I give to the Committee of the Board of Overseers an accurate statement of the injury I have sustained in my income, by the alterations that have been made in my lecturing in this place. In order to do this properly as it regards my medical lectures I beg leave to ask of you some information, for really I do not understand what I have read, and what comes to me by report from some of the senior class. I ask this information in the two fold capacity of a professor & a parent.

I learnt from the votes of the Corporation that we three professors were to give our lectures to the senior class *gratis*. This I told to several who enquired of me.

By the late vote I learnt that instead of it, the Seniors who attended were to be assessed 10 dollars each in their Q^r. bills. I now hear that the Prof^r of Anatomy has obtained from about 30 undergraduates a subscription of *15 dollars* each for that course which these young men expected and had a right to expect from what had been said to them, *gratis*, or at most for their 10 dollars assessment, which makes up the 25 dollars which that Prof^r. has for those students who attend him from abroad. Now I wish to enquire as a *parent*, whose son is to pursue medicine as a profession, if I am to be charged 10 dollars in the Q^r. bill, and then pay Dr Warren 15 dollars mcre for his attendance on the course. If this be the case I have two objections to it. First as a *professor* I deem it a thing that will injure the character of our medical school, for the public will pronounce it unjust, because the expences of a subject &c is very trifling. Second as a *parent*, I declare to you that I cannot afford it; for almost every *Lacteal* by which I & my family drew nutriment from college has been cut off; insomuch as I have been obliged as Judge Wendell & Dr Holmes know, to take my two sons from Andover, because I could not afford to keep them there, nor to bring them up to college, and because I have been compelled to borrow money to pay the college dues of that son who graduated last year. Before that period my income from my natural history lectures not only paid my sons bills, but procured me my *wood*, my *hay*, & my *cyder*. Mr Gannet can confirm this. Now I am indebted to the college treasury for wood and am paying interest for it, while the Corporation keep from me my compensation as Cabinet-keeper for about 8, or 9 months, & for my extra labour in three times arranging by their order the Cabinet, and which I presume will over ballance what I owe the Treasurer.

The Corporation also withhold the payment of a bill, which *I think* they are bound in honor to discharge, due to David Frost, & which I expect to be sued for every day, the particulars of which I mean to give to the committee of the overseers, because my character has been cruelly handled in its discussion by the late Treasurer & Judge Davis, & which has been the subject of coarse remarks by the mechanics of Cambridge for a year or two past, not very respectful to college.

I applaud honest Pickering for his bold appeal to the public, and shall follow his courageous example; but hope to do it in a less angry spirit. This wretched scrawl ought to be transcribed, but the headache forbids, and leaves me only to add sentiments of respect to you officially & personally

B. WATERHOUSE

By the fall of this year, the other Medical professors had become so estranged from him and so exasperated in their feelings, that they presented a memorial to the Corporation (November 18, 1811), stating particulars in the conduct of Dr. Waterhouse which forbade their further intercourse with him.   We cannot undertake to discuss the question how far their statements were justified, but they charged the Doctor (1) with having supported the design for a College of Physicians in Boston which would be injurious to the Harvard Medical School; (2) that " he evinced a want of veracity " in stating that he had no knowledge of the plan for extending the Medical School to Boston, and that he knew nothing in advance of two circular letters issued by his colleagues; (3) that he had printed in the " New England Palladium," May 3, 1811, a libel against the Professor and Adjunct Professor of Anatomy, " which had a tendency to injure their characters, was of a nature to be highly offensive to their feelings, and to diminish their usefulness in the University, and that later, in another article, he charged the other professors with a neglect of their official duties."

A copy of the memorial was sent to Dr. Waterhouse, and he was asked to attend at a meeting of the Corporation and face his accusers.   His letter to President Kirkland, November 28, 1811, is in part as follows : [1]

" I beg you, Reverend Sir, to be assured that my not answering your letter of last Saturday, enclosing that to the Corporation from the Medi-

[1] Harvard College Papers, vol. vii. p. 5.

cal Professors & their Adjuncts, did not arise from inattention or disrespect; but from a very different sentiment. It has so fallen out, in the course of the administration of your Predecessor, that I have, in one or two cases, answered some communications with full as much indignation as prudence. His lamented death dissipated everything like resentment, and has led me to form for myself a rule never to answer off hand, and on the first impression any communication having the complexion of the denunciating letter of my colleagues. I therefore, after reading the letter to my wife & my children; and after having shewn it to several friends out of doors, have taken up my pen to acknowledge the receipt of it from you, and to say that I will attend at the time & place prescribed.

" Two of the three charges appear not to be worthy my notice, or any one's else: but one of them is sufficiently serious to excite all my attention, and the attention of my friends, & the attention of the College Legislature.

" Scarcely a week has elapsed since I cleared myself from the imputation of *peculation* & other acts of dishonesty in the administration of the affairs of a public hospital when I find myself accused before the Corporation of being a LIAR. The Medical students here in Boston have already got hold of the story, and they are told that it will be only throwing away money to attend my course of lectures for that the Corporation are now in the act of removing me from a station which I disgrace. This and a *great deal more* has already reached the ears of *all* my family."

Referring to the case of a Frenchman who had some years before been in the service of the College and had been finally dismissed — " driven from College & from this country by the indignant voice of public opinion, and not by the intrigues of *professional Rivals,*" he continues:

" Now I, who have been a Professor in your College nearly 30 years, & have still a few friends left who are not ashamed to own me, ask of the Honb¹ & Revᵈ. the Corporation no more tenderness, no more fellow-feeling, sympathy or exercise of patience towards me, and consideration for my family, than what was exercised towards this notoriously immoral Frenchman."

The Corporation seems to have examined into the trouble with great care, and to have given all parties, and particularly Dr. Waterhouse, every opportunity to be heard, but finally (May 14, 1812) resolved that, harmony and confidence being destroyed, " the interest and reputation of the University require that he [Dr. Waterhouse] be removed from the office of Hersey Professor of the Theory and Practice of Physic," and it was voted that Dr. Waterhouse be and he is hereby removed from said professorship.

In spite of the peculiarities of temperament and perhaps the animosities of politics which seem to have made it impossible for Dr. Waterhouse and his colleagues to work together in harmony, we must not forget his good qualities and his valuable services to the College. Dr. Holmes describes him as a " brisk dapper old gentleman; with hair tied in a ribbon behind and, I think, powdered, marching smartly about with his gold-headed cane, with a look of questioning sagacity and an utterance of oracular gravity." It is pleasant to find in the recently published volume on the Harvard Medical School this paragraph in its account of Dr. Waterhouse: [1]

" Rather than the pompous old gentleman of Dr. Holmes' remembrance, let us think of Dr. Waterhouse as the enthusiastic student of science, striving in far-distant America to keep in touch with the best that was taking place in the centers of European learning, vigorous and practical in his ability to seize upon the medical event of the period, strong in the denunciation of existing evils, and with a breadth of mind that prepared the way for the advent of Gray and Agassiz."

Another letter, now in the Andover Pearson papers, also addressed to John Quincy Adams, must be our last glimpse of the irascible but warm-hearted doctor. It is undated, but being addressed to " Pres^t Adams," cannot be earlier than March, 1825, and from the allusions in it cannot be much later than that.

" I close with a word or two on this University — Dr. Pearson told me some years ago, that his father-in-law, President Holyoke, said to him, on his deathbed — ' if any man wishes to be humbled and mortified, let him become President of Harvard-college,' w^c, said the Dr., I then thought a very strange speech; but I now perceive the wisdom of it; for Pearson retired from it in utter disgust. Webber lost his life by it; and I do not believe that the chair, even now, feels, at all times, as if

[1] The Harvard Medical School, 1782-1906, p. 19.

stuffed with eider-down.   Pearson predicted to me, & to others, that the ingrafting the botanical & natural history professorship on the University would operate the destruction of the institution.   I every day see his prediction verifying.   Two of their ablest teachers,[1] men who have studied & travelled in Europe have recently left them, & are about establishing a seminary for the instruction of lads, near Northampton.   The Amherst college has lost, by sudden death, its Calvinistic President[2] but the institution is progressing, while 40 young men of spirit have left Harvard filled with resentment.   The establishment is in no small destress for money, owing principally to following the advice of some of the very wisest men that ever trod the soil of Essex, who persuaded them to sell out their 6 pr. cent stock when it was down to 85!   This was all owing to political blindness, & clerical ignorance.   It is said, & I believe it, that the funds of the Natural history professorship is nearly all consumed wasted without honor or profit.   If so, I think the history of Ahab, Naboth & Jezabel is about finished.   If this be a true state of things, they have the bitter reflection, that it is all owing to the advice of *one* man, who accepted a seat in the Corporation on the express condition of *doing as he had a mind to.*   I heartily wish the prosperity of this noble institution; but I am convinced, that one generation, with its rancorous politics, must pass away, before this college, and its adjunct, the Academy of Arts & Sciences, will be placed on a safe, honorable & prosperous footing.   I wish never to have any thing to do with them.   I have no more sons to listen to their instructions; and I think so little of them, that I wonder how I came to say so much of their affairs; for assuredly they very rarely occupy the thoughts of your old Leyden Friend

BENJ^N. WATERHOUSE.

Pres^t. Adams.

THE EARLY NINETEENTH CENTURY

Henry R. Viets

CHAPTER V

THE EARLY NINETEENTH CENTURY
1800–1846

WITH the opening of the century and even a few months before 1800, came the work of Benjamin Waterhouse on cowpox vaccination. It is rather strange that this man, so queer and difficult to get along with, always at odds with his colleagues, especially with John Warren in relation to the early days of the Harvard Medical School, should have made such a striking contribution to medicine in Massachusetts as were his vaccination experiments. He had the advantage, however, of a long English training and the friendship of a relative, John C. Lettsom, of London; it was from Lettsom that a copy of Jenner's classic book, 'An Inquiry into the Cause and Effects of Variolæ Vaccinæ, a Disease discovered in some of the Western Counties of England, particularly Gloucestershire, and known by the name of the Cow-pox,' reached Waterhouse in the beginning of the year 1799. Jenner's book had been published in June, 1798, giving his experiences with vaccination by cowpox virus as a means of preventing smallpox. The knowledge of the value of this procedure was not new even in Jenner's time, for many of the milkmaids in the vale of Gloucestershire had noticed that, after they had been innocently inoculated with cowpox on their hands from the cow's udders, they were *not* subject to the more terrible disease of smallpox.

Edward Jenner, however, put these casual observations to a scientific test and his discovery entitles him to a place in the first rank of those who have improved the art of medicine.

Waterhouse, keen to sense the value of Jenner's work, wrote: 'I was struck with the unspeakable advantages that might accrue to this country, and indeed to the human race at large, from the discovery of a mild distemper that would forever after secure the constitution from that terrible scourge, the smallpox.' He received, soon after this, a book by George Pearson, of London, confirming Jenner's discovery and, at once, drew up for the 'Columbian Sentinel,' a newspaper, a brief communication which was printed March 12, 1799. The paragraph, entitled 'Something Curious in the Medical Line,' simply gave the essential part of Jenner's work as well as the comments of George Pearson. This publication shared the fate of most new discoveries reported in newspapers, and it would have been soon forgotten except for the persistence of Waterhouse. He, at a meeting of the American Academy of Arts and Sciences held in Cambridge, with President John Adams in the chair, exhibited Jenner's book and explained the contents. 'The reception of this communication was much to my satisfaction,' reports Waterhouse, and he prepared a more formal contribution for the next quarterly meeting of the Society. Before this date came around, however, he had received another report from England; this in the form of a book by William Woodville, physician to the smallpox and inoculation hospitals in the city of London, giving a review of his cases, the results of which bore out in every way Jenner's original contribution.

Waterhouse sent to England for some of the vaccine or cowpox matter for trial and, after several fruitless attempts, obtained some 'by a short passage from Bristol.' He, without hesitation, inoculated his five-year-old son on July 8, 1800; later he inoculated another son, three years of age, and following that a boy of twelve. All the vaccinations apparently 'took,' but the real test of protection was to come later; it must be proved by actual experiment that the patient, so protected, was actually immune to smallpox. Waterhouse, therefore, turned to his friend, William Aspinwall, of Brookline, who conducted a smallpox hospital, where original inoculations by the method of Boylston were carried out. He wrote, in August, 1800, asking if Aspinwall would 'try the experiment on inoculating some of my children who have already undergone the cowpox'; Aspinwall consented at once and chose the boy of twelve, the third child inoculated by Waterhouse, as a test. Direct inoculation of the smallpox matter was used and, although the boy's arm became infected in a day or two, he was able to leave the hospital and return home on the twelfth day after the experiment, without having 'the slightest trace of the disease.' This crucial experiment was so successful that, later, other members of Waterhouse's family, including some of the servants, were subjected to the same test with the same results.

The first report of these vaccinations by Waterhouse appeared as a pamphlet forty pages in length, with the long title, 'A Prospect of Exterminating the

Small-Pox; being the History of Variolæ Vaccinæ, or
Kine-Pox, commonly called Cow-Pox; as it has appeared in England: with an Account of a series of
Inoculations performed for the Kine-Pox, in Massachusetts. Printed for the author, at the Cambridge
Press, by William Hilliard, and sold by him, and other
booksellers in Boston. 1800.'

Only a few physicians in Boston and elsewhere were
apparently interested in these experiments of Waterhouse; one or two visited his patients for the purpose
of learning something of the 'new inoculations.' There
were some malicious reports in regard to the success of
the inoculation, but they appear to have been ground-
less. Waterhouse soon received a number of applications to vaccinate families, but declined to try the
method on any person outside of Cambridge until he
was sure of the results from Aspinwall's hospital.
When it was obvious that these children were protected from smallpox, Waterhouse extended the benefits as widely as possible and introduced the method
into the hands of other physicians in whom he had
confidence. His method of treatment, however, fell
frequently into the hands of practitioners who disregarded his cautions and there were some untoward
results. A disagreeable incident took place in Marblehead, eighteen miles from Boston. Waterhouse had
vaccinated two persons in the town, one of them a son
of a physician. The physician took the virus from his
son's arm and with it vaccinated forty persons.
Another physician obtained some virus from the arm
of a sailor who had recently come from London. Apparently this material was a mixed virus containing

some smallpox matter; as a consequence, small-
pox spread rapidly throughout the neighborhood and
the public became so alarmed that the municipal
authorities took a hand. Waterhouse requested that
the Massachusetts Medical Society appoint a committee to visit Marblehead to inquire into the facts of
the disaster, but the committee did not execute their
commission, as only one of the three physicians
appointed saw fit to attend to it.

Not dismayed by the trouble, Waterhouse sent to
England for fresh vaccine, and recommenced his
vaccinations in March, 1801. He was rejoiced to find
that these new inoculations presented all the characteristics of the first cases in his own family.

The news of the final success of vaccination spread
rapidly, especially into the Southern States, and
Thomas Jefferson, then President, wrote to Waterhouse from Washington, December 25, 1800, 'In this
line of proceeding, you deserve well of your country;
and I pray you accept my portion of the tribute due
you, and assurance of high consideration and respect.'
After some difficulty with the virus sent to Jefferson,
which had apparently spoiled on the long trip to
Virginia, a new lot was conveyed to the President and
Jefferson was inoculated successfully August 6, 1801.
The President from then on became an ardent advocate of the method.

In spite of the success of vaccination in the South,
Boston and Massachusetts physicians did not accept
the work of Waterhouse. The man and his experiments could not be separated; many of the profession
hated the one and refused to grant the value of the

other. In 1802, when smallpox was again prevalent
in Boston, Waterhouse concluded to make another
serious effort to convince the profession and the public
of the power of vaccination and to secure its general
introduction into the town. He therefore communicated, May 31, 1802, with the Board of Health, setting forth the facts as he then visualized them. The
Board appointed promptly a committee of seven
reputable physicians, including Waterhouse, who, in
August, 1802, vaccinated nineteen children at the
health office. The physicians were James Lloyd,
Samuel Danforth, Isaac Rand, John Jeffries, John
Warren, and Charles Jarvis. A more representative
group of Boston physicians could hardly have been
chosen; the Board of Health treated Waterhouse
quite differently than had the Massachusetts Medical
Society. In November, twelve of these children were
sent to a special hospital erected on Noddle's Island,
where they were inoculated with matter taken from
a patient in the most infectious stage of the disease.
Some were inoculated a second time and control cases
were used. All the committee were convinced that
cowpox was 'a complete security against the small-
pox.'

This decisive experiment had the desired effect of
definitely establishing the practice of vaccination in
Massachusetts. Other experiments were tried near
by and all were successful. Waterhouse's second report was published in 1802 at Cambridge, a much
longer and more thorough communication than the
first, giving the actual notes of his cases as well as
numerous extracts from the literature.

The success of Waterhouse's vaccination was granted, at last, by his brother physicians; the man was never accepted, even by his closest colleagues. Things were not going well at the Medical School, and there was continued friction between Waterhouse, the Professor of Theory and Practice of Medicine, and John Warren, the Professor of Anatomy. Waterhouse was formally charged, before the Corporation of Harvard College, with 'embarrassing the affairs of the medical institute; secondly, being engaged in support of plans inimical to its interest, and, thirdly, being guilty of duplicity and want of veracity.' His defence was strong and he was able to show that his enemies were actuated by selfish motives. In spite of his victory, Waterhouse sensed the feeling against him and he resigned from the College in 1812, after a service of nearly thirty years. He withdrew largely from the profession and devoted himself to literary work, occasionally writing on medical subjects.

Waterhouse's character was a most unusual one. He deserves the greatest credit for the method by which he convinced the physicians of the New World of the value of vaccination. All his other work, including the development of his department at the Medical School, is insignificant compared with his work on vaccination, and he may truly be called 'the Jenner of America.' [1] He died in Cambridge in 1846, just before the public demonstration of the value of ether as an anæsthetic.

[1] Welch, W. M.: *The Jenner of America.* Philadelphia, 1885.

HOW THE PRESIDENT, THOMAS JEFFERSON, AND DOCTOR BENJAMIN WATERHOUSE ESTABLISHED VACCINATION AS PUBLIC HEALTH PROCEDURE

Robert H. Halsey

RECTOR ET SENATUS ACADEMIAE LUGDUNO-BATAVAE LECTORIBUS SALUTEM.

Laudabili instituto Majorum nostrorum receptae consuetudini ut ii qui Artis Medicinae sese peritiam et eruditionem coram nobis satis probaverint gradu et honoribus Doctoris ornarentur ... BENJAMIN WATERHOUSE, Anglicanus, aliquoties nobis satisfecit ... MEDICINAE ... CORPORIS HUMANI, ejusque in explicandis et curandis morbis necessaria consideratione ... MEDICINAE ... MEDICINAE ... BENJAMINUM ... Gulielmi Virginia Philadelphia ... MEDICINAE DOCTOREM MEDICINA ...

MEDICINAE DOCTORES
DOCTORI

... die XV Junii MDCCLXXX

J.J. Mohr
Promotor

J.P. Ruttinh
Secretarius

How the President, Thomas Jefferson,
and
Doctor Benjamin Waterhouse
ESTABLISHED VACCINATION AS
A PUBLIC HEALTH PROCEDURE

HISTORY OF MEDICINE SERIES
ISSUED UNDER THE AUSPICES OF THE
LIBRARY OF THE NEW YORK ACADEMY OF MEDICINE
No. 5.

How the President, Thomas Jefferson,

and

Doctor Benjamin Waterhouse

ESTABLISHED VACCINATION AS A PUBLIC HEALTH PROCEDURE

By ROBERT H. HALSEY, M.D.

PRESENTED BEFORE THE SECTION OF HISTORICAL AND
CULTURAL MEDICINE, NEW YORK ACADEMY OF MEDICINE
MARCH 14, 1934

PUBLISHED BY THE AUTHOR

NEW YORK

1936

ACKNOWLEDGMENT

As I have gathered this material from many sources I have received much cordial assistance and many helpful suggestions. To all of these generous givers, though their names remain unpublished, I wish to acknowledge my indebtedness and express my sincere appreciation.

R. H. H.

In the last week of September 1932, I was at the University of Virginia, at Charlottesville, Va. To pass a few unscheduled moments, I sought the library to learn if there was anything unique I might see. I was shown a photostat copy of the letter written by Thomas Jefferson, September 12, 1801, to Dr. John Shore, of Petersburg, Va.[1] The description of the technique of inoculation and the record of results resembled in every way such a table as a practitioner of today might present in reporting a series of cases, and it aroused and stimulated my interest to learn more of the interest in smallpox evidenced by the President and Dr. Waterhouse. When I returned to New York City it was not a difficult task to find in the library of the Academy of Medicine the published letters of Thomas Jefferson to Dr. Waterhouse, but nowhere could I find a hint of the existence of, nor a reference to, any letters from Dr. Waterhouse to President Jefferson. My interest was stimulated by the difficulty, since they would complete the history of the episode. After visiting the libraries and historical societies of New York, Boston, Worcester, New Haven, as well as the Medical Libraries of Boston and New York without finding a reference, the Library of Congress suggested itself as a possible repository of information and there I was delighted to discover and rescue all but one of the letters from Dr. Waterhouse to President Jefferson.

In this correspondence the story of how and why Dr. Waterhouse sought the aid of the President elect was revealed and as the story develops it is a fascinating description of the application of empirical medicine to public health. The letters to and fro between them tell the cogent reasons for each step in the development of a new public health procedure: a procedure which has made possible the increase in population and development of this country and the world at large, along lines and with a speed which would have been impossible without the wide application of the cowpox vaccination promulgated by Jenner: a procedure which performed and continues to perform a miracle for community health, happiness, and the preservation of life.

The introduction of any new medical procedure affecting public health is attended by certain very definite reactions by the medical profession and the public. Objections are often raised by the profession because of doubt as to the validity of the claims until they can be fully

[1] P. 41.

[1]

substantiated, and, also, because of professional jealousies and rivalries. Objections are made by the public from ignorance of the procedure and from fear of the imposition of restrictions, and the public, too, may be jealous because of local, city, or state political rivalries.

The episode of introducing vaccination aroused both the personal and professional jealousies of New England, and evoked the bitter opposition of all the influences which made the political questions of Federalism and Jeffersonism contribute so much heat to the social life of the University and the community. The result of these social and political forces was disastrous to the professional and financial fortunes of the doctor. To understand Jefferson's interest in the medical problem it is necessary to survey briefly his broad experiences, for it will be understood why he was prepared to accept eagerly the suggestions of Dr. Waterhouse.

The letters have led to an inquiry concerning the technique of inoculation, the preparation and after treatment, the legal obstructions to its use and the political difficulties, social and medical, which weave into and in fact are controlling forces. The essential items are included.

Thomas Jefferson was born in Shadwell, Albemarle County, Virginia, April 2, 1743, and he died at Monticello, July 4, 1826, a few minutes before John Adams, who died in Boston. He was always interested in new ideas, inventions or discoveries. He was inoculated with matter of smallpox by Dr. William Shippen,[2] of Philadelphia, when aged twenty-three.[3]

The method of preparation and care of the person to be inoculated with small-pox is described by the recognized authority of the times— Baron Dimsdale. Whether the method was used by various men advertising to inoculate and care for the person is not told, but as described by Thomas Dimsdale [3a] it is as follows: "Abstain from all animal food, including broths, also butter and cheese, and from all fermented liquors, excepting small beer, which is allowed sparingly, and from all spices, and whatever possesses a manifest heating quality. The diet is to consist of pudding, gruel, sago, milk, rice-milk, fruit pyes, greens, roots, and vegetables of all the kinds in season, prepared or raw. Eggs, though not to be eat alone, are allowed in puddings, and butter in pye-crust; the patients are to be careful that they do not eat such a quantity as to overload their stomachs, even of this kind of food. Tea, coffee, or chocolate are permitted for breakfast, to those who choose or are accustomed to them. In this manner they are to proceed about nine or ten days before the operation; during

[2] Surgeon in the U. S. Army, 1776–1781,—died 1808.
[3] A. J. Nock, pp. 12–14; "Life and Letters of Jefferson," Francis W. Hirst, Macmillan, 1926.
[3a] "The present Method of inoculating for Small-pox,"—Second Edition, London, 1767.

[2]

this period, at nearly equal distances, they are directed to take three doses of the following powder, either made into pills, or mixed with a little syrup or jelly, at bed-time, and a dose of Glauber's salt, dissolved in thin water gruel, each succeeding morning.

"The powder is composed of eight grains of calomel, the same quantity of the compound powder of crabs claws, and one eighth part of a grain of emetic tartar. Instead of emetic tartar, I have sometimes substituted two grains of precipitated sulphur of antimony. In order to facilitate the division of the doses, a large quantity is prepared at once, and great care taken that the mixture is well performed."

In the *Annual Register* 1781, London, 1782, the method of after-care is described by the Baron as follows: "After the inoculation is performed, the rules laid down concerning diet are to be observed; and a proper attention being paid to prevent costiveness. No more medicines are usually given till the fifth or sixth evening after the operation; On one of which, according to the greater or less apparent inflammation of the infected arms, I repeat the same quantity of the powder as before. As this quantity commonly produces in children two or three stools on the following day, no further medicine is necessary for them. But to adults I usually prescribe a gentle purgative the morning after the exhibition of the powder, and the repetition, or omission, of the powder in all cases, is to be regulated according to the symptoms. Sometimes a third dose is ordered about the time of the eruption."

Later, in September 1782, after the death of his wife, Jefferson took "his children and his wards, the Carrs, to be inoculated at Amphill, the residence of Col. Archibald Cary, who had lent it to him for the purpose." [3b] He acted as their chief nurse and it was while he was there with them that he received the notification from Congress that he had been appointed for the third time Plenipotentiary to Europe.

He found leisure to work out several devices of his own but never patented one. He expressed his views in the sentence that: "Never having thought of monopolizing by patent any useful idea which happens to offer itself to me," and whenever he had devised anything useful he stated that: "As soon as I can speak of its effect with certainty I shall probably describe it anonymously in the public papers, in order to forestall the prevention of its use by some interloping patentee." He would have nothing to do with patents for he had no taste for money made from any form of monopoly. He is said to have written to Madison that: "No sentiment is more acknowledged in the family of agriculturists than that the few who can afford it should incur the risk and expense of all new improvements, and give the benefit freely to the many of more restricted circumstances."

[3b] Gene Lisitzky, "Thomas Jefferson," The Viking Press.

[3]

While he was Ambassador to France he traveled during a leisure period to Italy and brought back some rice seed, because of an embargo, in his overcoat pockets. These samples were sent by different routes to Charleston, S. C. Later, in 1800, while he was Vice-President, he distributed "one hundred varieties of rice from the Philippine Islands. Several gentlemen took samples to determine whether either of the species ought to be introduced into this country. Some of the samples are of rice which grows on high land." Whenever he heard of a new device that bore upon farming, he promptly looked it up and wrote about it to his fellow farmers. Thus while his services to practical agriculture netted him little or nothing, they were of great benefit to the farmers to whom he contributed new knowledge.

When drafting an ordinance for the temporary government of the Northwestern Territory he showed his opinions of slavery by inserting an anti-slavery clause which, however, was struck out by Congress by the narrow margin of only one vote.

He was Vice-President during John Adams' administration and in 1800 was nominated as an opposition candidate. Claud G. Bowers in his "Jefferson and Hamilton" [5] states that Hamilton approached Jay in a letter about Jefferson with the statement, "In times like these, it will not do to be over scrupulous. There should be no objection to taking of legal and constitutional steps to prevent an atheist in religion and a fanatic in politics from getting possession of the helm of state." The popular vote for Jefferson was so large that there was no doubt of the will of the country but the vote of the electors was a tie between Thomas Jefferson and Aaron Burr, who had not been even a candidate for the presidency. According to the law the greatest number of electoral votes indicated the President and the candidate receiving the next lower number of electoral votes became the Vice-President. The election was thus thrown into the House of Representatives for decision. Alexander Hamilton, chief of the Federalists, who had become embittered against Burr, stated that, "Upon every virtuous and prudent calculation Jefferson is to be preferred." Thus Alexander Hamilton who fought against Jefferson's election, expressed the judgment which finally made him President.

Life was hectic indeed during the months of the campaign and election; because under the Sedition Act it was possible and easy to arrest and convict any critics of the government's methods or acts, and impose a fine and imprisonment.

The clergy of Connecticut, to be able more powerfully to assist the Federalist party, organized a form of "jehad" or religious war, under

---

[4] "Medical Repository," 1800, I, p. 115. [5] P. 454.

the leadership of the Rev. Dr. Timothy Dwight, president of Yale and related by blood or marriage to nearly the whole of the little politico-economic oligarchy that had controlled Connecticut from its colonial beginnings. Some person tabulated and published this connection during the campaign of 1800. Dr. Dwight was called * the "Pope," and was said to dictate the policy and prayers of the "Illuminati." In a "discourse preached on the Fourth of July 1801," at New Haven, he included a list of some thirteen influential members. The printed oration with informing notes occupied a large share of several editions of the newspaper, the *New York Spectator,* and this oration is illuminating reading as it contains the expressed belief that secession of New England might be the solution of the political problems as they then appeared to the defeated Federalists. It shows the lengths to which they felt it might be necessary to go.

Jefferson, however, was tactful and pacific and in his first Inaugural address, March 4, 1801, expressed in the following words this sentiment; intending thereby to strengthen the union of the country and overlook the bitterness of the campaign: "Let us, then, fellow-citizens, unite with one heart and one mind. . . . Let us restore to social intercourse that harmony and affection without which liberty and even life itself are but dreary things. . . . But every difference of opinion is not a difference of principle. We have called by different names brethren of the same principle. We are all Republicans, we are all Federalists. If there be any among us who would wish to dissolve this Union or to change its republican form, let them stand undisturbed as monuments of the safety with which error of opinion may be tolerated where reason is left free to combat it. . . ."

Notwithstanding all these many interests and political obligations, the correspondence with Dr. Waterhouse shows Jefferson to have been from the first profoundly impressed with the promise of eliminating smallpox, a disease whose ravages in death and disfigurement he knew were great. He had early appreciated this and on two occasions demonstrated his fear of the disease and his acceptance of the then only known method of acquiring immunity—by inoculation with the disease.

When, therefore, Dr. Waterhouse revealed a new and benign method of preventing the disease, he was prepared, from his knowledge and by his personal experience, to accept it, and his enthusiasm and confidence were increased by trying the procedure on his slaves and relatives, and by persuading and teaching physicians whom he knew to use it.

* A. J. Nock, "Life and Letters of Jefferson," 1926.

[5]

In 1803 he instructed Capt. Meriwether Lewis, his secretary, whom he loved "as if he had been my own son," when about to leave on the expedition up the Missouri and Columbia Rivers, to "Take them some cowpox for vaccination." [7] This is probably the earliest instruction bearing on preventive medicine ever given by a President to the officers of an American government expedition.

Having demonstrated that cowpox did prevent smallpox and that he had introduced into Virginia the real disease of cowpox, he was eager and glad to ascribe to Dr. Waterhouse the credit for the public health accomplishment. Dr. Waterhouse on his part ascribed to Jefferson the credit of accelerating the introduction of cowpox inoculation into Virginia by "at least two years."

Doctor Benjamin Waterhouse [8] was born in the house at the corner of Marlborough and Farewell Street, Newport, Rhode Island. His father, Timothy, was born at Portsmouth, New Hampshire, the son of a Timothy and moved to Newport, Rhode Island, where he married Hannah Proud, May 1738. [9] Hannah Proud [10] was the daughter of Rebeckah Fothergill, [11] an aunt of Dr. John Fothergill, a celebrated London physician. [12]

At the age of sixteen he was apprenticed to Dr. John Halliburton of Newport, Rhode Island, to study medicine. Having worked with the doctor for several years it was decided that he should go to London to study with Doctor Fothergill, who was at the height of his fame. He sailed in 1775 in the last boat to leave Boston before the British blockade, arriving in London in April. In the following autumn he entered the medical school at Edinburgh and studied under William Cullen, [12a] Joseph Black, [12b] and Alexander Munro, [12c] who were at the height of their influence. The next year, 1776, he returned to London and worked with Dr. Fothergill. While living and studying with Dr. Fothergill it is probable he met John Hunter, John C. Lettsom, Edward Jenner and many others who were intimate with the doctor and prominent in medical circles.

He enrolled as a student at Leyden in 1778, and signed himself, "A citizen of the free and United States of America." This statement aroused discussion and fear of international difficulties, if permitted to

[7] Charles Morrow Wilson, "Meriwether Lewis of Lewis and Clark," 1934, Thomas Y. Crowell Co., New York.
[8] Born March 4, 1754, died October 2, 1846.
[9] Recorded in "Book of Minutes of Monthly Meeting of Friends," Newport Historical Society, Newport, R. I.
[10] Born November 30, 1712, died at Cambridge, Mass., May 18, 1802.
[11] Born at Carr End, Yorkshire, England, July 7, 1684 and died at Newport, R. I., May 16, 1732.
[12] Records in Society of Friends Library, London, Eng.
[12a] Born 1710, died 1790.　　[12b] Born 1728, died 1799.　　[12c] Born 1733, died 1817.

remain. He delivered a graduation dissertation in Latin on the subject of "Sympathy" and received a diploma April 19, 1780.

He devoted much time to the study of experimental philosophy, mineralogy and botany, as well as to medicine. His knowledge of these subjects made it possible later for him to give courses in them at Brown University and at Harvard, where his collections formed the nucleus of the subsequent collections of minerals and botanical specimens.

While a student on the Continent he met and lived with John Adams and his two sons. A volume of letters from John Adams to Waterhouse have been published by Mr. W. C. Ford under the title of "Statesman and Friend" and a subsequent group in the *Atlantic Monthly*, 1927, entitled "John Adams as He Lived." The letters of Waterhouse to Adams have not been published so it is not known what suggestions or statements of his may have colored these replies. During his travels he became acquainted with Benjamin Franklin.

After receiving his degree for his medical studies he set out for home. Because of the unsettled state of the political relations between Great Britain and the Colonies, which had become the United States, Dr. Waterhouse traveled down to Spain in September 1781, then across to Teneriffe and from there to Cuba where he arrived in January 1782. He visited some of the Bahama Islands and arrived at Rhode Island in June 1782. He probably intended to practice in Newport where he arrived just after Dr. Haliburton, his former preceptor, had left, possibly because of his royalist sympathies, for Halifax.

After his arrival in Newport, events brought Dr. Waterhouse in contact with the Governor of Massachusetts, who was so impressed that he persuaded the young doctor to present a copy of his dissertation to the University at Cambridge; and there is in the minutes of the Corporation [18] this paragraph: "Dr. Benjamin Waterhouse of Newport, having through the hands of his Excellency the Governor presented his Latin dissertation of Sympathy to this University, Voted that the thanks of this Board be given to the Doctor for this mark of his esteem and regard for this literary Society."

During the preceding winter of 1780–1781, Dr. John Warren had given a course of anatomical demonstrations at the Military Hospital in Boston to medical men and others. These clinics were received with so much enthusiasm that on November 30, 1781, the Boston Medical Society voted that "Dr. John Warren be desired to demonstrate a course of anatomical lectures the ensuing winter." Among those who attended this series of lectures were President Willard, of the University, and

[18] "College Book No. 8," p. 123, September 17, 1782.

[7]

some other members of the Corporation. The outcome of the courses were several conferences and Dr. Warren was requested to submit a plan for a medical school. He wrote to Thomas L. Shippen of Philadelphia for information as to the manner in which the University of Pennsylvania Medical School was administered. He learned among other things that the professors of anatomy were paid five half Joes—in Philadelphia £15-0-0 (£6-10-0 Sterling)—and the other professors six Pistoles—in Philadelphia £8-8-7 (£4-0-0 Sterling).[14] The minutes of the Corporation[15] state that a committee was appointed to "take up the subject at large and report at some future meeting."

In September 1782 it was noted in the minutes,[16] "that as soon as ways and means can be devised for raising sufficient funds for the encouragement of Professors of Anatomy and Surgery, the theory and practice of physic, the materia medica and chemistry, Professorships of these branches be founded in the University."[17] On November 22, 1782, the Corporation voted the three professorships and Dr. John Warren "was chosen," the "first elected Professor" who was to "superintend all branches so far as may be consistent." Further consideration of the candidates for the professorships of theory and practice of physic and of chemistry was postponed.

Such then was the professorship situation at the end of November 1782 in Cambridge University—one professor elected and two to be elected. An eligible physician, lately returned from travel and study in Europe with a degree in Medicine from the, at that time, world famous Leyden, who had met the Governor of the State and through him had been invited to present his graduation thesis to the Corporation which had accepted and officially thanked him for it, was an available candidate. It is with little astonishment that we read the record in the minutes[18] of the Corporation for December 24, 1782, that "Written votes being brought in for a Professor of Theory and Practice of Physic it appears that Benjamin Waterhouse, M.D., was chosen," and "The President [John Willard] and Treasurer and the Rev. Mr. Lathrop" were appointed a committee "to wait upon Dr. Waterhouse with the above vote and desire his acceptance of the Professorship to which he is chosen, provided the Overseers vote their concurrence."

But the Overseers, who met on January 2, 1783, saw no reason for haste and postponed consideration to January 20, when the "Vote of the Corporation electing Dr. Waterhouse Professor was taken up and after some debate," it was "voted that consideration of this election be further referred to the adjournment of this meeting." Thus it was not

---

[14] London value and rate of exchange from "Poor Wills Almanack 1784."
[15] "College Book No. 8," May 16, 1782.
[16] *Ibid.*, p. 117.   [17] *Ibid.*   [18] *Ibid.*

until February 3, 1783, that the Overseers [19] "voted to concur with the Corporation in the election of Benjamin Waterhouse, M.D., to be Professor of Theory and Practice of Physic."

It was not until May 22, 1783, that Dr. Aaron Dexter was chosen to the third professorship, and it was September 1st before the Corporation "Voted to induct the professors into office the first Tuesday in October, if agreeable to the Honorable and Reverend Board of Overseers," and the Overseers "Voted it be agreeable."

It is quite evident, therefore, from these minutes of the Overseers that there was a serious and powerful opposition to the election of the young doctor, aged twenty-eight, from Rhode Island, and justified in great measure the statement written by Dr. Waterhouse in a letter—the original in the Warren Papers—to Dr. Lettsom in 1789, that: "The Corporation elected him Professor of the Theory and Practice of Physic and invited him into the Massachusetts . . ." and "When he came he experienced a strong torrent of opposition from the Physicians of Boston, who thought themselves overlooked and affronted by this preference given to so young a man, and who was not a son of their college, and [some illiberally added] a Quaker." To be a Quaker was even then a serious charge against any person, for it was only a century earlier, in the years 1656 to 1663, that the people of Boston, or the Massachusetts government, had sold Quaker children into slavery in the West Indies and tortured or killed members of the Sect.[20] And further in the same letter he complains that he was constrained to move from Boston to Cambridge, "because no Professor can be entitled to a salary who does not reside in Cambridge," "since which the Corporation has done all in their power to settle the Herseian donation upon him, trifling as it is . . . but the Overseers have at length determined that even that, cannot be legally given to him, as his title does not correspond with the words of the will, which says, 'the interest of a Thousand pounds to a Professor of Anatomy and Physic.' "[21] The will of Dr. Hersey which was proved in 1770 stated that the fund was for the "Support of a Professor of Anatomy and Physic and for that use only."

It was not until September 1791 that it appeared to the Corporation, after the widow of Dr. Hersey had bequeathed an additional thousand pounds, "that the design of these worthy Benefactors can be better answered by placing two Professors upon those funds and dividing those branches between them, than by having them united in one." It was May 1792 when the Overseers voted "that the interest of these legacies be equally divided between the Professor of Anatomy and

[19] *Ibid.*, p. 258. [21] "College Book No. 4," p. 332.
[20] J. T. Adams, "The March of Democracy," Charles Scribner's Sons, 1932.

Surgery and the Professor of the Theory and Practice of Physic, and that the former be stiled Herseian Professor of Anatomy and Surgery and the latter Herseian Professor of the Theory and Practice of Physic." Thus for nine years the matter had dragged on with an evident undercurrent of opposition to Dr. Waterhouse. During this time he had offered his resignation [22] which had not been accepted and he had been persuaded to withdraw it. During the next few years Dr. Waterhouse was involved in litigation with a former student for a matter of forty dollars and he had appealed the court decisions and the matter had dragged on for several years, during which time he had endeavored by letters and conferences to persuade his confreres, Dr. Warren and Dr. Dexter, to make certain definite statements in court but they appear to have been irritated the more, rather than persuaded. The organized profession had developed such an antagonistic state of mind toward the doctor that they were inclined to oppose anything emanating from him, not so much because of a low estimate of the value of the procedure, but because they were out of patience with the doctor.

Dr. O. W. Holmes,[23] a Professor of Anatomy and Physiology from 1847 to 1882 of the medical school, some years later has described in several of his essays with a dry and incisive humour his knowledge and opinion of the doctor as follows:

Benjamin Waterhouse, honorably known for having been the introducer of vaccination into America, was the first Professor of the Theory and Practice of Medicine. I remember him well, and carry the scar of the vaccination he performed on me. His powdered hair and queue, were familiar to me from my boyhood. Dr. Waterhouse had his degree from Leyden, where he wrote and defended a thesis, *De Sympathia, Partium corporis Humani, ejusque in explicandis et curandis morbis necessaria consideratione.*[23a] He had some learning, which he was disposed to make the most of, as perhaps we all are if we have it, and laid himself open to the playful sallies of the students of his time, one of whom announced a course of Lectures on Oudenology, which was supposed to be a travesty of some of his prelections.[24]

Dr. Holmes describes Dr. Waterhouse as rather a comical figure about Cambridge, "a brisk, dapper old gentleman, with hair tied in a ribbon behind and, I think, powdered, marching smartly about with his gold-headed cane, with a look of questioning sagacity and an utterance of oracular gravity. The good people of Cambridge listened to his learned

[22] *Boston Polyanthus*, 1806, Vol. II, p. 73.   [23] Born 1809, died 1894.
[23a] Quoted from the diploma.
[24] P. 5. The Address delivered in Huntington Hall by Oliver Wendell Holmes, "Addresses and Exercises at the One Hundredth Anniversary of the Foundation of the Medical School of Harvard University, Oct. 17, 1883, Cambridge." John Wilson & Son, University Press, 1884.

DOCTOR BENJAMIN WATERHOUSE

From the painting by Gilbert Stuart who was a fellow student and intimate friend of Dr. Waterhouse. The original painting is at the Redwood Library and Atheneum, Newport, R. I.

(Published by courtesy of the Frick Art Reference Library, New York)

PRESIDENT THOMAS JEFFERSON
From the Birch enamel miniature in the collection of Mrs. A. K. W. Mitchell
(Published by courtesy of the Frick Art Reference Library, New York)

talk when they were well, and sent for one of the other two doctors when they were sick. He probably liked to write and talk about medicine better than to practice it." [25]

In his novel, "Elsie Venner," Dr. Holmes refers to Doctor Waterhouse rather critically in the paragraph on testimonials, as follows:

"It was harder still, if he had been induced to venture a few tremulous remarks, to be obliged to write them out for the *Rockland Weekly Universe,* with the chance of seeing them used as an advertising certificate as long as he lived, if he lived as long as the late Dr. Waterhouse did after giving his certificate in favor of Whitwell's celebrated Cephalic Snuff." [26]

In his essay "Some of my Early Teachers" he writes: "Dr. Benjamin Waterhouse, whom I remember, came back from Leyden, where he had written his Latin graduating thesis, talking of the learned Gaubius and the late illustrious Boerhaave and other dead Dutchmen," and in the essay, "Scholastic and Bedside Teaching," Holmes writes of "that somewhat peculiar personage, who took it hardly when Dr. James Jackson succeeded to his place as Professor of Theory and Practice."

The real story of the introduction of vaccination begins in 1799, when Dr. Waterhouse received a copy of the work of Jenner. He was so impressed with its value that he appreciated the importance of informing the public and the profession concerning it. He published a report of the method and its effectiveness in the *Columbian Sentinel,* entitled, "SOMETHING CURIOUS IN THE MEDICAL LINE."

EVERY body has heard of those distempers, accompanied with pocks or pustlees, called the *smallpox,* the *chicken-pox* and the *swine-pox,* but few have ever heard of the *cow-pox,* or if you like the term better, the *cow small-pox;* or to experts it is in technical language, the *variolae vaccinae.* There is, however, such a disease, which has been noticed here and there in several parts of England, more particularly in Gloucestershire, for sixty or seventy years past, but has never been an object of medical inquiry until very lately.

THIS *variolae vaccinae* or *cow-pox,* is very readily communicated to those who milk cows infected with it. This malady appears first on the teats of the cows in the form of irregular pustles or pocks. [27] They are commonly of a palish blue, somewhat approaching to livid, and surrounded by an erysipelatous inflammation, resembling the St. Anthony's fire. These pustles, unless timely remedied, degenerate into those ragged ulcers known by the surgeons under the name of *phagedenic.* The cows soon become sick, and the secretion of milk is lessened, but I never heard of one dying with it. Those who milk cows thus effected, seldom or ever

[25] "The Harvard Medical School, 1782–1906," p. 16.
[26] Dr. Oliver W. Holmes, "Elsie Venner," p. 165, Riverside Press Edition, 1861.
[27] See Jenner, pp. 3 and 4.

fail catching the distemper, *if there be cracks, wounds, or abrasions in the hands.* That is to say, they are *inoculated.* When infected, there appear on different parts of the hands and wrists, inflamed spots, having the appearance of blisters, produced by burns. These run quickly on to suppuration. These superficial suppurations have a circular form with their edges more elevated than the center, very much resembling a certain stage of the small-pox. These depressed pustles or pocks, are of a colour approaching to blue. Absorption now takes place, and a soreness and sometimes tumors appear in the arm pits. Then the arterial system becomes affected; the pulse is quickened, and shivering with a general lassitude and pains in the back and limbs supervene, and these symptoms are not unfrequently accompanied with vomiting. There is too, a pain in the head and dizziness. These symptoms varying in their degrees and violence, generally continue from one day to three or four, leaving ulcerated sores about the hands, resembling those on the cow teats, from whence they sprung. The lips, nostrils and eye-lids are sometimes affected with sores, but these evidently arise from their being rubbed or scratched with the patient's infected fingers. This is the common course of the disease with the human species. *No person was ever known to die of this distemper,* but what makes this newly discovered disease so very curious, and so extremely important is, that every person thus affected, is EVER AFTER SECURED FROM THE ORDINARY SMALL-POX, *let him be ever so much exposed to the effluvium of it, or let ever so much ripe matter be inserted into the skin by inoculation.* In other words—a person who has undergone the *local* disease and *specific fever* occasioned by the cow-pox infection, is *thereby rendered ever after unsusceptible of the small-pox.** It is worthy of remark that the infection of the cow-pox can be conveyed to the human species by the ordinary mode of inoculation. And it is observed, that there is no difference in the effects of the matter taken from the cow, and of the matter generated successively in the second, third, fourth or fifth human creature.

SUCH are the outlines of a mild disease, the knowledge of which may lead to consequences of the utmost importance to the whole human race, no less indeed than that *of superceding, if not extinguishing, that terrible scourge, the small-pox.*

DR. EDWARD JENNER, is the physician in England, who has collected and arranged a series of facts and experiments respecting the disease called there the *cow-pox.* His short work is commended on by DR. GEORGE PEARSON, physician to St. George's hospital, London.

THIS imperfect sketch is thrown into the newspaper at this time, with a view of exciting the attention of our dairy farmers to such a distemper among their cows. It may also be gratifying to some of the faculty of medicine, who, it is presumed, are not yet generally informed of an

* See Dr. Pearson's Publication.

epizootic disease, capable of being communicated from the brute to the human kind, and which when communicated, is *a certain security against the small-pox.* The public anxiety has been routed of late, to search after the cause of a destructive *fever.* Their attention has been directed merely to *effluvia, vapours* or *gasses,* while they may here see a disease, the *nearest a kin* to the small-pox of any yet known, which is never communicated by effluvia, or medium of the air. It is highly probable that some of the most distressing diseases which afflict mankind, have an *animal* origin; and time may prove, that small-pox, whooping-cough, and one kind of quincy, have like the hydrophobia, a similar source."[29]

Cambridge, March 12, 1799.

In June 1800 he received some "matter" from Dr. John Haygarth, of Bath. To convince himself he tried it at once on his family, Daniel Oliver Waterhouse, age 5; Benjamin Waterhouse Second, age 3; Mary Waterhouse, age 1; and Eliza Watson Waterhouse, age 7; and successfully produced the kine pox. To prove the value of the cow, or kine, pox as a preventative against smallpox he now arranged with Dr. Aspinwall and published in the *Columbian Sentinel*[30] the result of the exposure to smallpox of his wife, four children and two domestics. He planned first to prove the fact of the potency of kine pox as a protection against smallpox and second to diffuse the knowledge of the procedure and of the technique.

Dr. Waterhouse (p. 67)[30a] relates that "In the beginning of the year 1799, I received from my friend Dr. Lettsom, of London, a copy of Dr. Edward Jenner's 'Inquiry into the causes and Effects of the Variolae Vaccinae, or Cow-Pock,' a disease totally unknown in this quarter of the world. On perusing this work, I was struck with the unspeakable advantages that might accrue to this country, and indeed to the human race at large, from the discovery of a mild distemper that would ever after secure the constitution from that terrible scourge, the small-pox."

.   .   .   .   .   .

Having thus traced (p. 70) the most important facts respecting the causes and effects of the kine-pock up to their source in England, and having confirmed most of them by actual experiment in America, one experiment only remained behind to complete the business. To effect this, I wrote the following letter to Dr. Aspinwall, physician to the Smallpox Hospital in the neighborhood of Boston.

[29] *Columbian Sentinel,* March 12, 1799.
[30] September 20, 1800.
[30a] Dr. John Coakley Lettsom, "Observations on the Cow-Pock," Edition 1800.

Cambridge, Aug. 2, 1800.

Dear Doctor,

You have doubtless heard of the newly-described disorder, known in England by the name of the cow-pock, which so nearly resembles the small-pox, that it is now agreed in Great Britain, that the former will pass for the latter.

I have collected everything that has been printed, and all the information I could procure from my correspondents, respecting this distemper, and have been (p. 71) so thoroughly convinced of its importance to humanity, that I have procured some of the vaccine matter, and therewith inoculated seven of my family. The inoculation has proceeded in six of them exactly as described by Jenner and Woodville; but my desire is to confirm the doctrine by having some of them inoculated by you.

I can obtain variolous matter, and inoculate them privately, but I wish to do it in the most open and public way possible. As I have imported a new distemper, I conceive that the public have a right to know exactly every step I take in it. I write this, therefore, to enquire whether you will, on philanthropic principles, try the experiment of inoculating some of my children who have already undergone the Cow-pock. If you accede to my proposal, I shall consider it as an experiment in which we have cooperated for the good of our fellow-citizens (p. 72), and relate it as such in the pamphlet I mean to publish on the subject, I am, & &

B. W.

Hon. William Aspinwall, Esq.
Brookline.

To this letter the Doctor returned a polite answer, assuring me of his readiness to give any assistance in his power, to ascertain *whether the Cow-pock would prevent the* small-pox; observing, that he had at that time fresh matter that he could depend on, and desiring me to send the children to the hospital for that purpose. Of the three which I offered, the Doctor chose to try the experiment on the boy of twelve years of age, whom he inoculated in my presence by two punctures, and with matter taken that moment from a patient who had it pretty full upon him. He at the same time inserted an infected thread, and then put him into the hospital, where was one patient with it in the natural way. On the 4th day, the Doctor pronounced the arm to be infected. It became every hour sorer (p. 73), but in a day or two it dried off, and grew well, without producing the slightest trace of a disease; so that the boy was dismissed from the hospital, and returned home the 12th day after the experiment. One fact, in such cases, is worth a thousand arguments.

Following the definitely conceived plan the doctor, desiring to spread the knowledge of kine pox, published articles in the newspapers, which was an ethical procedure in those days as there were no journals exclusively medical. He appealed, also, to his old friend John Adams, the then President of the United States, as well as the president of a scientific organization, sending him a copy of the newspaper article and a booklet. He received a reply dated September 10, 1800,[81] in which the President stated: "I have received and will communicate to the American Academy of Arts and Sciences, your 'Prospect of exterminating the Small Pox.'

"I have read this history of the Kine Pox with pleasure. Your Zeal and Industry to give the experiment fair play in America deserve the thanks of all the Friends of Science and Humanity.

"To disarm the Small Pox of its contagion is an enterprise worthy of a Hercules in Medicine."

Dr. Waterhouse desired to have the Massachusetts Medical Society take some action, but it was undoubtedly influenced by the medical men who were unsympathetic to any action the doctor might sponsor. He describes his plan for proving the efficacy of the technique in the fifth paragraph of the appendix of "A prospect of exterminating the Small-pox":

To those of the faculty who have applied to him by letter to supply them with matter for inoculation—he would just observe that as he has taken much pains in this business, run no small risk of reputation, as well as of personal feelings, there are *few* he trusts, that will wonder he is anxious to have the matter under his own eye until the practice is more firmly established by the public opinion. Some unsuccessful cases at the beginning, deprived Scotland of the blessings of inoculation for the small pox for more than 20 years. He hopes this idea will operate as an excuse at present, even in the mind of his ci-devant pupils. . . . Dr. Waterhouse is happy to find that every GENTLEMAN of the faculty in Boston and its vicinity, has understood this, and conducted accordingly.[82]

The strength and character of the opposition of one of the professors of the medical faculty to a discussion of the use or application of vaccination is evident by the disinclination of Dr. John Warren, who wrote to his son, John Collins Warren, addressing him as a, "Student of Physick," Borough of London. This letter is dated a few weeks after Dr. Waterhouse had published the account of the successful vaccination of his son and his exposure to virulent smallpox without taking the disease. The paragraph from the letter follows:

[81] W. C. Ford, "Statesman & Friend," Little Brown & Co., 1927.
[82] "A Prospect of exterminating the Small-pox," Benjamin Waterhouse, 1800 (Cambridge Press by William Hilliard, Boston, 1800), N. Y. Academy of Medicine, Bound Pamphlets, Vol. 29.

"The Cow or Kine pox is making some noise here—I wish you had thought of procuring and sending me some matter as Dr. Waterhouse is the only Physician who has received it from London and has begun to practice and the other Physicians can not readily obtain it. John and I like to know from you what its present character is and if you can easily obtain it and send in a closely sealed Phial. I may possibly have it in that way sooner than any other." [33]

There were other and quite bitter opponents, who heaped calumny upon the doctor and made his life dangerous by persecution as they believed that taking the virus of cowpox from a cow and putting it into a child had the effect of slowly but surely turning the human into the animal kind. One of these unseen and anonymous opponents who was fearful of the effects of the kine pox, possibly on what he considered his own vested interests, desiring to express his doubt and disapproval prognosticated the certain outcome of the doctor's sagacity, but fearing the revelation of his name, published in the newspaper a paragraph entitled "KINE POX."

It happens however that sagacity is not quite monopolized, by faculty, and that the public can faintly discern without the assistance of an occulist; which being the case, I am ready to predict, that not only the sensibility of this *Philanthropist*, but his *popularity* will require both philosophical, and medical aid, to become perfectly hale: and that the practice, with which he commences will silently pilot him back to his native dunghill.

PEDRO. [34]

From his contacts in Boston, Dr. Waterhouse became convinced that President Adams was too preoccupied, or disinclined, to assist him in establishing the reputation of kine pox inoculation. The reasons for his conviction of Mr. Adams' disinterestedness are contained in the abstract from a letter to Dr. Tilton:

Cambridge 24th March, 1815.
When Mr. Jefferson came into office, the late Judge Lowell, a leading man of the *Junto,* and a very influential governor of this University, and a warm friend of mine, gave us, of the college to understand, that the church and all our other sacred institutions were in danger, particularly the University, that therefore it behoved us Professors to rally with the clergy, and together form *the front rank* in the Massachusetts *army of federalism,* in opposition to infidelity, Jacobinism and Jeffersonism. My associates, and

[33] Letter from John Warren, Boston, Aug. 30, 1800, to John Collins Warren, Student of Physick. No. 3 St. Thomas St., Borough London. Original in the Warren Papers, Massachusetts Historical Society.
[34] *Columbian Sentinel,* September 6, 1800.

the clergy very generally swallowed and relished this doctrine, while I remained rather silent.[85]

He considered, therefore, some action by him to be necessary as he was completely satisfied that kine pox would prevent smallpox and he was also persuaded that he owed it to the community and to the public generally to diffuse this knowledge among both the profession and the laity. To have the method brought to the key men of the profession through reliable channels became his immediate objective. Convinced of the merit of his plan he wrote to the Vice-President, who was then the popular candidate for election to the Presidency, Thomas Jefferson, on December 1, 1800, and received a prompt reply, dated December 25, 1800, at Washington.

Cambridge, Mass[t] Dec[r] 1, 1800.

Sir,

Having long regarded Mr. Jefferson as one of our most distinguished patriots & philosophers, I conceived that a work which had for its end the good of the community would not be unacceptable to him.—Under that impression I have here sent him *"a prospect of exterminating the small-pox,"* and am with the utmost consideration and respect

his very humble serv[t]

Honb[e] Thomas Jefferson.

Benj[n] Waterhouse.[86]

Washington, Dec. 25, 1800.

Sir:

I received last night, and have read with great satisfaction, your pamphlet on the subject of the kine-pock, and pray you to accept my thanks for the communication of it.

I had before attended to your publications on the subject in the news-papers, and took much interest in the result of the experiments you were making. Every friend of humanity must look with pleasure on this dis-covery, by which one evil more is withdrawn from the condition of man; and must contemplate the possibility, that future improvements and dis-coveries may still more and more lessen the catalogue of evils. In this line of proceeding you deserve well of your country; and I pray you accept my portion of the tribute due to you, and assurances of high consideration and respect, with which I am, Sir,

Your most obedient, humble servant,

Dr. Waterhouse, Cambridge.

Thomas Jefferson.[87]

[85] Abstract from letter of Benjamin Waterhouse to Dr. James Tilton.
[86] Benjamin Waterhouse to Thomas Jefferson, December 1, 1800, (MS.) Thomas Jefferson Papers, 108, 1800–1801. All the letters of Benjamin Waterhouse to Thomas Jefferson contained herein are to be found in the Library of Congress, Washington, D. C., and hitherto have been unpublished.
[87] Henry A. Martin, "Jefferson as a Vaccinator," *North Carolina Med. J.* 1881, VII, pp. 1–24. All the letters from Jefferson to Waterhouse are published in the *North Carolina Med. J.* 1881, VII.

As part of his plan to educate the public and the profession and refute false statements, Dr. Waterhouse went to Marblehead to investigate a smallpox epidemic reported by Drs. Story and Drury, as kine pox. He found the "matter had been taken from the arm of a sailor, on the passage between London and Marblehead by one of his brothers who was on board the ship." This is published in the newspaper of September 19, 1800.

To peep behind the scenes there is in the Warren Papers [38] a note by Dr. Warren that "the corresponding secretary of the Massachusetts Medical Society was to write to the physicians of Marblehead respecting cowpox and smallpox."

There is another note that "at the meeting of the Council of the Massachusetts Medical Society, a committee of three was to go to Marblehead. The three appointed were the president, the vice-president and Dr. Waterhouse." There is another note dated "June 3, 1801. In Council, two of Committee prevented from going, hence no official return and letters received by the corresponding secretary prevented the necessity of any further attention to the subject. Voted to publish such answers of the doctors of Marblehead as the President and Recording Secretary shall think proper." Another note states that, "Letters received from Dr. J. D. Treadwell, Elisha Story, Thomas Messinger and Dr. Waterhouse, Dr. Thomas Bartlett, two letters read giving account of his application to the Vaccine Institution for Cowpox."

In January 1801 the *Connecticut Gazette* published the news of the relief of the town of Marblehead.

The town of Marblehead, we are glad to hear, is relieved from the distresses occasioned by the Small pox. Sixty eight have died of the infection—of whom two were men, 12 women, 3 lads, 4 young women, and 47 children mostly infants. It is gratefully astonishing, that there has been but *two* adult funerals arising from any other sickness, during the prevalence of the small pox by inoculation which was from Nov 10 to Jan 11th. and these were languishments: whereas the week before, four women were interred belonging to one society only—A degree of health never known in the town before.

The *Kine-Pox* inoculation has failed in Marblehead, the details of which ought to be given by the physicians for the benefit of the public. However, it is only justice due to Dr. Waterhouse to acknowledge, that the two patients whom he inoculated with the Kine-Pox were exempted from the general contagion; whereas the other persons, who were supposed to have received the Kine-Pox were afterward the subjects of the small-pox to the number of 48. [39]

[38] Vol. V.
[39] *Connecticut Gazette and the Commercial Intelligencer,* Jan. 21, 1801.

A few days later the *Connecticut Journal* gives a gruesome picture of the dramatic effects of SMALLPOX inoculation in Halifax.

"We learn from Halifax that a general inoculation for the small pox, has been lately permitted there: and that the mortality has been very considerable, particularly among children. One letter mentions 800 deaths, infants and adults, and that one family lost seven persons." [40]

Nurse Toothaker, in "Edward Fane's Rosebud," says:

"She remembers when small-pox hoisted a red banner on almost every house along the street. She has witnessed when typhus fever swept off a whole household, young and old, all but a lonely mother, who vainly shrieked to follow her last loved one. . . ." [41]

In the Warren Papers there is a note by Dr. Warren indicating how serious were the effects of smallpox and inoculation:

"Particular account of Small pox by a Committee of the town of Boston in September and October 1792

Whites inoculated	8804
Died	158
Whites natural way	214
Died	27
Blacks inoculated	348
Died	7
Blacks natural way	18
Died	6"

The difficulties surrounding vaccination became complicated and April 24, 1801, Dr. Waterhouse wrote a letter to Jenner with an expression of appreciation of his aid and suggestions and the relating of some humorous comparisons and a note of recognition of the value of vaccination by the artillery engineers of the Coast Military Service. He describes with care and exactness the comparison of the local appearance of the inoculation with vaccine virus with the colored engravings sent by Jenner. It is indicative of his logical and scientific method that he wished to prove melons grown from seeds of melons raised by him in New England should grow melons similar to melons from which his seed was obtained and the similarity was to be judged by the person, Dr. Lettsom, who had sent the seed to him. Later he describes the accomplishment of the successful completion of a similar circuit of cowpox by vaccination with matter from cases of Mr. Jefferson. He then asserts the importance of Jenner's clarifying statement "for the benefit

[40] News item dated Boston, Jan. 20. *Connecticut Journal*, Jan. 29, 1801.
[41] Nathaniel Hawthorne, "Twice Told Tales."

of the Western World." He also relates the ingenious method of holding the public attention until he could procure new matter from Jenner by asserting that "the winter was an unfavorable season for this new inoculation." He describes experiments on cows by inoculation and he notes the benefit of vaccination upon weakly children with whooping-cough.

It is interesting to note his expression of astonishment at the fact that "not a single case of cow-pox inoculation has yet occurred in Philadelphia" and he pokes some fun at the "leading physician [probably Dr. Rush] who had pronounced it too beastly and indelicate for polished society!" He relates briefly the history of the library of Harvard and the loss of a large portion of the books by fire during a small-pox epidemic and closes by stating that "such an accident from such a cause can never happen again. Thanks to Dr. Jenner!"

Cambridge, April 24th, 1801.

DEAR SIR,

Being just informed of a ship's sailing to-morrow for London I have only time to acknowledge the receipt of your most excellent letter: the answer to it must be postponed a week or two longer. With it I received a supply of vaccine matter, which came to hand thirty-eight days after the date of your letter, for which you have my most cordial thanks. I have inoculated with it, and found it good, and here send you the first crop from it. When my good friend Dr. Lettsom has sent me curious melon seeds I have sent him as soon as possible some seed raised from them, that he might see whether our soil, atmosphere, and mode of culture effected any alteration from the original stock. The same I have now done with your Vaccine virus. It was taken on the 9th day, for the pustule afforded none on the 8th. I took the patient into my own house that I might watch the progress of the local affection, which I did with the microscope. It is now the tenth day in the morning, and I expect the efflorescence will, in ten or twelve hours more, put on the appearance of your *tenth day representation* in the coloured engravings.

It is impossible for me to express the great satisfaction your letter gave me. The subject was before involved in a mist: your letter was a ray of light, which ray must be reflected for the benefit of the western world. Oh! that it were possible for this ray to become still more brilliant and even generative at the point of repercussion.

I entirely agree with you as to the cause of our late failures in inoculation. The case at Geneva, under Dr. Odier, was ours exactly. One inch and a half of infected thread from Dr. Haygarth was the whole stock from whence perhaps 3,000 persons have been inoculated, but I fear the greatest part of them have been spurious. I here enclose a newspaper containing a communication written in the *clouds* last December. I will allow you to

[20]

smile at my mercurial and antimonial process, and likewise at my sextuple quantity of *deteriorated* virus! You know not what it is to be perplexed in this business. That prince of physiologists, John Hunter, once told me that "he loved to be puzzled, for then he was sure he should learn something valuable." Burthensome as it was at the time I do not now regret my perplexity. When I had lost my way, and wandered into the wilds of conjecture, I stood still. I gave out that the winter was an unfavourable season for this new inoculation, and by that means I suspended the practice throughout the country from that period until the arrival of fresh matter and your letter. Now we are going on again, but not with the faith and spirit of the last season. Some unlucky cases have damped the ardour of a people who received this new inoculation with a candour, liberality, and even generosity, much to their credit. The first political and literary characters in our nation are still warm advocates for the practice. I have lately received a request from head-quarters to supply the matter, and give the instructions to the regimental surgeons for inoculating the corps of artillerists and engineers stationed at different places on our coast.

Accept my thanks for the coloured plate.⁴² It is indeed a happy expedient, and honours the graphic art. It is thought here to be so important that I am anxious to know if I can with propriety procure more of them. I should wish to possess a couple of dozen to be deposited in the hands of some of our leading practitioners, or clergymen, in different parts of the United States by way of standards. If this could be done I would propose that your artist or bookseller should send them to my bookseller, Mr. Mawman in the Poultry, who will pay for them and transmit them to me. Could I procure two or three, delineating the appearances on the skin of the negro, I would send them into such of our southern states as are blackened by these degraded beings. I have lately had letters from Virginia, respecting matter, instruction, &c.

I have been informed from a quarter not likely to be deceived, that cows (contrary to my assertion in page 22 of my pamphlet) have been known to have the small-pox.

The account is this. At one of our periodical inoculations, which occurs in New England once in eight or nine years, several persons drove their cows to an hospital near a populous village, in order that their families might have the daily benefit of their milk. These cows were milked by persons in all stages of the small-pox: the consequence was, the cows had an eruptive disorder on their teats and udders, so like the small-pox pustule, that every one in the hospital, as well as the physician who told me, declared the cows had the small-pox. Since the cow-pox has been talked of this account has been revived and credited. Have you found any thing like this in England?

I inoculated one of my cows with the Vaccine virus, and obtained from her a crop of matter on the ninth day, which produced the disease in the

⁴² One of these is in the Library of the New York Academy of Medicine.

human subject to perfection. Is this experiment known among you? As I operated myself there was no avenue opened for deception in the whole experiment.

I have invariably found that weakly children have been benefited by the vaccine inoculation, and some it has cured of the whooping-cough.

Could you believe that not a single case of the cow-pox inoculation has yet occurred in Philadelphia? A young physician applied to me a few days since from that for the infection. It seems that the leading physician there pronounces it too beastly and indelicate for polished society! It is impossible to think of this without calling to mind Mr. Ring's solemn appeal to Dr. Moseley respecting *cows' milk, beef steaks,* and *mutton chops.* Please to present my best compliments to that gentleman, and tell him that this single stroke of wit, so much in the spirit of our *Franklin* who always decorated philosophy with a smile, has done me more service than half the publications I have read on the philosophy of vaccination.

You very politely express a wish for more of my letters on the Vaccine or any other subject. In order to damp this desire and surfeit you at once, I have directed my bookseller to send you a whole volume of them, which the partiality of Dr. Lettsom has brought into light.

I here send you the Massachusets Register for the present year. It may possibly afford you some information as to our literary societies, &c. and may give you some new ideas respecting the present state of a country which was characteristically denominated by the English a century ago "THE WILDERNESS."

I need not, I think, say how highly I should prize the correspondence of Dr. Jenner on any subject; but more especially on that for which he is so deservedly celebrated; and who, according to my understanding, is the only *clear, consistent,* UNCONFUSED writer on the cow-pox that has yet appeared.

I reiterate my thanks for your kindness, and beg you to accept the assurances of high consideration and esteem!

BENJAMIN WATERHOUSE.

P.S. As the library of this University is by far the largest in the United States, and is the grand deposit of rare and valuable books in this quarter of the world and will long continue so, I cannot resist expressing my wish that a copy of your invaluable work may be deposited there by its author. I presume my motives for wishing this, and hinting it, stand in no need of an apology. By a law of the Commonwealth, an author to secure his copyright must deposit a copy of his work in this library; and books sent to it come free from duty. This library, museum, and other public rooms are constantly visited by strangers as among the curiosities of the country. When I had the honour of waiting on the Duke of Kent through them, he expressed his surprise at such a collection of books and natural productions in about thirty years, *for the small-pox destroyed the chief of what had been collected since* 1638: that is to say, it raged in Boston, and the legislature on that account occupied one of the public rooms in the hall, which contained the library; when it by some accident took fire and was, one alcove excepted, totally destroyed. Thanks be to Dr. Jenner, such an accident from *such a cause* can never happen again.[48]

In March he found "such a rage for the matter" in various parts of New England and by some the actual encouragement by some physicians of children to inoculate one another merely to destroy the business of a rival physician. This spurred him again to publish a statement in the papers and he sent this in the form of a letter to Timothy Dwight, president of Yale, a long exposé and description which the editors gladly received and printed.[48a]

In this letter to the Rev. Dr. Dwight he describes the reason for his desire, expressed early, to be conservative just as modern research workers are urged to do in promulgating any new treatment of disease—he says, "It was my plan to have seen more of this new disease in conjunction with one long conversant with inoculated small pox [44] before the matter should pass into many other hands, and the reason I gave for it in my publication, was, that some unsuccessful cases at the beginning deprived Scotland of the blessings of inoculation for more than twenty years. But I soon found such a rage for the matter as to defeat all views of that kind, so giving up all hopes of a rigid set of experiments, I went, I fear, into the opposite extreme." He points out the caution of England and Paris and emphasizes the importance of the publicity given to rash conduct as at "a place not far distant from us [Marblehead]." He published at this time the information that Dr. Trotter of Plymouth had written to the Editor of the *Medical and Physical Journal*, that Jennerian inoculation had contracted the scope of human misery in the Navy of Great Britain. And Dr. Marshall at Gibraltar had inoculated the garrison and expected to perform the same action at Minorca.

Mess. GREENS,
  The inclosed letter from Doctor Waterhouse contains so much and so valuable information concerning the Cow-Pox, that I am persuaded it cannot but be acceptable to the public. I request you, therefore, to give it a place in your paper; and am, Gentlemen, yours, &c.

TIMOTHY DWIGHT.

[48] Baron's "Life of E. Jenner, M.D.," Vol. I, 1838.
[48a] *Connecticut Journal*, Vol. XXXIV, Wednesday, April 29, 1801, No. 174.
[44] Dr. Aspinwall who was in charge of the inoculations at the Small pox hospital at Boston.

REVEREND SIR,

YOUR letter introducing Dr. Curtis was very acceptable. Should a similar occasion occur, I beg that the circumstance you mention of not having a personal acquaintance, may never operate as an impediment, but that you will honor me with a line without hesitation, or an idea of an apology.

Dr. Curtis's errand was to gather information respecting this recently noticed *epizootic* distemper the *Cow,* or *Kine-Pox,* to know the most approved mode of inoculating for it, as well as to collect the *criteria,* by which he should at all times be able to discriminate the *genuine* disorder from the *spurious;* a matter of the first importance in this new inoculation: I communicated every thing I knew and thought valuable on that subject, and only regret I could not give him more, because he appears to be one of those who carries his views beyond the mere pecuniary consideration of it.

I was surprised to hear the erroneous notions, which were circulating in some parts of Connecticut, respecting this inoculation and the promoters of it! My surprize, however lessened, when I learnt that no written accounts had circulated with you, excepting a few detached pieces of mine in the News-Papers. In order to exhibit a juster view of things, I shall give you a brief sketch of the business, as far at least, as it regards myself.

In March 1799, I first published in one of the Boston papers, an account of a pustular distemper among the Cows in some of the western counties of England, known there by the name of the *Cow Pox,* which disease has this strikingly singular property, that it can be transferred from the Cow to the human kind, producing a mild distemper, never fatal, *and which would secure the person so inoculated, ever after from the Small Pox.*

In November following, after receiving further information from England, I made a second communication through the same medium, and strengthened my first account by the respectable testimony of the first philosophic and medical characters in Great Britain, and to give further satisfaction, I referred the public to the writings of Drs. *Jenner, Woodville* and *Pearson.* for more minute information. The first is a physician, of long experience and high reputation. The second is physician to the small pox hospitals in London, and long known as a medical, botanical, and medico historical writer. Dr. (George) *Pearson* ⁴⁴⁴ is physician to St. Georges hospital, and head of the *Vaccine Institution.* a man "to whose active zeal, the world is indebted for much of the early and far extended intelligence, respecting this invaluable discovery."

Being firmly persuaded of the efficacy of this vaccine inoculation, in securing the person (when *fairly* infected with the genuine virus) from the small-pox, I sent to England for some of the matter, & in July last, inoculated four of my own children and 3 others of my family, and I found that I produced the very same disease as that described by these cele-

⁴⁴⁴ Born 1751, died 1828.

brated physicians. But one thing still remained behind to complete the business, and that was to prove that it absolutely secured the system from small-pox, and this was accomplished the month following, by placing them in the small-pox hospital, where they were inoculated by Dr. *Aspinwall*, and all came out at the end of ten days, without any signs of infection, and thus my leading assertions passed the test of *demonstration*, and in that light it was viewed by an anxious public. At this period I published the whole history of the business in a pamphlet, a copy of which, I here send for your acceptance. In this publication I took special care to apprize the reader of a degenerate or *spurious* disorder, which would not secure the system from small-pox, as you may see from p. 25 to 29, and laboured to guard him against so serious an accident, but it has not been enough attended to. People are not willing to believe what they do not wish.

It was my plan to have seen more of this new disease in conjunction with one long conversant with the inoculated small-pox, before the matter should pass into many other hands, & the reason I gave for it in my publication, was, "that some unsuccessful cases at the beginning, deprived Scotland of the blessings of inoculation for more than 20 years." But I soon found such a *rage* for the *"matter,"* as to defeat all views of that kind, so giving up all hopes of a rigid set of experiments, I went, I fear, into the opposite extreme. Practitioners came from all parts of this state, from Vermont, from N. Hampshire & other quarters,;—a dozen sometimes in a day. This pressing call for the matter, had a doubly bad effect, which I did not at first foresee, but which I was sensible of when they began to apply for it from Connecticut, which accounts for my refusal of them. But the motives of my refusal was misconstrued & they obtained some sort of matter elsewhere.

When many of these inoculations failed, those who were most zealous in the business, and who had formed to themselves *extravagant* expectations, were the first to cry out that it was all a delusion, a mere money speculation! Can we wonder that spurious cases have occurred, when we know that the sleeves of shirts, that had been worn three, and even four weeks after inoculation, where the arm discharged very much, were cut up into small strips and sent into the country as good kine pox matter! matter which was said to have come direct from me, because the person was unluckily my patient. More than an hundred people were inoculated with these strips, when the matter they contained had no more efficacy than if taken from an horse's sore back. It however produced a sore. Can we wonder at the accidents complained of, when we know that a practitioner has inoculated for 50 cents, then *gratis,* and lastly encouraged children to inoculate each other, merely to destroy the business of his rival, who had got the start of him? I hope I may not be provoked to publish names and places. Contrast this abominable conduct with the extreme care and caution exercised in England and lately at Paris in this new inoculation. (*See the report of the Committee for Vaccine Inoculation signed by* THOURET,

Director of the National Medical School.) When I reflect on the consequences which may follow from such rash conduct, my regret at the failures which have happened in a place not far distant from us, is considerably diminished, because it required something of that magnitude to rouse the public attention, and to direct it to the only true line of conduct in prosecuting a business in which the whole American people are peculiarly interested.

It is not amiss, perhaps, to mention that attempts have been used by some interested in the small pox inoculation to injure the credit of the kine pox. An affidavit appeared in two of the Boston papers signed *Abraham Hedge* declaring he had the small-pox *after* the kine-pox. But his brother who inoculated him, has publicly contradicted the assertions, which his weak brother had published. By what I have lately heard from Connecticut, I suspect that the experiment has not had *fair play* with you.

But the disagreeable sensations arising from such proceedings has been compensated, nay more than compensated by the many letters received from the first characters in the three learned professions in different parts of the Union respecting this new inoculation. I shall select an extract from two, not that they speak in the strongest terms of it, but on account of their high authority in our nation as well as in the philosophic world. PRESIDENT ADAMS says, "I have read your history of the kine-pox with pleasure. Your zeal and industry in giving these experiments fair play in America deserve the thanks of all the friends of science and of humanity. The disarming the small-pox of its contagion is an enterprise truly worthy of an Hercules in Medicine."

PRESIDENT JEFFERSON, in a letter I received from him this winter says, "I have read with great satisfaction your pamphlet on the kine-pox, and I pray you to accept my thanks for the communication of it. I had before attended to your publications in the news-papers, and took much interest in the result of the experiments you were making. Every friend of humanity must look with pleasure on this discovery, by which *one evil more is withdrawn from the condition of man;* and must contemplate the possibility that future improvements and discoveries may still more and more lessen the catalogue of evils. In this line of proceedings *you deserve well of your country,* and I pray you Sir, to accept my portion of the tribute due to you." To further counteract the opinion which has prevailed in some places in your state that this inoculation is a mere money speculation, may I be allowed to quote the sentiments of one of the latest English writers on the cow-pox.** "It is to the credit of the cow pox inoculation that it has been introduced by no illiberal arts or empirical pretention, on the contrary, its supporters have contented themselves with laying before the public the event of experiments conducted with ability and perfect impartiality; so that all the reputation which the practice has hitherto acquired may be considered as fairly earned."

** Aikin, "Concise View of the most Important Facts concerning Cow-pox."

Within a week or two I have received from England a very great additional weight of evidence, confirming my first assertions respecting the salutiferous efficacy of the *Cow*, or *Kine Pox*, together with a fresh supply of matter, under the seal of the *Vaccine Institution*. Its power in securing the system from the Small-Pox contagion, seems established in England beyond all doubt or dispute. It is more than a year since the British adopted the vaccine inoculation in their army, and since that into their navy. Dr. *Trotter*, of Plymouth ** writes to the editor of the Medical and Physical Journal, thus: "If the value of any improvement in the practice of medicine is to be established by its contracting the scope of human misery, the *Jennerian Inoculation* will be deservedly recorded as one of the greatest blessings to the navy of Great-Britain that was ever extended to it."

Dr. *Marshell* writes from Gibraltar, "We have inoculated the soldiers of the garrison and their children, tomorrow we expect to sail for Minorca, with recommendations to inoculate the English army now lying there. I am further happy to add, that all are equally convinced of the efficacy of the Cow-Pox in resisting the Small Pox, and of the great reward due to our friend Dr. *Jenner*, for the benefit he has conferred upon society and the world at large, by his investigation of this so peculiarly mild and safe disease."—But why need I add more?—I could quote a volume to the same effect. I think I have written enough to convince those who doubt, and to afford comfort to those who believe "that this inoculation when once fairly brought before the bar of the public is not likely to sink into neglect, so long as it possesses such intrinsic value as really to merit the patronage of the candid and liberal part of the community." I have long had in contemplation a *vaccine institution* for inoculating the poor *gratis*, and for bringing the Kine Pox, to the test of Small Pox, for until that is done here, we shall in a great measure grope in the dark. Whatever some misinformed persons may have imagined, I think I can say with the illustrious *Jenner* that truth in this and every other physiological inquiry that has occupied my attention, has ever been the object of my pursuit and should it appear in the present instance that I have been led into error, fond as I may appear of the offspring of my labours, I had rather see it perish at once, than exist and do a public injury.

Accept, Reverend Sir, of the assurances of high consideration and esteem.

BENJAMIN WATERHOUSE.

To the Rev. President DWIGHT.

By this time Waterhouse had become more confident of his technical methods and now he writes another letter to President Jefferson and sends some matter. Jefferson forwards this at once to Dr. Edward Gantt of Washington, who retained this and all subsequent communications but never replied to any letter from Dr. Waterhouse.

** Author of "Medical Nautica."

It was in May 1801 at a suburb of Baltimore that Dr. James Smith vaccinated Nancy Malcom with matter received from a Mr. Taylor who had received it from his brother in London. This notice was published in the *Daily Telegraph* of Baltimore, Dec. 3–5, 1801.

With all the knowledge of smallpox that Jefferson had and his contacts with public men it is remarkable that nowhere in the correspondence is there a note of this incident.

Jefferson tells of the failure of the inoculations by Dr. Gantt and expresses the hope Dr. Waterhouse would continue to send matter until "we can inform you that it has at length taken."

On this letter Dr. Waterhouse has written a note that the first letter from Jefferson he had sent as a gift to Dr. Jenner.

Washington, June 26, 1801.

Sir

Your favor of the 8th. inst. came safely to hand with the several matters accompanying it. as the longer the vaccine matter should be unemployed, I knew the chance of its success would be the less, I thought it would be more likely to answer your benevolent views by having it employed here rather than risking it by a further mission to Virginia. I therefore put it immediately into the hands of Doctor Gantt a long established, judicious & successful physician of this place, together with your letter & the pamphlet & papers accompanying it. it turns out that it had still been too long unemployed; for of numbers inoculated with it from the 18th to this time, no one appears to have taken the infection. in the meantime a great anxiety is produced here to obtain a successful inoculation. I know not however how it will be obtained unless you could continue your goodness so far as to inclose by post new matter two or three times successively until we can inform you that it has at length taken you need not be at the trouble of writing a word, for it is making it troublesome enough to you to put the matter under cover & into the post office the benevolence which has dictated the measures for which we are already indebted to you, will I hope plead my excuse in this new request. I pray you to accept assurance of my high consideration & respect.

Th Jefferson.[47]

Doctr. Benjamin Waterhouse.

N.B. The first letter I received from Mr. Jefferson was dated Dec[r] 25th, 1800. It is printed in my Treatise page 2. I sent the original a present to Dr. Jenner, thinking that coming from the Chief Magistrate of the Americas it would not be unpleasing to the originator of vaccination.

By July 13, 1801, he believed there was need of more education of the "profession and humanity," so he sends to the editors of several

[47] Letter, "Jefferson as a Vaccinator."

newspapers duplicate reports on the work. One of these was published in the *Connecticut Courant* with the superscription "A Card" and a duplicate was published in *The Spectator*, July 4, 1801, New York.

☞ Dr. Waterhouse takes this method, most respectfully to suggest something to his bretheren at a distance, in which the honor of the profession, and the cause of humanity are particularly concerned.—It is well know to the faculty, that notwithstanding thousand of well attested cases of kine-pox resisting the infection of the small pox, can be obtained from *England,* and other parts of *Europe,* yet as it is found, that people are not so ready to believe what happens a good while ago, or a great way off, it is necessary to collect and lay before the American public, all such cases as have occurred among ourselves, before every one will be convinced that the kine-pox is a perfect security against the small pox. More than two hundred cases can already be enumerated among ourselves, where persons have been inoculated with the small pox, *after having gone through the kine pox,* without the least trait of infection. *Connecticut* alone can furnish more than an hundred.

It seems really necessary to establish a central point, to which everything relating to this new inoculation may be directed, and from whence every ray of light that comes from a single place, may be reflected, and everywhere extend its power of illumination. It has been hoped and expected, that some *Medical* or *Philosophical Society,* would form such a center; in which case, the reflecting ray would become not only more brilliant, but even generative at the point of repercussion. But as a propitious season is fast passing away, without any prospect of such an advantage, *Dr. Waterhouse* is constrained to adopt a more diminutive plan, and to go on in this business as he began it—*alone.*

He, therefore, in a most respectful manner, would request all those practitioners who have already put off the kine-pox to the *test* of the small pox, with success, to transmit to him all such cases through the medium of the post office. Many that have already come to hand, are not clothed in that particular and specified form, in which he would choose to lay them before a scrutinizing public. To specify every particular is needless, but names, ages, dates, and places of abode, are absolutely necessary. That such a procedure is requisite to establish the credit of this most precious discovery, will appear to every one, who considers the prejudices, and rigid laws in some parts of the Union, in regard to the promiscuous inoculation for the small-pox.

Although this benign disease is now passing with a rapid step through all ranks of society in *Europe;* and although it has full credit with characters most distinguished for information in every profession among us, yet a great many others still remain doubtful of its affording a complete shelter from the attack of the most loathsome of diseases. From the spurius, and all explained cases that have occurred, (arising from taking the *matter* at too late a period) this state of doubt is not to be wondered at, and nothing can effectually dissipate it, but submitting one disease to the test of the other. In this situation one fact is worth a thousand arguments.

A subscription has already commenced, to ennable a few dozen people (whose *time* is their *estate*) to repair to the Hospital at *Brooklyne*, to try if they can take the small pox, after having gone fairly through the kine-pox. Seven have already been tried in that hospital, and twice the number at *Ipswich* and *Marblehead*, AND ALL ESCAPED INFECTION.

The Printers from these states are requested to incert this, and *Patriotism* will carry it to their credit. Those of Virginia are particularly requested to notice it, because the kine-pox inoculation is about commencing in that extensive and populous state, under very favorable auspices.[48] Cambridge, June 25th, 1801.

By this time Thomas Jefferson, while at Washington, had received the printed publications and some matter which he sent to Dr. Wardlaw at Monticello, and wrote about it to his daughter, Mrs. (Thomas Mann) Martha Randolph. This letter is in the Pierpont Morgan Library in New York. He requested Dr. Wardlaw "to make himself acquainted with them" and at the end of the paragraph he states his conviction "there is no doubt it prevents the Small pox."

Washington, 16-VII-1801.
[Thomas Jefferson to Mrs. Martha Randolph.]
. . . I this day inclose to Dr. Wardlaw some publications on the Kine pox, with a request to make himself acquainted with them. I shall probably be able to carry on some infectious matter with a view of trying whether we cannot introduce it there. The first essay here has proved unsuccessful but some matter received 6 days ago & immediately used will prove this day whether it takes or not; & I am promised by Dr. Waterhouse of Boston successive weekly supplies till it takes. If the matter be genuine there is no doubt it prevents the small pox. . . .[49]

On July 24th, Dr. Waterhouse writes a few lines accompanying some vaccine virus stating that the needle "will communicate the disease if it be thrust under the scarf skin, and drawn slowly through it."

. . . The thread enclosed in this Quill was imbued in the vaccine virus on Thursday Evening the 23rd of July. At the same time the needle was infected in the same fluid and it is highly probable will communicate the

[48] *Connecticut Courant*, Monday, July 13, 1801. Also appeared in *The Spectator*, N. Y. Saturday, July 4, 1801, dated June 26, 1801.
[49] Extract from letter. Original in The Pierpont Morgan Library, New York City.

disease if it be thrust under the scarf skin, and drawn slowly & gradually through it.

Benjⁿ Waterhouse.

Cambridge, July 24th 1801.[50]

On July 25th, Jefferson acknowledges receipt of matter July 17th, but this letter is missing. He expressed the hope this third supply may be more successful than others which had failed Dr. Gantt of Washington. He tells of the time approaching when he will leave for Monticello where he hoped to introduce the cowpox. To avoid future failures of matter which might be due to transportation he suggests the ingenious method depending upon water to insulate against heating of an inner bottle. Dr. Waterhouse wrote a note at the bottom of the letter stating that the matter sent agreeably to this direction was the fourth that succeeded.

Washington July 25. 1801

Dear Sir,

Your favor of the 17th arrived last night, together with the new Vaccine matter which was immediately sent to Doct^r Gantt. the 2^d as well as the 1^t supply of matter had failed. we hope the 3^d will be more successful. how might it answer to put the matter into a phial of the smallest size, well corked & immersed in a larger one filled with water & well corked. it would be effectually preserved against the air, and I doubt whether the water would permit so great a degree of heat to penetrate to the inner phial as does when it is in the open air. it would get cool every night, and shaded every day under the cover of the stage, it might perhaps succeed. I leave this place on the 30^h inst. for Monticello being unwilling to work myself on the tidewaters during the months of Aug. & September, when situations which generate bilious complaints are most dangerous. my own is entirely exempt from that danger. should you be so good as to continue forwarding matter till it succeeds, it will now be best to address the packages to Dr Gantt, from whom, so soon as he succeeds, I shall ask a transmission of fresh matter to Monticello, where I shall endeavor to introduce it. it will be a great service indeed rendered to human nature to strike off from the catalogue of its evils so great a one as the small pox. I know of no one discovery in medicine equally valuable. Accept assurances of my great esteem and respect.

Th Jefferson.[51]

P.S. I re-inclose Doct^r Lettsom, tre.

The matter sent agreeably to this direction was the fourth that succeeded.   B. W.
Doct^r Benjamin Waterhouse.

[50] Library of Congress.   [51] "Jefferson as a Vaccinator."

On July 26, 1801, Dr. Waterhouse sends another thread and needle and statement of the weather at the time of taking.

. . . Vaccine virus on a needle and on the thread, taken Sunday morning 26 of July, from a young and healthy subject, on the 8th day of the disease or rather inoculation. The weather moderate and rainy for several days in succession.

Benj[n] Waterhouse.

Cambridge 26th July 1801.[52]

On August 1, 1801, Dr. Waterhouse sends another toothpick and two plates of glass covered with lead from Dr. Jenner and describes the method of transportation. Dr. Waterhouse makes a request for the result of the trials. This material from Dr. Jenner was sent by Jefferson to Dr. John Shore of Petersburg. The original letter is in the Massachusetts Historical Society, Boston.

Cambridge August 1st 1801.

. . . Vaccine matter on the toothpick taken July 31st in the evening, the thread taken at the same time. The two plates of glass, which he I have covered with lead is just come to hand from Dr. Jenner being taken May 19 in London. Two other plates containing some of the virus taken at the same time has been proved to be perfectly active. It adheres to the glass like gum, water warm steam, or a little hot water is necessary to dilute it for use. . . . Dr. Waterhouse is anxious to hear from Washington respecting the success of his endeavours.[53]

On August 8, 1801, Jefferson acknowledges receipt and delivery of matter to Dr. Gantt. He tells of Dr. Wardlaw as the skilled physician and expresses hope of "planting" the cowpox where it will be "as salutary as anywhere in the union." He then refers to the laws governing inoculation and comments:

Monticello, Aug. 8, 1801.

Dear Sir

I had the pleasure of writing you on the 25th of July and of acknowledging the receipt of yours of July 17. with the vaccine matter which was immediately delivered to Doct[r] Gantt. your previous favors of the 24th & 25th came to me at this place on the 6th inst. and the matter accompanying them was, by a skilful physician of the neighborhood, Dr. Wardlaw, immediately inserted into six persons of my own family. we shall thus stand a chance of planting the disease here where I imagine it will be as salutary

[52] Library of Congress.   [53] Ibid.

as anywhere in the union. our laws [54] indeed have permitted inoculation of the small pox, but under such conditions of consent of the neighborhood as have admitted not much use of the permission. that disease therefore is almost a stranger here and extremely dreaded. I will take care to inform you of the result of our operation. Accept my esteem and respect.

Th. Jefferson.[55]

Doctᵣ Benjamin Waterhouse.

The law referred to was passed by the General Assembly in 1777 and was an amendment to the original act of 1769. Both laws are examples of how cumbersome public health regulations could be when ignorant fear dictated the methods of thought.

In 1769—the tenth year of the reign of King George III—the Burgesses of Virginia passed "an act to regulate the inoculation of small-pox within this colony." The preamble reads, "Whereas the wanton introduction of the Small pox into this colony by inoculation, when the same was not necessary, hath, of late years, proved a nuisance to several neighborhoods, by disturbing the peace and quietness of many of his Majesty's subjects, and exposing their lives to the infection of that mortal distemper, which from the situation and circumstances of the colony, they would otherwise have little reason to dread."

The law enacted that; any person who shall wilfully, or designedly, presumed to import or bring into this colony from any place whatever the small pox, with a purpose of inoculating any person, or by any means to propogate the said distemper within this colony shall forfeit and pay the sum of one thousand pounds. One moiety shall be to the informer and the other moiety to the church wardens of the parish, for the use of the poor of the parish.

But forasmuch as the inoculation of small pox may, under peculiar circumstances, be not only a prudent but necessary means of securing those who are unavoidably exposed to the dangers of taking the distemper in the natural way, and for this reason it is judged proper to tolerate it, under reasonable restrictions and regulations:

Therefore if any person shall think him or herself exposed to the immediate danger of catching the said distemper such person may give notice to the sheriff of any county who "shall immediately, and without loss of time, summon all the acting magistrates of the county, to meet at the most convenient time and place to consider whether, upon the whole circumstance of the case, inoculation may be prudent or necessary, or dangerous to the health and safety of the neighborhood and thereupon grant a licence for such inoculation or prohibit the same as shall seem expedient.

[54] W. W. Hening, "The Statutes at Large of Virginia," Vol. VIII and IX.
[55] "Jefferson as a Vaccinator."

"And if any person shall inoculate, or procure inoculation of the small-pox within the colony, without obtaining a licence in the manner before directed, he shall pay for every offence, the sum of one hundred pounds.

"And whereas checking the progress of the said distemper, where it may accidentally break out, or the regulations which may be established for carrying on inoculation, may be attended with some expense . . . it may be lawful for the justices of the court, at the time of laying their levy, . . . to levy on the tithable persons in their said county, so much tobacco or money as will be sufficient to defray the expences necessarily incurred for the purposes.

"And if any sheriff or mayor or chief magistrate shall upon application to him made, in manner aforesaid, refuse, or unreasonably delay, to summon the magistrates . . . or if any magistrate so summoned, shall refuse or neglect to attend according to such summons . . . every such shall forfeit the sum of one hundred pounds."

In 1777—the Second year of the Commonwealth—the General Assembly amended an act intituled, "an act to regulate etc."

The preamble reads whereas the small pox, at this time in many parts of the commonwealth, is likely to spread and become general, and it hath been proved, by incontestible experience, that the late discoveries and improvements therein have produced great benefits to mankind, by rendering a distemper which taken in the common way is always dangerous and often fatal comparatively mild and safe by inoculation.

Any person. having first obtained, in writing, to be attested by two witnesses, the consent of a majority of the housekeepers residing within two miles, and not separated by a river, creek or marsh, a quarter of a mile wide, and conforming to the following rules and regulations, may inoculate, or be inoculated for the small pox, either in his or her own house, or at any other place.

Every physician, doctor, or other person undertaking inoculation at any house, shall cause a written advertisement to be put up at the nearest publick road, or other most notorious adjacent place, giving information that the small pox is at such house, . . . under penalty of forty shilling for every day that the same shall be omitted or neglected. . . .

On August 14, 1801, Jefferson relates the successful inoculation of cowpox and describes the results of the infection—success by Dr. Wardlaw at Monticello and failure by Dr. Gantt at Washington.

Monticello, Aug. 14, 1801.

Dear Sir

I wrote you on the 8th. inst. that your favor of July 24 & 26 had come to me here. Doct^r Wardlaw on the 7th inoculated two persons with the matter of the 24th & with that of the 26th the latter has no effect, but the two former show inflammation & matter. some of them complains of pain under the armpit, & yesterday was a little feverish. the matter is of this size & form ⬭ the inflammation about ½ an inch all round from the pustule. we have considerable hopes he has the true infection. yesterday I received your favor of the 1ˢᵗ inst. Dʳ Wardlaw immediately inoculated 5 of the former subjects with it, & one other. he also inoculated one from the pustule above described. you shall be regularly informed of the progress & success of this business. I learn from Washington indirectly that Doctʳ Gantt's essays have all failed. should ours succeed he shall be supplied hence. I am very anxious to obtain the disease here. Accept my best esteem & respectful salutations.

Th. Jefferson.[56]

Doctʳ Benjamin Waterhouse.

It may be interesting to note here that Dr. John Crawford [57] received from Dr. John Ring [58] who served with Dr. Jenner, the vaccine matter on a cotton thread rolled up in paper and covered with varnish which excluded the air. This material came some time in 1801 and was used on patients of Dr. Crawford in the suburbs of Baltimore.

It is particularly interesting to recollect that at no time does one find reference in Jefferson's letters to any suggestion of cowpox matter being obtainable from any other source than Boston. One may well be incredulous of a statement that vaccination was very widely known in or about Baltimore and yet unknown and, if heard of, unmentioned in these letters of Jefferson and Waterhouse.

On August 21, 1801, Jefferson reports of further successes statistically. Impregnated thread and toothpicks with matter to be forwarded to Dr. Gantt at Washington, where all inoculations had failed.

Monticello Aug 21. 1801.

Dear Sir

I had the pleasure of informing you on the 14ᵗʰ inst. that i supposed the inoculation of the kine pox to have taken effect in two subjects. these were from the matter you were kind enough to send July 24. that of July 26. succeeded with 2 others. that of Aug. 1. with 4. on the 16ᵗʰ inst we inoculated from the 2 first subjects 15. others, 14 of whom very evidently have the infection, so that we have 20 now of my family on whom the disease has taken, besides some recent inoculations. some of them have slight fevers, headache, kernels under the arms, & one only, has a very sore arm. most however experience no inconvenience; and have nothing but the inoculated pustule, well defined moderately filled with matter,

[56] "Jefferson as a Vaccinator."
[57] Born 1746, died 1813.
[58] Born 1756, died 182–.

& hollow in the center. I have this day impregnated some thread, & half a dozen toothpicks which I forward to Doct^r Gantt, who writes me that his inoculations all failed. Doct^r Wardlaw of this neighborhood has so much other business that he has been able to be with us only twice. however I expect that the account of my experience will encourage the neighborhood generally to engage him to introduce it in their families. to you they will be indebted for it, and I am sure they will be sensible of the obligation. accept assurance of my great esteem & respect

Th. Jefferson [59]

Doct^r Benjamin Waterhouse.

On August 28, 1801, a letter from Waterhouse indicated the thrill of very great emotion, enthusiasm and joy at the conviction that at last Jefferson had obtained the real cowpox. So great is his pleasure at the success that he cannot delay a moment from expressing his congratulations yet can write only a "hasty scrawl."

He also expresses his belief in there being an art of inserting the matter which Dr. Wardlaw had and Dr. Gantt had not acquired.

Boston August 28th, 1801.

Sir,

I have this moment taken your letter of the 14th inst from the Post-Office, and have step'd into the first house to write a line, and pray you to excuse me until I return home before I can answer it properly.

I congratulate you, Sir, in having produced the true disease, of which I have little or indeed *no doubt.* I hope Dr. Wardlaw will inoculate from the part affected as soon as he finds a drop of pellucid fluid, that is to say on the 8th day, or even the seventh and when the inoculated part is affected at no greater distance from the incision than this or if a simple scratch or puncture be made, as in case of using the recent fluid when it is of no greater size than this or even less. I believe there is an art in inserting the matter, which Dr. Gantt had not acquired, & which Dr. Wardlaw has. I hope he will inoculate from patient to patient, and never trust to the thread when he has a recent pustule to take it from.

Excuse this hasty scrawl, and accept of my profound respects.

B. Waterhouse. [60]

On September 2, 1801, Waterhouse writes the longer letter promised in the previous and he asserts that the announcement of a successful production of cowpox gave him "pleasure inexpressible." He describes his improved technique in obtaining virus. He tells of the use of the double bottle idea to forward virus to Dr. Gantt but had not received any reply. He suggests a possible effect of hot weather on the

---

[59] "Jefferson as a Vaccinator." [60] Library of Congress.

virus and remarks on the hot weather which had prevailed in Boston. He expresses the opinion that by Jefferson's influence the "practice of vaccination had been forwarded at least two years." He then reviews the acceptance of the practice geographically in Newfoundland, Halifax, Geneva, France, Hamburg, African side of the Mediterranean, Minorca. He tells of a practical joke of a medical student who inoculated a cow and the existence of the disease in this case had been certified as evidence that the disease cowpox existed in this country. He had discovered the trick but only after he had reported its presence as an endemic disease. He, therefore, was compelled to acknowledge the error. He shows his appreciation of humor and relates a pun on the claimed finding of vaccine virus among the "leaves" in Switzerland and his retort that the work should be spelled "Beaves." The Irish word Shinnaugh meaning a cow's teat was used for the cowpox and there was a general opinion that persons once affected never take the smallpox. He then writes that Dr. Jenner with a "Franklian sagacity first transferred it from the brute to the human kind." He announces that he had underway a second pamphlet, on "Observations on the local appearance, symptoms and mode of treating the Variola Vaccinee." He states the double significance of the "Hyndostan" word "gooty" indicating smallpox and chickenpox.

Cambridge Septr 2d. 1801.

Sir

I know not if I acknowledged the receipt of your letter of the 8th ult^o in the hasty scrawl I lately wrote from Boston. That of the 14th. gave me pleasure inexpressible, as it informed me that you had succeeded in planting the benign remedy against the small-pox in the vast region of Virginia. I have written to Dr. Wardlaw on the important subject of preserving the active fluid-virus for inoculation, in constant succession from patient to patient. I wish he had inoculated as many as he possibly could, from the pustule, and not trusted to the thread, as the fresh fluid never, or very rarely fails communicating the infection, even when no other instrument is used than a cambric-needle.

I have referred Dr. Wardlaw to the letter I wrote to you at Washington for more minute directions. I have repeated to him, and hope to be excused for re-iterating it here, to take the matter on the 8th day, nay the 7th if possible, and never later than the 9th. The efflorescence is a sign that the absorption has commenced, and the nicety of the business is to take the virus just before that period. I have watched this process with a microscope in a number of persons whom I had taken into my house for this express purpose, and experience has now taught me a sure procedure, somewhat different from my early theory, which was to take the matter at the very acme of the inflammation. I now take it before the virus is so

[37]

far absorbed as to affect the lymphatics in the arm-pit with pain; and by so doing, I always succeed. In consequence of the hint in your letter just on your departure from Washington, I sent Dr. Gantt the virus in a phial of water, but have not heard of its reception. This matter I took on a cool & rainy day and put it up with great care; and can hardly conceive that it should fail. The weather has been oppressively hot,—98 in the shade! an occurrence not easily accounted for in this northern latitude, and in our situation. On a journey this time 12 months, I found it as hot an hundred miles east of us, and more like a *sirocco* than anything I ever felt. "There is something in this, which our philosophy has never dreamt of."—I carefully avoided taking matter for transportation during such hot days, for I presume the mercury must have risen to 100, in the open fields.

I may be mistaken, but I at present believe that my thus sending the vaccine matter to President Jefferson has forwarded the practice in Virginia at least a year if not two. The rivalship of physicians, the desire of taking and keeping the lead in this new inoculation has retarded the advancement of the *true* inoculation, while it has diffused the *spurious* far & wide. I therefore presume that a number of decidedly perfect cases in the neighborhood of Montecello, will give the genuine disease a currency through Virginia. The vaccine inoculation is progressing at Newfoundland. The physician general at Halifax has just written to me on the subject of introducing it there. At Geneva it is now the custom with the ministers of religion to impress on the minds of every parent, who presents a child for baptism the duty of giving it this newly discovered disease. The minister of the interior, directed Professor Odier to make him a report of the state of *vaccinism* in France. But the most eloquent production I have yet seen on the subject, is by a physician at Hamburgh, so that the practice is becoming universal in Europe. What a blessing will this discovery be to the inhabitants of the African side of the Mediterranean where the small-pox has always raged with a peculiar malignity! We already know that the kine-pox has preserved (?) its characteristic mildness at Minorca.

I have had a number of communications from different parts of New England, tending to induce a belief, that this disease has been found among the kine of our own country. I am not, however, entirely convinced of it. I gave full credence to one account transmitted to me by our Attorney General. I even sent the history to London, which may possibly be already published. I communicated it also to the Massachusetts Medical Society as a proff of the domestic origin of the kine pox. And it is not many days since I discovered that the cow was inoculated by a mischevous medical-pupil, who took this method to convince an old, unbelieving country practitioner that there really did exist such a disease; this rustic physician's daughters were his milk maids. They being soon disabled from milking the diseased cow, their mother performed that office and took the disorder also. In the height of the disorder they were seen by Chief Justice Dana, Judge Sulivan, and some other gentlemen who had seen the disease in their own families. I gave more credit to this account coming from gentlemen belonging to that order whose very essence is *evidence,* than if it were related by physicians, yet my account sent to England must be followed by this explanation.

There appeared in almost all the News-papers in the Union a paragraph saying that a Dr. Lacci had discovered the vaccine-virus among the *Leaves* in Switzerland, to which the printers added three notes of admiration!!!—I wrote to one of the Boston printers that he might change the *L.* into a *B.* and then erase the three notes of admiration. This epizootic distemper has existed so long in Ireland as to be known there by a *Celtic* name, viz *"Shinnaugh";* which word is found on dissection to mean *"a Cow's teat."* To a knowledge of this disease has been connected an opinion that persons once affected with the *Shinnaugh* could never take the small pox. But Dr. Jenner, a learned, skillful, and philanthropic physician was the first who took this knowledge so long vaguely floating on the breath of the vulgar and impressed upon it the stable form of science. He, with a Franklian sagacity first transferred it from the brute to the human kind, and demonstrated it to be a perfect security against the small pox. This extraordinary fact came forth from his masterly hands in so perfect a form, that were all other writings on the Cow-pox but his, destroyed, posterity would have a clear & unconfused idea of this singular disease & its salutiferous consequences.

I am preparing a second pamphlet, being "Observations on the local appearance, symptoms & mode of treating the Variola Vaccinee, with some rules for determining the *true* pustule from the *spurious,"* but my collegiate duties will scarcely allow me to publish it very soon, my course on Natural History having just commenced, and when that terminates my medical Lectures begin.

In the course of my researches, I have learnt that the pustular disease denominated *chicken pox* originated in those domestic birds, which having no specific name in the english language are called by the general one of *fowls,* or by the still more vague one of *Cocks & Hens.* It originated in Hyndostan. The small pox and that disease in the poultry having, with the natives, the same denomination viz *"gooty."*

With the highest respect for your station and character I remain your very humble serv^t

Benjn Waterhouse.[1]

On September 4, 1801, Dr. Waterhouse expressed the opinion that it was "quite unnecessary to send you any more matter" as he was convinced that Jefferson had planted the genuine disease. He then emphasized the need of keeping a succession of cases from which matter might be taken on the eighth day.

[1] Library of Congress.

To complete the proof of the type of disease which Jefferson had developed Dr. Waterhouse requested that he, or any of the physicians who had received matter, should send some matter to him for inoculation. The same logical method as he had used for melon seeds. As a last thought in his letter he laments the need of paper manufactories sending to Hamburg for a ship load of rags.

Cambridge Sept. 4th. 1801.

Sir

Since closing the letter I had the honor of writing to you yesterday, yours of the 21st ult. came to hand. I think it quite unnecessary to send you any more matter, being thoroughly convinced that you have planted the genuine disease in your family. I cannot, however, too emphatically recommend to all concerned in this new inoculation to keep up a *succession of cases,* from which matter may be taken on the 8th day. I should be gratified, could any of your physicians have sent me some on a tooth-pick, and some on a little cotton thread, secured with some of the sheet lead. I have found the advantage of such an exchange, and should wish to propose it to Dr. Wardlaw or any other physician in your quarter. They shall have some in return from this neighborhood. I should be please likewise to prove that your cases were what I am well convinced they are, genuine.

I increased the bulk of the packet I sent you yesterday by one or two printed papers, of besure very little consequence, excepting indeed that on the new manufactory of paper. It is deplorable that one of the first manufacturers of paper in this State, sent to Hamburgh for a ship load of rags. Accept sentiments of the highest respect.

Benjn Waterhouse.[42]

On September 17, 1801, Jefferson relates the receipt of a letter from Dr. Gantt at Washington who had three takes in subjects inoculated with matter sent from Monticello. He relates that he had sent matter to Richmond and Petersburg (Dr. John Shore) and is optimistic that it will be spread notwithstanding the incredulity which had been produced by ineffectual experiments at Richmond and Norfolk.

He then mentions his desire to publish the first letter Dr. Waterhouse had written, which he had sent to Dr. Gantt as he considered: "it is just our countrymen should know to whose philanthropic attentions they will be indebted for relief from a disease which has always been the terror of this country."

[42] Library of Congress.

Monticello Sep. 17. 1801.

Sir

I received by the last post your favor of Aug. 28. and by the same a letter from Doct^r Gantt informing me that the matter I first sent him from hence had taken in three of the subjects in to whom it had been inserted that from these he had inoculated others, so that they are now in full possession of the disease at Washington. I have also sent matter to Richmond, Petersburg, and several other parts of this state so that I have no doubt it will be generally spread through it, notwithstanding the incredulity which had been produced by the ineffectual experiments of Richmond & Norfolk. the first letter you were so kind as to write to me on the subject, & which contained a great deal of useful information, I put into the hands of Doct^r Gantt and we concluded it would be useful to publish it as soon as the public should be possessed of the disease. it is still in his hands, and as you have been so kind as to permit us to make any use of it which the general good may require, I shall propose to him to have it published immediately on my return to Washington, which will be within a week from this time. it is just our countrymen should know to whose philanthropic attentions they will be indebted for relief from a disease which has always been the terror of this country. Accept my particular thanks for this great good, and assurance of my high esteem & respect.

Th. Jefferson.[**]

Doct^r Waterhouse.

Monticello Sep. 12. 1801.

Doct^r Shore.

Sir

I received about a month ago some vaccine matter from Dr Waterhouse of Boston, and by a second conveyance some which he had just received from Doct^r Jenner of London. Both have succeeded perfectly. They were inserted into different arms of the same subjects, and exhibited precisely the same appearance. I have inoculated about 50. of my family and Mr Randolph & Mr Eppes about 60. or 70. of theirs. We have had in the whole one instance of a little delirium, two of considerably sore arms, from too large incisions about one third have had slight fevers, & the greater part have intermitted labours 1. 2. or 3. days on account of kernels under their arms. None changed their diet or occupation previously. It is now disseminating through this part of the country, & has taken in Georgetown from matter I sent there. Understanding that a former trial had failed in Richmond, I have sent some matter there, & presuming it might be acceptable to you also, now inclose a phial in which are half a dozen tooth picks, the points impregnated with virus, and a thread well soaked. By Doct^r Waterhouse's advice we have confined ourselves to inoculate from a subject

[**] "Jefferson as a Vaccinator."

on the day sennight from his inoculation, or the day after. Later than this there is danger of communicating the disease in a spurious form, & one which is not preventative of the small pox. This seems to be the only danger attending this inoculation, & renders it necessary to be vigorously attentive neither to inoculate from the mere lymph which the pustules yields in its first stage, nor the ripened pus of the latter. The matter at the time prescribed is a thin pellucid liquid, & is said to be then only proper. We barely draw a speck of blood. The pustule is of this size & form ⓘ generally, the middle depressed, the edges defined. Perhaps larger than I have drawn it. Accept assurances of my high consideration & Respect.

Th. Jefferson.[64]

On October 1, 1801, Dr. Waterhouse relates again his pleasure at the intelligence that vaccine inoculation was effectually planted in Washington and other parts of Virginia, and declares his conviction that "the matter commences its career in Virginia and Columbia under more favourable circumstances than it has in any other State in the Union." Then he tells of the prevention of the "cool, and deliberate train of experiments which I presume has taken place under your auspices." After this he relates the various monopolies publicity and financial plans which had been proposed until "before I well knew the spirit and extent of the plan, I found myself the center of a vile speculation." A little further he writes that he "checked, however, this vile traffic in that quarter [Connecticut], by exposing the trick in a letter to the President of Yale College [Timothy Dwight], which he published." This appeared in the *Connecticut Journal* in April and was quoted above.[65] In closing he quotes Dr. Jenner's directions for obtaining the virus.

Cambridge October 1st 1801.

Sir

Yesterday I was honored with your letter of Sept. 17th from Monticello informing me that the Vaccine inoculation was effectually planted at Washington, as well as at and near your own residence, and that you had sent the matter to several parts of the State of Virginia. I rejoice, beyond what a person less zealous than myself can realize at this intelligence, being convinced that the matter commences its career in Virginia & Columbia under more favourable circumstances than it has in any other State in the Union. Avarice, rivalship, and mistrust have accompanied its incipient practice in most parts of the Eastern States. These unworthy passions have prevented that cool & deliberate train of experiments which I presume has

[64] Original letter in the Massachusetts Historical Society, Boston, Mass.
[65] P. 23.

[42]

taken place under your auspices. Before I had determined on sending the matter to President Jefferson, I perceived symptoms of a similar disposition in Virginia, for I had not a few letters from different parts of the State, in which the practitioners held out what they conceived living baites to send them the matter & instructions to the exclusion of their bretheren. Several practitioners rode night & day from the extreme parts of Connecticut & Vermont to Cambridge to get before hand of their neighbors. Sometimes the two rival Doctors of the same town were at my house at the same time, each wishing to outbid the other! An association of six practitioners in New Hampshire absolutely new districted the State, and then applied to me for the matter, and offering me their conjoint bonds to give me a fourth part of all that were inoculated by them & their subordinates! so that before I well knew the spirit & extent of the plan, I found myself the centre of a vile speculation. Some went through Vermont & Connecticut calling themselves my agents, commissioned from me to sell the *matter* & spreading a spurious disease & endangering the lives of the people, by the abominable cheat. The keenest apostles in this new doctrine went out from Connecticut. I checked, however, this vile traffic in that quarter, by exposing the trick in a letter to the President of Yale-College, which he published, with a suitable introduction in his own name. I believe that such speculations would not be so apt to show themselves in the southern States, I however perceived by letters from that part of the Union that some wished to monopolize the practice within certain circles, but the mode I adopted has effectually checked that disposition, and has at the same time given the practice a dignity, which it has never acquired in some parts of the Union.

I here enclose a few unpublished pages by Dr. Jenner, on the origin of the inoculation. He has also sent me two or three fine representations of the Disease in all its stages, and these contrasted with the small-pox; one of which I here send for your acceptance. From a letter I received from the worthy Dr., dated London July 18th. I transcribe the following paragraph—"I don't care what British laws the Americans discard so that they stick to this.—*never to take the virus from a vaccine pustule for the purpose of inoculation after the efflorescence is formed around it. I wish* this Efflorescence to be considered as a sacred boundary over which the lancet should never pass." My own experience entirely corresponds with the above injunction of Dr. Jenner. I never take the matter *after* the 8th day as represented in the colored plate, never so late as the 10th.—I should be still pleased to hear of the progress of this new inoculation among our bretheren of the South, and should I receive any thing further of importance to the practice, from England, I will transmit it.

With the highest respect for your character & station, I remain your very humble serv^t

Benjn Waterhouse.

P.S. The paper on which this letter is written is made from *old paper, written* or *printed on;* the ink being discharged by a process which is cheap, & easily performed. This paper is six shillings sterling the ream, cheaper than that of the same quality made from rags.

B. W.

On November 5, 1801, Jefferson writes to a Mr. Vaughan from Washington and relates the general statistical results of his own experience and his desire to try inoculating the vaccinated patients with variolous matter to test the genuineness of his cowpox matter. He asks Dr. Coxe to send him in exchange for the cowpox matter, "some fresh variolous matter, so carefully taken and done up, as that we may rely on it. . . ." He then emphasizes the importance of having active uncontaminated variolous matter as a negative reaction would indicate an immunity to smallpox—and he is acting in accord with the melon-seed philosophy.

The following is the letter with which Jefferson transmitted that supply of virus to Dr. Coxe, of Philadelphia, which, as before intimated, inaugurated vaccination in that city.[66]

Washington, Nov. 5th, 1801.

Dear Sir: I received on the 24th ult., your favor of the 22d, but it is not till this day that I am enabled to comply with your request of forwarding some of the Vaccine matter for Dr. Coxe. On my arrival at Monticello in July, I received from Dr. Waterhouse, of Cambridge, some vaccine matter taken by himself, and some which he at the same time received from Dr. Jenner, of London. Both of them succeeded, and exhibited precisely the same aspect and affection. In the course of July and August, I inoculated about seventy or eighty of my own family; my sons in law about as many in theirs, and including our neighbors who wished to avail themselves of the opportunity, our whole experiment extended to about two hundred persons. One only case was attended with much fever and some delirium; and two or three with sore arms which required common dressings. All these were from accidents too palpable to be ascribed to the simple disease. About one in five or six had slight feverish dispositions, and more perhaps had a little headache, and more of them had swelling of the axillary glands, which in the case of adults disabled them from labor one, two or three days. Two or three only had from two to half a dozen pustules on the inoculated arm, and no where else, and all the rest only the single pustule where the matter was inserted, something less than a coffee-bean, depressed in the middle, fuller at the edges, and well defined. As far as my observation went, the most premature cases presented a

[66] It is reprinted from Dr. Waterhouse's book into which it was copied from Dr. Coxe's "Practical Observations on VACCINATION, or inoculation for the COW-POCK," Philadelphia, 1802. Page 120, *et seq.*

pellucid liquor the sixth day, which continued in that form the sixth, seventh, and eighth days, when it began to thicken, appear yellowish, and to be environed with inflammation. The most tardy cases offered matter on the eighth day, which continued thin and limpid the eighth, ninth, and tenth days. Perceiving therefore that the most premature as well as the tardiest cases embraced the eighth day, I made that the constant day for taking matter for inoculation, say, eight times twenty-four hours from the hour of its previous insertion. In this way it failed to infect in not more I think than three or four out of the two hundred cases. I have great confidence, therefore, that I preserved the matter genuine, and in that state brought it to Dr. Gantt, of this place, on my return, from whom I obtained the matter I now send you, taken yesterday, from a patient of the eighth day. He has observed this rule as well as myself. In my neighborhood we had no opportunity of obtaining Variolous matter, to try by that test the genuineness of our Vaccine matter; nor can any be had, or Dr. Gantt would have tried it on some of those on whom the Vaccination has been performed. We are very anxious to try this experiment, for the satisfaction of those here, and also those in the neighborhood of Monticello, from whom the matter having been transferred, the establishment of its genuineness here will satisfy them. I am, therefore, induced to ask the favor of you to send me in exchange, some fresh Variolous matter, so carefully taken and done up, as that we may rely on it; you are sensible of the dangerous security which a trial with effete matter might induce. I should add that we never changed the regimen nor occupations of those inoculated; a smither at the anvil continued in his place without a moment's intermission, or indisposition. Generally it gives no more of disease than a blister as large as a coffee-bean produced by burning would occasion. Sucking children did not take the disease from the inoculated mother. These I think are the most material of the observations I made in the limited experiment of my own family. In Aikin's book which I have, you will find a great deal more. I pray you to accept assurances of my esteem and respect.

(Signed) Thos. Jefferson.

Mr. John Vaughan.

On November 10, 1801, Dr. Waterhouse relates the success of a trial of vaccine matter sent on quill and thread by Jefferson so that he could observe the character of the disease. He then makes some technical suggestions for taking the matter on the thread. He describes tactfully the fact that there were enemies of the new inoculation and enclosed a newspaper clipping on this professional opposition.

He then proposes to sum up and publish a "Report on the progress of the vaccine inoculation during the year 1801" and promises to forward a copy and he concludes with the statement that: "as I have attained the ultimate object of my views, the planting the true Kine-pox in the most populous of the southern states, under the most favourable auspices, I shall have no further occasion to encroach on your valuable time, but conclude with wishing you long to possess the highest honor our country can bestow, with health to enjoy it."

Cambridge Nov. 10th. 1801.

Sir

The vaccine matter, which you were so good as to transmit to me 4 or 5 weeks ago, on quills & on thread, has been tried. I communicated the genuine disease with some from one of the tooth-picks, but am not absolutely certain that it ever took from the thread. This induces me to make an observation that may be useful to your inoculators.

I was, at first sight, suspicious of the goodness of the thread you sent me merely from it's *quantity;* for if I understood you right, it was all taken from one patient. I think myself pretty fortunate if I obtain 2, or 3 inches of perfectly infected thread from one patient. Frequently I can procure not more than two inches, whereas the phial you sent me contained, perhaps, as many feet, and that two of very *fine* thread. I set more value on two inches of *coarser* thread, repeatedly soaked in the fluid, so as to have acquired the stiffness of a wire; in which case, the contortions of the thread are nearly obliterated by the coat of matter, whereas that which I received scarcely agglutionated the fibrillae of the cotton. My requesting a sample of the virus from your own-cases, was with a view of demonstrating that your cases were genuine; and of judging if your physicians conducted the process of taking the virus (for transportation especially) in the manner, which we find by experience to be best. They will therefore, I hope, excuse my observing that it is better to imbue repeatedly an inch or two *very well,* than merely to moisten ten times that quantity. By the first procedure they will very seldom, if ever be disappointed, by the latter frequently.

I have gone on inoculating with an almost undeviating success throughout the spring, summer, & this autumn. When I used the fresh virus, warm from the pustule, I *never failed;* but with the thread, I, in the very hot weather, was sometimes foiled.

The enemies of this new inoculation (for in this inferior walk, prejudice, envy, & other unworthy passions, will for a while hang heavily on the wheel destined to bring forth anything new in science) have lately rallied round one of our principal small-pox-inoculators, and gave a momentary check to the progress of truth & humanity, by publishing five cases (clearly spurious, except to the eye of ignorance) to whom he gave the small-pox. By placing a fact with it's wrong end foremost, some uneasiness was created in the public mind. Rumour generated from a simple fact, so placed, an apparently formidable structure, which on close examination was, however, discovered to have neither foundation, nor sides to it,—a mere illusion, calculated to deceive, & to retain a little while longer their

[46]

old *friend*, the small-pox. Not but what there are still many unbelievers among that class of people, where we may not dispair of making them believe anything but truth.

I have enclosed part of a News-paper containing some observations on this professional opposition. In the course of a few weeks, I propose to publish a *Report of the progress of the Vaccine-inoculation during the year 1801*, a copy of which I will transmit to you: after which, as I have attained the ultimate object of my views, the planting the *true* kine-pox in the most populous of the southern-States, under the most favourable auspices, I shall have no further occasion to encroach on your valuable time, but conclude with wishing you long to possess the highest honor our country can bestow, with health to enjoy it.

Benjamin Waterhouse.

President Jefferson,
Washington.

On December 25, 1801, Jefferson assures Dr. Waterhouse that the effort to inoculate with smallpox those who had been inoculated with cowpox had proven he had preserved the cowpox matter in its genuine form. He believes, too, that Dr. Coxe of Philadelphia had ascertained this and, since the vaccine he had used had come from Jefferson and Waterhouse had shown by test that the same vaccine produced cowpox, it made secure those in Virginia who had received the matter from him.

He then states the criteria he had depended upon to recognize the difference between genuine and spurious matter and asks Dr. Waterhouse to repeat what the sure rule was.

This request—enclosed in brackets—is printed without Jefferson's name in the *Medical Repository* for 1802 with "The Answer" signed by Dr. Waterhouse under date of January 28, 1802.

Washington Dec 25. 1801.

Dear Sir

I am indebted to you for several favors unacknowledged. I have waited till I could inform you that some variolous after vaccine inoculation had proved that I had preserved the matter of the cowpox in it's genuine form. Dr Coxe of Philadelphia has ascertained this, having secured his vaccine matter from hence. to this is added your information that the matter I sent you produces the genuine disease and consequently those in Virginia who received the matter from me are now in security.** [knowing how little capable the people in general are of judging between genuine & spurious matter from their appearance, or that of the sore, I endeavored in the course of my inoculations at home to find some other criterion for

** Printed in "Medical Repository," 1802, V, 348.

[47]

their guide. with this view I was very attentive to discover whether there be not *a point of time* counted from the vaccination, when the matter is genuine in all cases. I thought the 8. times 24. hours furnished such a point, I governed myself by it, and it has been followed here successfully by Dr Gantt. but your experience, so much greater, can inform us whether this rule is a sure one. whether any other point of time would be still more certain. to the eye of experience this is not necessary: but for popular use it would be all important for otherwise the disease degenerates as soon as it gets into their hands and may produce a fatal security. I think some popular criterion necessary to crown this valuable discovery.] Accept assurance of my great esteem & respect.

Th. Jefferson.

Dr Benjamin Waterhouse.

On the Necessity of establishing a Point of Time for taking the Vaccine Virus for the Purpose of Inoculation, as a Popular Criterion; in a Letter from ——— ——— to Dr. Waterhouse, dated Washington, Dec. 25, 1801.

Knowing how little capable the people in general are of judging between genuine and spurious matter from their appearance, or that of the pustule, I endeavoured, in the course of my inoculations at M——, to find some other criterion for their guide. With this view I was very attentive to discover whether there be not a point of time, counting from vaccination, when the matter is genuine in all cases. I thought the eight times twenty-four hours furnished such a point; I governed myself by it, and it has been followed here successfully by Dr. Gantt: but your experience, so much greater, can inform us whether this rule is a sure one, or whether any other point of time would be still more certain. To the eye of experience this is not necessary; but for popular use it would be all-important; for otherwise the disease degenerates as soon as it gets into their hands, and may produce a fatal security. I think some popular criterion necessary to crown this valuable discovery.

The Answer

I was forcibly impressed with the necessity of fixing one some point of time, by way of popular guide, when to take the vaccine fluid for the purpose of inoculation, in order to prevent the evils you suggest.

I know that the perfection of the virus differs somewhat in different subjects; but in the formation of a general rule it is necessary to impose a limitation. Dr. Jenner says, "I prefer the fifth day, or the sixth, or the seventh, eighth, or (if the efflorescence is not far advanced beyond the margin of the pustule) the ninth day." But I conceive this is impossible to be discovered with requisite precision on the skin of the African. The criterion of LIMPID matter is fallacious: for, in the rising of a vesicle from almost any cause, the scarf-skin separates from the true, and a portion of the superfluous water of the blood, and sometimes of the coagulable lymph, is found under it. I have known this limpid fluid exude in considerable quantity from the vaccine pustule that has been too much irritated by pricking, and exhausted of its virus. It gives a shining, glazy appearance to the thread. I know of no writer or practitioner who has made this distinction.

Were I, then, to fix on a point of time, of all others, as a general or popular rule, I should say EIGHT TIMES TWENTY-FOUR HOURS: this being the result of my own experience.

Benjamin Waterhouse.

Cambridge, Jan. 28, 1802.

On January 11, 1802, Dr. Waterhouse states he is "inoculating almost every day, and with undeviating success. We scarcely see anything like a spurious taint, and when we do, the cause is apparent and the remedy certain."

.　　　.　　　.　　　.　　　.　　　.

He then states that "altho this new inoculation prospers, it is not without its opponents among the faculty here" and he mentions the stumbling-blocks slyly thrown in his way not by way of complaint, but merely to apprise Jefferson of the falsehoods and misrepresentations that are floating on the breath of ignorance. He mentions the fact that articles had been sent to the newspapers "without the writer's name to it"—probably similar to the "Pedro" advertisement previously quoted.

The effect of tracing every case and dissecting it before the public is indicated as impressing caution on the enemies and at the same time informing the printers of Boston so that public opinion had become crystallized against the smallpox inoculation and in favor of kine pox.

In the next paragraph he imparts the details of his plan to print part of the Jefferson letter. Evidently Jefferson did not object to the use of his query without his name as it was printed.** He then asks Jefferson if the letter sent to Dr. Gantt was ever printed in Washington as Jefferson had suggested in his letter of September 17, 1801.

In the last paragraph he tells of Dr. Valentine Seaman in New York "conducting the business with perfect success." He informs him, too, that he has sent by sea some virus to Dr. David Ramsay of Charleston.

** See p. 48.

Sir

The enclosed letter came to my hands two days ago. I return it from an apprehension that it is a mistake. I conjecture that Aiken's publication, as also some pieces from the news paper, were sent to some person to whom you wished to communicate information respecting the vaccine inoculation, and that by mistake you directed this letter to me, as no such articles came with it. It gives me however, the pleasing hope, provided I am right in my conjecture, of being soon honored with a letter from you.

I am inoculating almost every day, and with undeviating success. We scarcely see anything like a spurious taint, and when we so, the cause is apparent and the remedy certain. The weather is favourable to the practice, for instead of frost & snow, we have showers like spring and the weather continues so warm that we are endanger of a double vegetation, after which "may come a frost, a killing frost!" and nip the hopes of the cultivator.

Altho this new inoculation prospers, it is not without its opponents among the faculty here, as well as elsewhere. Some are loath to give up their old *friend* the small-pox. They slyly throw stumbling blocks in my way, while others plant themselves like reptiles in the high road of improvement & try to hiss back all that would advance. I mention this not in the tone of complaint, but merely to apprise you of the falsehoods & misrepresentations that are floating on the breath of the ignorant, intrested, envious & malignant. I have been so attentive in tracing every case that has been brought forward to injure us, & so careful to dissect it before the public that our enemies are rather cautious in their movements, especially as they know the popular opinion is against them. None of the printers in Boston will admit any pieces against the practice without the writers name to it. It was early attempted, but the public voice cried out against it. Nay more, the printers of all parties in Boston have not only declined printing such pieces but in several instances sent them to me.

The most mischievous idea spread abroad is this,—"the kine-pox will secure you for *a few years only* from the pox, after which you are as liable as ever to this disease." It is here, after being beaten from every post, that our enemies have entrenched themselves with an air of defiance.

As the practice now stands on the firm ground of experiment, I mean to continue the history of it in the form of a communication to next number of the Medical Repository at New-York. In that paper I could wish to make use of the whole, or a part of one of your letters to me, merely to aid the cause by showing the American people that you think well of the discovery & the practice: unless indeed you would think fit to express your *present* opinion, as you have been able to form one from your own knowledge of the business. If this idea accords with your own, I should rejoice at it, but otherwise, I must beg you to excuse the suggestion, while I remain satisfied that it would be improper. I never knew if the letter which you thought had best be published at Washington, ever has appeared. Col. Varnum used to send me the National intelligenser, but he has forgotten me this session.

I have just sent the vaccine virus to Dr. Ramsey of Charleston by sea; he writes very earnestly for it. At N. York the worthy Dr. Seaman conducts the business with perfect success by matter I sent him. He says he shall hereafter make *a point of conscience never to inoculate another person for the small-pox* unless it be after the vaccine process by way of trial.

Accept the sentiments of esteem & veneration from

Benjn Waterhouse.[99]

In the *Medical Repository* [999] for this same year (1802) is the notice of the organization of the New York Vaccine Institution with its directors, officers and medical board. Also the notice of the appointment of Dr. Jenner and Dr. Waterhouse as "perpetual honorary directors" of "New-York Vaccine Institution." [70]

A number of the citizens of New-York, impressed with the importance of substituting the inoculation of the vaccine disease for that of the small-pox, lately agreed to associate, and to contribute to the establishment of a public institution for that object. The design of this institution is three-fold; to extend the advantage of vaccine inoculation to the poor—to maintain a permanent supply of genuine matter for the use of the community —and to disseminate a knowledge of this inoculation among the physicians of the adjacent country. After public meetings, held by the contributors for the purpose, they formed and adopted a constitution suited to their design; and then proceeded, in pursuance of the constitution, to elect the officers of the institution, when the following gentlemen were elected:

Directors.

James Watson,	Samuel Bowne,
John Keese,	Robert Bowne,
Samuel L. Mitchill,	Isaac Hicks,
Gilbert Aspinwall,	William Moore,
Thomas Buckley,	Samuel Miller,
Willet Seaman,	Andrew Cock,

James Robertson.
Thomas Franklin, Treasurer.
Adrian Hegeman, Secretary.

[99] Library of Congress. [70] Page 347.
[999] Volume V, 1802.

The Directors made choice of the following gentlemen to perform the various duties assigned to their offices by the constitution:

James Watson, President.
Gilbert Aspinwall, Vice-President.
Medical Board.

| Valentine Seaman, | Edward Miller, |
| Wright Post, | Samuel Borrowe. |

Samuel Scofield, Resident Surgeon.

The Directors having procured a suitable apartment, and made other neccessary arrangements, the Medical Board have commenced inoculation, and are now proceeding in it with every prospect of carrying into effect the benevolent intentions of the founders of the institution.

At the last meeting of the contributors, the following resolution, moved by Mr. Samuel Bowne, was unanimously adopted, viz.

"Resolved, that in testimony of the high estimation in which this meeting of contributors hold the philanthropic and able exertions of EDWARD JENNER, M.D.F.R.S. &c. of London, and BENJAMIN WATERHOUSE, M.D. professor of the practice of physic in the University of Cambridge, in Massachusetts, relative to the inoculation of the Kine-Pock, they are hereby appointed perpetual honorary Directors of this institution."

On January 17, 1802, Jefferson writes to his daughter and tells of the failure of attempts to cause smallpox in those vaccinated. This was tried by Dr. Gantt in Washington and probably Dr. Coxe and others in Philadelphia. Jefferson is pleased because it established the genuineness of his matter and placed his family and neighbors in perfect security.

Washington, January 17, 1802.
[Thomas Jefferson to Martha (Mrs. R.)]

. . . Dr. Gantt has inoculated six of his cow-pox patients with the small pox, not one of which took it. Many have tried in Philadelphia & with the same issue. As the matter here came from Monticello, and that at Philadelphia from this place, they establish the genuineness of our inoculations and may place our families & neighbors in perfect security. . . .[71]

On January 29, 1802, Dr. Waterhouse reviews the "criteria as to the precise time of taking the matter" and quotes Jenner's dictum. He takes exception to the suggestions of Mr. Aikin and says he "is not a

[71] Original letter in the Pierpont Morgan Library, New York City.

good guide on this subject" as neither he nor "his very learned and classical father, Dr. Aikin, had any experience in the disease."

He says he has written several times to Dr. Gantt "but never had an answer." There is no intimation of the reason for this persistent silence in any of Jefferson's letters.

He apologizes for the printing of Jefferson's first letter to him by Lettsom and its republication by the editors of Aikin's new edition.

He describes the criteria of the differential in thought which he considered should be made between the private citizen and the chief magistrate of a nation in the sentence: "Anti-monarchical as I am, I nevertheless think that a strong line of distinction should always be drawn between the private citizen and the chief magistrate of a nation, toward whom I am disposed to say in the language and meaning of that old book which all New England folk sware by, 'Ye are Gods.' "

In the closing paragraph he asserts that because Lettsom printed the Jefferson letter in the book, it would check his inclination to spread abroad the useful and philanthropic volume. Lastly he claimed kinship to Dr. Fothergill, who was a nephew of his grandmother.

Cambridge Jan^{ry} 29th. 1802.

Sir

Your letter of the 14th ins^t enclosing one of the 25th ult^o came duly to hand.

I was struck with the expediency of establishing a popular criterion as to the precise time of taking the matter, and I entirely coincide with you in opinion that it should be fixed on *eight times twenty four hours,* this being the result of my own observation during the last season. I know that it differs somewhat in different subjects, but in the formation of a general rule it is necessary to impose a limitation. Jenner says "I prefer the 5th. 6th. 7th. 8th. and (if the efflorescence is not far advanced beyond the margin of the pustule) the 9th."—But I conceive this is impossible to be discovered with requisite precision on the skin of the African? Mr. Aikin is not a good guide on this subject. His publication was not the result of his *own* experience; nor do I believe that Dr. Aikin, his very learned & classical father, had any experience in the disease.

As to the criterion of *limpid* matter, I know it to be fallacious; for in the rising of a vesicle, or blister from any cause, the scarf-skin separates from the true, and a portion of the *superfluous water* of the blood, & sometimes of the *coaguable lymph* is found under it; and I have know this *limpid* fluid exude from the vaccine pustule, especially after being too much exhausted and irritated in procuring virus. This exudation gives a shining glary appearance to the thread. I know of no writer, or practitioner who has made this distinction.

I am glad to find that other physicians are following the lead of Dr. Cox in Philadelphia. I have heretofore been surprised at the fastidious style of some of the fathers in the art in that city.—I have never heard anything respecting Dr. Gantt's progress in the business. I have written to him several times, but never had an answer.

I have been made uneasy at one occurrence. In an unrestrained & perfectly confidential correspondence with my intimate friend Dr. Lettson, I transmitted him a copy of your first letter to me dated Dec. 25th. 1801. acknowleding the receipt of my pamphlet & altho I did this in the pride of my heart, I meant that he and Jenner only should partake of my satisfaction; but my friend Lettson printed it in his volume on the cow-pox; and the Editors of a new edition of Aikin's little book just published at Philadelphia have prefixed it to that work. Anti-monarchical as I am, I nevertheless think that a strong line of distinction should always be drawn between the private citizen & the Chief Magistrate of a nation, towards whom I am disposed to say in the language and meaning of that old book which all we New England folks sware by, *"Ye are Gods!"*

My friend Lettsom has taken one method to check my inclination of spreading abroad this useful & philanthropic volume. My venerable kinsman Dr. Fothergill used to say, "a man's *conduct* should be his *picture."* Accept the sentiments of profound respect.

Benjamin Waterhouse.[72]

On April 8, 1802, Dr. Waterhouse, writing a letter to Dr. Jenner, stated that: "The ship had but thirty-two days passage." The statement would seem to suggest astonishment at the "speed" and that thirty-two days was a rapid voyage.

Just as one judges animals the next thought expressed is the use of the "Lombardy virus" just put into "a fine female arm of about two and twenty years standing."

The last step in public health programs is the printing of the technique in single sheet or folder form and it seems Dr. Jenner has done this and sent copies which are acknowledged and at the same time we learn of the tiresome task of repetition.

He acknowledges receipt of a copy of the eloquent lecture by which Dr. Rush of Philadelphia had "come out full and strong in praise of the new inoculation and the blessings of the Jennerian discovery."

He relates in some detail the visit to the city of Washington of "a grand embassy of certain tribes of Indians" and the supplying of virus to them.

It is also noteworthy that the Rev. Dr. Gantt, chaplain of Congress, vaccinated the chief and nine or ten more warriors.

[72] Library of Congress.

MY DEAR SIR,

Four hours ago I received your polite and very interesting letter dated 24th February. The ship had but thirty-two days passage. I have just put your Lombardy virus into a fine female arm of about two-and-twenty years' standing, and shall give you the result by the return of the ship which brought it. I am highly gratified by your written, printed, and engraven communications. I shall send one of each to the President of the United States directly. You have executed the very plan I had in contemplation, viz. printed directions on a page of a sheet for a common letter; for my numerous correspondents in these States have rendered the repetition of the task respecting directions so tiresome that I had resolved on a printed letter like yours. Now I shall just reprint yours, with the additional weight of your name to it.

Dr. Rush has come out full and strong in praise of the new inoculation, and has sent me a copy of an eloquent lecture of his on the blessings of the Jennerian discovery. I believe I informed our friend Dr. Lettsom that the vaccine inoculation was carrying on its salutiferous powers into the wilderness of the new world. If I did not, I will repeat it here.

Last December a grand embassy of certain tribes of the Indians came to the city of ·Washington while the Congress was sitting, or as they phrase it, while the sixteen *fires* or *lights* were burning. Our Government continued to do every thing to ameliorate their condition. They had sent them seventy ploughs, ten looms, and fifty spinning-wheels, with every common utensil in husbandry, besides establishing blacksmiths, bricklayers, &c. They had taught them to plant orchards, to rear and manage horses, to use scales and weights and measures (for heretofore the white traders used to put in the scales their *foot* or right *hand* against their beaver and ermine skins.) In short, Washington, Adams, and Jefferson have done every thing to civilize that shrewd people. The chief of this embassy was named *Little Turtle.* The President one day sent for this warrior and his interpreter, and told him that he had a matter of great importance to communicate to him, for the benefit of the whole nation of his *Red Children,* for these savages always call him *Father.* He then told him that the GREAT SPIRIT had lately made a precious donation to the enlightened white men over the great water, first to a single person, and from him to another on this side the waters, and then explained to him the history of the cow or kine-pock as a gift from Heaven to preserve them from the small-pox, and even to banish it from the earth. The chief heard him with marked attention, and desired first to receive the benefits of it himself. This was performed soon after by the Rev. Dr. Gantt, chaplain of Congress, and also upon nine or ten more warriors in his train. On their departure the President caused them to be supplied with the virus; and the interpreter (a white man) took a copy of the directions for conducting the process I had transmitted to the President.

When the Minerva returns I may possibly write you a *letter* instead of this *receipt* for your valuable favours; as it is, you will receive cordial wishes of an affectionate friend,

Benjamin Waterhouse.[73]

On December 27, 1802, Dr. Waterhouse was still curious and continuing his efforts to find the cause of cowpox. In a letter to Dr. Eustis he discusses "remote and proximate causes" and states Dr. Jenner's idea that the vaccine disease originated with the horse.

Cambridge, Dec. 27, 1802.

Disorder was in the heels of horses, which the English farriers, and after them, Dr. Jenner, call the *grease* . . . "but they do not agree as to the remote or proximate cause, or even as to the diagnosis of the distemper. Mr. Bowdoin . . . says, we have not the disease in the country. Dr. Jenner you know, has asserted, that the vaccine disease is of equine origin. Altho. this matter has been much controverted, he says in a late letter to me, that *"wherever in the same dairy, there should happen to be* the *peculiar intercourse, which he* has *pointed out, between* the *horse,* the *man,* the *cow* and *its milker,* there *the cow pox will be called into existence."* . . . Has it ever been know that farriers, or shoers of horses, have resisted the s pox inoculation? Besides giving the information to Dr. Jenner, I wish to mention the subject in a work now in the press. . . ."[74]

On March 1, 1803, Dr. Waterhouse sends to Jefferson a copy of his "Treatise on Kine-pox"—this was probably Part II. He relates the enthusiasm of the press in the United States and in Great Britain where it was published that the beneficial practice of vaccination is patronized by "Jefferson in the New World," by the Emperor of Germany and the Empress Dowager of Russia.

Cambridge March 1st 1803.

Sir

I here transmit for your acceptance, a copy of my Treatise on the Kine Pock, which, though dated Nov[r] 1802 is just out of the press. The first part contains the history of the progress of this new inoculation in America; The second contains the theory of morbid poisons, together with practical rules & observations.—

Being aware that this first narrative would probably be referred to, in time to come, I was desirous to give it all the dignity in my power, by recording the patrons of this new discovery & practice. The unreserved applause which some of its most distinguished patrons have received in *all*

[73] Baron's "Life of E. Jenner, M.D.," Vol. I, 1838.
[74] Benjamin Waterhouse to William Eustis, Cambridge, December 27, 1802, in Emmet Collection, Number 5341, New York Public Library.

the newspapers in this part of the Union, has given us high satisfaction. The same strain of eulogism pervades many of the British publications, especially the volume of public characters for 1803 just come to my hands, in sheets. In Jenner's character page 47, a paragraph begins thus,—"This beneficial practice is patronised by *JEFFERSON* in the New World, & by the *EMPEROR OF GERMANY*, the *EMPRESS DOWAGER OF RUSSIA* in the old." Then follows a copy of the letter from the Empress to Dr. Jenner, dated Paulowsky Aug. 10ʰ 1802.

A second edition of this Treatise will I believe follow in a few months, before which I hope to receive from my friend & correspondent such corrections, hints for additions, or omissions as will make it less exceptionable to the scholar & physician. With high respect, I am

Your very humble servᵗ

Benjⁿ Waterhouse.[75]

President Jefferson.

In the review of this episode it is evident that Dr. Waterhouse had recognized immediately the great value to the public health of vaccination. He conceived and followed the same practical course of promulgating the new medical procedure that even now would be adopted. That is, he desired first, to prove to his satisfaction that vaccination would prevent smallpox; second, he wished to perfect the technique so he might teach it to others. Thus having prepared himself he reported the whole problem to the profession and invited discussion and criticism and hoped he might obtain the assistance of an organization to proceed to gather, classify and tabulate cases for a statistical study. When he perceived his efforts were misinterpreted and considered to be an endeavor to monopolize the procedure he immediately desisted. Nowhere do we find the least intimation that he desired to restrict the knowledge or the use of the procedure, but, on the contrary, we find him making every effort to spread the knowledge of its value to both the laity and profession. Though offered large financial inducements for exclusive rights he refused them as a "vile conspiracy" and took every adequate means to prevent the organization of monopolies in various states and towns.

Failing to enlist the active support of President John Adams, an old friend, or the co-operation of an influential scientific or medical society, he felt compelled to "go it alone." He wrote to the newspapers requesting statistical help but the physicians and the communities gave little or no response. The influential men, medical or scientific, of Boston or New England apparently would not organize to promote the procedure. At last convinced of this unwillingness the doctor en-

[75] Library of Congress.

deavored to enlist the President elect, Thomas Jefferson, as one who could exert the greatest and most widely recognized influence in the promulgation and control of kine pox inoculation. The man, Jefferson, from his wide experience and travel had displayed his inquiring and scientific sympathy and a viewpoint similar to that of physicians respecting public health measures—the application of all available knowledge without restrictions of monopoly or patent.

The appeal to Thomas Jefferson aroused his complete and enthusiastic accord. He answered within twenty-four hours the letter initiating the definite plan which resulted in enlisting the interest of the profession and laity of Virginia, Washington, Philadelphia and other places.

To Dr. Waterhouse is due, therefore, the credit of devising the method and inviting Jefferson to lend his influence in the execution of the procedure and thus expediting the introduction of vaccination as a preventative of smallpox and establishing it as a recognized public health measure.

AN EPISODE IN THE EARLY HISTORY
OF
SMALLPOX VACCINATION IN NEW HAMPSHIRE

Morris C. Leikind

AN EPISODE IN THE HISTORY OF SMALLPOX VACCINATION IN NEW HAMPSHIRE [1]

MORRIS C. LEIKIND [2]

Although much has been written on the beginning of smallpox vaccination in America, most of the accounts have been largely confined to biographical sketches of the early vaccinators, discussions of the clinical phenomena and descriptions of early vaccination techniques. Very little has been written on the economic and social factors involved in establishing vaccination as a recognized medical procedure. For light on the question of fees, the relationships of doctors to each other and to their patients we must study contemporary documents such as fee bills, letters and contracts. It is in fact on the study of just such a collection of manuscript material, much of it hitherto unpublished,[3] that this paper is based. Fragmentary though the account is, it provides some insight into the economic and social factors involved in the practice of vaccination and distribution of vaccine virus to physicians and their patients.

In 1799, Dr. Benjamin Waterhouse, Professor of the Theory and Practice of Physic at the Harvard Medical School in Cambridge, Massachusetts, received from his friend Dr. Lettsom of London a copy of Jenner's " Inquiry into the causes and effects of the variolae

---

[1] Read at the Annual Meeting of the American Association of the History of Medicine in Atlantic City, N. J., May 1, 1939. Also read in part before the Washington Branch of the Society of American Bacteriologists at the Army Medical School, Washington, D. C., March 21, 1939.

[2] From the Institute of the History of Medicine, The Johns Hopkins University, Baltimore, Md., and the Library of Congress, Washington, D. C.

[3] This study is based in part on hitherto unpublished letters and papers found in the Josiah Bartlett Collection owned by the Library of Congress. All the documents transcribed and reproduced are marked here with the symbol (B). In studying the material it was found that some of the letters in the Bartlett Collection fill gaps in a collection of letters previously published in a life of Dr. Lyman Spalding (Dr. Lyman Spalding . . . , by Dr. James Alfred Spalding. Boston, W. M. Leonard, 1916, viii, 380 pp.). In order to give continuity to the story here recounted certain of the letters were borrowed from the Spalding biography. They are marked with the symbol (S) with the page reference immediately following.

vaccinae, or cowpox." Waterhouse [4] tells us, ". . . On perusing this work, I was struck with the unspeakable advantages that might accrue to this country and indeed to the human race at large from the diffusion of a mild distemper that would ever after secure the constitution from that terrible scourge the smallpox. . . . As the ordinary mode of communicating even medical discoveries in this country is by newspapers, I drew up the following account of the cowpox, which was printed in the Columbian Sentinel, Mar. 12, 1799, under the title: 'Something curious in the medical line.'" This was essentially a resume of Jenner's book. From Waterhouse again, we learn of the reception of this notice: "This publication shared the fate of most others on new discoveries. A few received it as a very important discovery, highly interesting to humanity, some doubted it; others observed that wise and prudent conduct which allows them to condemn or applaud as the event might prove: while the greater number absolutely ridiculed it as one of those medical whims which arise today and tomorrow are no more." But this ridicule did not dismay Waterhouse. He was determined to try the new protection against the dreaded smallpox and see its action for himself. In Ju'y, 1800, having secured some of the vaccine matter from England, he proceeded forthwith to vaccinate his children and several domestics, seven persons in all. Soon after they recovered from the effects of the vaccination they were sent to a licensed smallpox hospital in Boston where they were inoculated with smallpox virus as a test of the protection afforded by the Kine-pox. All proved resistant. These first experiments of Waterhouse were a complete and triumphant vindication of Jenner's claims.

This successful experiment encouraged patients of Dr. Waterhouse to try the treatment. Some fifty persons were inoculated in a short time, there were no ill effects and the word began to spread that vaccination was indeed all it was claimed to be. Waterhouse soon found himself deluged by requests from physicians for the vaccine matter.

Among those who wrote to him was Dr. Lyman Spalding of Portsmouth, New Hampshire (b. 1775, d. 1821). Dr. Spalding

[4] A Prospect for exterminating the small-pox . . . by Benjamin Waterhouse. Boston, W. Hilliard, 1800, 40 p.

was co-founder with Nathan Smith of the Dartmouth Medical School, father of the U. S. Pharmacopoeia and Secretary of the New Hampshire Medical Society. Waterhouse replied in a letter dated Sept. 6, 1800, as follows:

(S, p. 54)

> Cambridge, September 6, 1800. Dear Sir. I have only time to say that I have received your second letter and that I will accommodate you with the " matter," etc., at the same pay which has been offered to me, but I declined, namely for One Quarter of the profit arising from the inoculation, and the contract to remain for 14 months from this time. Abandon the idea of inoculating for the small pox and throw all your attention to the Kine-pox. If this idea suits you and Dr. Cutter [5] you shall be accommodated at once, for half a dozen practitioners stand ready to jump at that offer, and two of them are not a very great distance from you. In haste, I am Yours, etc.
>
> BENJAMIN WATERHOUSE.

Spalding's reply to this letter is as follows:

(S, p. 54)

> Portsmouth, September 10, 1800. Dear Sir. The terms are accepted, and I promise that you shall have One Quarter part of the next profit arising from my inoculation with the kine pox for the space of 14 months, provided it be not made public before that term expires, and then the contract to remain in full force only to the time of its becoming public. However, on your part it is expected that the like privilege will not be granted to others in my vicinity. Yours, etc., L. SPALDING.

In the words of Spalding's biographer, " we have here a ' Vaccination Trust.' " But not only is there evidence of attempts at monopolistic practice in connection with the new discovery. We even find evidences of " muscling in on a good racket." On Sept. 12, 1800 Waterhouse again writes to Spalding:

(S, p. 54)

> Cambridge, September 12, 1800. Yours of the 19th [5a] informs me that you accede to my proposal " provided it be not made public before that time expires." Now that is too vague to proceed on. Sam Brown [6]

---

[5] There were two Drs. Cutter, father and son, in Portsmouth. It is not clear which one is referred to.

[5a] The date 19th is probably a misprint and should be read " 10th."

[6] A classmate of Spalding's at Harvard. He was attempting to buy scabs from patients inoculated, and tried to use these scabs for treating his own patients.

may steal it before a month expires, and then in six months it may be diffused all over Boston, or it may not. I therefore propose that shall be for twelve months and that will leave you to yourself during the three autumn months of 1801. You however will have got the start of all others, so much that no one can rival you entirely; besides it will fix you in business. My fee is Five Dollars. You must engage not to supply any other practitioner. Your acceeding to this will fetch the infection next post. If you wish to come and see the disease, and my practice, you shall have that in the bargain. Yours, B. WATERHOUSE.

P. S. I have a similar application from Amherst in your state and another from a young doctor going to settle at Hampton. But, if Dr. Cutter and you and I make the contract proposed, this gentleman will not be supplied. I will supply none within twenty or thirty miles of you and perhaps further.

Letters were shuttled back and forth, Waterhouse holding out for more pay and insisting that Spalding take an older man as a partner, thus further increasing the royalties; Spalding holding out for an individual contract in order to be the first in Portsmouth, thus giving him a monopoly of the practice. In an undated letter, Spalding writes to Waterhouse as follows:

(S, p. 55)

Dear Sir: . . . I applaud your policy of making a few guineas for yourself considering what pains you have taken in procuring and experimenting upon the Kine-pox. Now Sir, far from inoculating gratis or endeavoring to procure the infection by stealth, if you will permit me to inoculate I will give you ten per cent upon the fees received for it, till you shall, or by other means, and not through my carelessness, it shall be made public. If these terms coincide with your ideas, you will forward the infection IMMEDIATELY, for " Now is the appointed time " and I promise you shall receive your premium without the least shadow of fraud.

With fidelity

LYMAN SPALDING.

P. S. How do you obligate your patients to prevent the infection being taken from their pustules ! !

N. B. I expect the same privilege will not be granted to any other person in this vicinity !

Waterhouse finally yields to Spalding. He writes on September

18th that he is enclosing a bond [7] to be executed whereupon he will send the virus. He also outlines a scheme to divide the State of New Hampshire into vaccination districts. The letter follows:

(S, p. 56)

> Cambridge, September 18, 1800. Dr. Spalding, Dear Sir: I am sorry, very sorry that you did not come in person to negotiate the business of inoculation instead of doing it by letter, because every day brings me fresh applicants on the same subject. I have had three physicians from New Hampshire with me these two days, and during their waiting for my determination, I received what I absolutely waited for, your letter, which when read I was disappointed in finding no mention made of Dr. Cutter, whose name you mentioned as connecting in your plan in your first letter. As these gentlemen could not tarry any longer, I finally concluded and exchanged bonds, of which the enclosed is a transcript (Mutatis Mutandis) to inoculate the three counties of Strafford, Grafton and Rockingham, excepting the town of Portsmouth, Newington, Rye, Kittery, Greenland and Dover, on an intimation that Dr. Cutter practiced considerably in the last-named town. Thus, have I endeavoured to do what I conceived right, just, and honorable towards you, Dr. Cutter and them. I wished exceedingly that you had been present, but pressed as I have been on all sides I feel as if I had done for the best. I have reserved from our agreement Hanover and six miles around it in Grafton County, because I thought the physician, whoever he might be in that quarter, should have his chance under the same patronage I gave to others.
>
> I have sent the enclosed form, which is just like the one I interchanged with Dr. Rowe in Vermont, and Doctors Stowe, Ranney and Dr. Billings of Bristol County, Massachusetts and Three Dr. Bartletts [8] in your State, for three seasons with the reserve, that if you

---

[7] The bond is mentioned in Spalding's biography but I have not been able to find any existing copies in Washington.

[8] The three Drs. Bartlett are Levi, Josiah and Ezra. They were the sons of Governor Josiah Bartlett (1729-1795), physician, Revolutionary patriot and Signer of the Declaration of Independence, Governor of New Hampshire and Chief Justice of its Supreme Court. He was the father of 12 children, 3 of whom became physicians.

Of the three doctors, Levi was the oldest. Born at Kingston, N. H., 1763. Active as a physician and surgeon, he served also in the State Legislature, was a Colonel in the militia and was a Chief Justice of the Court of Common Pleas and Judge of the Circuit Court. Married twice and had three children by his second wife. He died in 1828.

Josiah Bartlett was born in 1768. Began study of medicine as an apprentice to his

do not close with my proposals, Portsmouth, Dover, etc., etc., will be
included in their district. If you and Dr. Cutter feel disposed to sign
such a paper as they have, I will, on receipt of yours, send another
properly executed and with it the matter for inoculation.

B. WATERHOUSE.

And finally to make a long story short, Waterhouse for a consideration of $150, the bond being duly executed, sends Spalding a thread
on which was the vaccine virus. In his letter dated Sept. 25, 1800,
Waterhouse cautions the young man,

(S, p. 58)

. . . You must be very attentive to collecting the matter from the
arm for I cannot supply more than the first thread.

The reader by this time is aware, and it will be noted later in this
story, that the matter of a constant supply of vaccine matter was an
acute problem in the early days. In fact this uncertainty of supply
was probably the chief source of the difficulties attendant on the
establishment of vaccination. The first supplies came to this country
as lymph dried on bits of thread. These threads of course were not
bacteriologically pure and so gave rise quite often to secondary infections. But aside from that not many persons could be vaccinated
from one thread. Spalding apparently tried to get a maximum yield
from his one thread for he vaccinated thirty patients from his first
bit of string. But he soon ran into trouble and Waterhouse replied
to his plea for help as follows:

(S, p. 59)

Cambridge, October 12, 1800 Dear Sir: I write immediately to
inform you that you must take the matter from the inoculated part in

---

brother Levi of Kingston. Completed his medical education at Harvard. Began
practice of medicine at Stratham in 1789. Sent to Congress in 1810. Served two
years. Succeeded Dr. Nathan Smith as president of the New Hampshire Medical
Society. Although he was twice married he had no children. Was blinded by
cataract and died in 1838.
   Ezra was the youngest of the three Bartletts. Born 1770, died 1848.
   For further data on the Bartlett family see,
      Bartlett, Levi, Geneological and biographical sketches of the Bartlett family in
         England and America. Lawrence, Geo. S. Merrill, 1876.
      Sanderson, John, Biography of the Signers to the Declaration of Independence.
         Rev. by Rob't T. Conrad. Philadelphia, Thomas Cowperthwaite, 1847.

its limpid state, before purulency comes on and never from the pustules which very rarely occur. I find great difficulty in procuring matter for my own inoculation.

I have had applications from Portsmouth and from its neighborhood and do most strenuously recommend that you offer the matter to Dr. Brackett and Cutter. With their assistance you will make it more profitable to yourself as well as to me. I never was, you know satisfied with our bargain and I never shall be unless those old established practitioners are included. Dr. Jackson has not the matter. He applied to me for it last week. He brought some but failed. In haste, I am, etc. B. WATERHOUSE.

P. S. The febrile symptoms are the criterion.

As is obvious from the above letter, the method used to keep the virus going was arm to arm transfer. A doctor would inoculate a patient and then on the fifth to the eighth day after insertion of the virus he would examine the pustule. If the lymph was clear he would take some of this for his next patient or family group. Direct arm to arm transfer was preferred by the patients as they thus could see that the donor was a " neat, clean person " and they felt more satisfied that they were getting the real stuff. Where direct transfer was not possible, threads were soaked in the lymph, dried and sealed in vials for use. Crusts and scabs were also used. But aside from the obvious danger (obvious to us) arising from material that was not bacteriologically pure, another problem arose. This was an economic one. Since the patient was the source of supply of the virus there arose the problem of controlling the patient. As will be recalled from some of the previous letters, doctors were not above buying vaccine virus from patients vaccinated by another physician. And patients, as human then as now, were not averse to making an " honest " penny when opportunity offered. In the following group of letters, the question of how to control the patient is repeatedly asked. Dr. Spalding's correspondence with Waterhouse was coming to a close and now we find Spalding entering into a correspondence with Dr. Josiah Bartlett of Stratham, New Hampshire. On October 9th, 1800, Bartlett writes to Spalding:

(S, p. 60)

Stratham, October 9th, 1800. Sir: Having no personal acquaintance, yet seeing an advertisement notifying your inoculating with the

varioloid vaccine, I write, wishing to know the Method you take to
prevent persons from inoculating with Matter from your patients.
From the little experience had in the business as yet I am much pleased
with similarity of the Kine. to the Small Pox, three patients having
passed through the former under my care with little disturbance except
the arms, one having about two hundred pock, but no pustulation, the
other a less number. If it will not trouble you too much, I wish you
to write and inform me respecting the Matter. With Esteem, your
Humble Servant, JOSIAH BARTLETT.

Although the distances were not great between the towns of Portsmouth and Stratham, the mail service must have been excellent for
Spalding received Bartlett's letter the day it was sent and he promptly
replied and sent a scab from a vaccine pock.

(B)   Portsmouth Oct. 9, 1800.
    Dear Sir:
    Yours of this date is before me. I am happy in becoming acquainted
with the physicians in this part of the State; but lament that I cannot
give you more, & satisfactory information on the subject of the kine
pox. My first inoculation was on the 30th ult. He has had no indisposition, nor eruption, although the arm has been somewhat sore— I
have inoculated 15 patients; one, only, has the appearance of eruption— I find some trouble in procuring infection for future
inoculations.
    All the patients, which I have inoculated, are of the first families
in town, & their honor or that of the parent, has been deemed sufficient
to prevent any clandestine inoculation. As yet, I have taken nothing
but the pledge of honor not to suffer any person to take infection from
them. When the lower class of people are inoculated I shall lay
them under some obligation not to suffer the infection to be stolen.
                            Sir, I am with much respect
                                & esteem, your humble
                                        Servant
Dr. Bartlett, Stratham   LYMAN SPALDING

    To this letter Bartlett replied in the following note sent by mes-
senger:

(S, p. 61)
    Doctor Bartlett's Compliments to Doctor Spalding, and would
inform him that the Kine Pock scab produced a spurious tumor in one
case and in others, where inserted, did not take or produce any effect.

If you have some on a thread will you be kind enough to let me have some if you think it is not effete or if it is fresh? Pardon my frequent applications and the trouble I give you. The bearer, George Wingate, Esquire will take the virus to me. Accept my Respects and good wishes, JOSIAH BARTLETT.

And a few days later, Spalding writes again to Bartlett asking for the loan of Jenner's publication on the Kine-pox.

(B)   Portsmouth Oct 28th.
Dear Sir:

Having learned that you have a publication on the kine pox (I suppose Jenner) with plates, I must beg the favor of the loan of it for a few days. I find it extremely difficult to determine when the patients are infected. If you will send me this volume by the Exeter stage—it shall be returned very soon with the best thanks of your humble servant   L. SPALDING

Can this work be procured in Boston?

Bartlett promptly replies:

(S, p. 61)

Stratham, October 30th, 1800. Dear Sir. Your inquiries concerning Jenner received. Doctor S. Ranney of Brentwood now has the Book. I will endeavor to get and send it to you next week. We could find only this, (one) that we purchased in Boston when visiting Dr. Waterhouse. By a late letter from him I find that the failure within his practice is equal to ours. I frequently inoculate in both arms at the same time; in general, on the 5th day (tho' sometimes not till the 9th or 11th) after effectual inoculation, there is a circular ridge around the puncture, which is pretty certain to produce a good inflammation. We find, that producing a slight irritation by friction on the arm, before inoculation will tend to accelerate the absorbtion of the virus. I wish, Sir, when you write me you would inform me of any symptoms that occur out of the common line in this disease, and we will do the same by you. I am Sir, with Esteem, Your Ob'dt Serv't,

JOSIAH BARTLETT.

and on November 3rd, Bartlett sends out the book with the following letter:

(S, p. 61)

Stratham, November 3d, 1800. Dear Sir. Jenner's publication you herewith will receive. After you have sufficiently perused it, please to return it. The Kine Pox is now inoculated by many Physicians within our neighborhood, although I believe the Matter was procured in a clandestine manner, and it appears that Dr. Dwight [9] is endeavoring to push himself by inoculating all, indiscriminately. I believe that Doctor Manning [10] has spread the Matter in this State, by way of Newbury. If he received the Matter from Dr. Waterhouse, as I heard that he did, and has spread it (as is reported of him) openly, Dr. Waterhouse ought to be informed of it. I wish you success, and am with Respect, etc., JOSIAH BARTLETT.

Spalding's reply on the 11th follows:

(B)   Portsmouth Nov. 11, 1800

Dear Sir: I have to acknowledge your politeness of the 30th ult. & 3rd. inst. & particularly your favouring me with Jenner, which I return herewith.

It is a fact that many physicians are inoculating in our neighborhood—but in what manner Cutter or Dwight procured their infection, I cannot discover—they are silent on this head, as also on every other particular that relates to Kine-pox, you will see that one advertises to inoculate without distinction & the other without discrimination—still I know not what is meant by this—unless it be that they inoculate without a fixed price, taking what they can get from each patient. I have had two cases were [sic] erysipalatous inflammation took place about the tenth day & was rather troublesome. I perceive that the temperature of the atmosphere in winter weather, has some effect in making the arms sorer—more than a quarter part of my patients have had eruptions of a vivid red color. Also when the arms are very sore I find chilliness very common. I shall inoculate for the small pox (next spring) some of my patients who have had the Kine-pox. If any of yours desire it they will be cordially received as I have promised my attention gratis.

Sin.   yours with due respect

L. SPALDING

After this letter we can no longer follow the story as it developed in Stratham and Portsmouth as no more manuscripts are available.

[9] Dr. Josiah Dwight of Portsmouth. Born 1775 in Connecticut. Came to Portsmouth as a young man and was so impressed by the beauty of the ocean that he settled there for life. Although a general practitioner he officiated at some 6000 births during his lifetime. Was blinded by glaucoma in his seventieth year and died in 1855.

[10] Dr. Samuel Manning (1780-1822) graduated from Harvard and practiced medicine in Cambridge. He was reputed to have received a supply of vaccine virus from Jenner.

But Spalding is not the only correspondent of Josiah Bartlett. He receives two letters from his brother Levi who lives in Kingston, New Hampshire, and we can pick up more of the story from them.

(B)   Kingston, Nov. 4, 1800.
Dear Brother:

. . . As to the Kine Pox affair I have not inoculated any since I saw you but expect to inoculate Mr. Peake's family Friday.

I approve the plan of obtaining liberty to sell the matter to other physicians, and shall write to Dr. Waterhouse tomorrow & desire liberty of selling upon conditions to any in this state excepting those places he has previously disposed of; but if he chuses not to grant this—to any in our district upon such conditions as he chuses, as you have not mentioned any conditions.

This I believe is the only way we shall make much money by it & even so after a little time it will not be so lucrative as other practice. . . . I will write you immediately upon receiving a line from Dr. Waterhouse & if he concludes in the affirmative wish you to ride up here & I will send for Stow to proceed as we chuse. I will meet you and Stow after a little time about this affair when you shall think fit and make a business of it.

You will see by the papers that matter is dayly carried from Boston & disbursed to anyone who chuses. Dr. Hunt has been inoculating for the Kine Pox in Boston about three weeks without discrimination, Bond or any other security & anyone can I believe take matter from him but more of this later.

Your Affectionate Brother

L. BARTLETT

(B)   Kingston Nov. 28 1800
Dear Brother

Last week I rec'd a letter from Dr. Waterhouse dated 10th of Nov. in answer to the one I wrote him wherein he wishes us to explain ourselves more particular " that he will accede to anything that is just, reasonable and liberal " and presents his compliments to you and Dr. Stow. I intended this week to have visited you and taken the letter and a copy of mine, but domestic affairs prevented which is the reason I did not write you sooner and cannot for several days to come, therefore wish you to come up on Thursday if you can or soon to consult with Stow about matters.

I have not inoculated any since I saw you as Dr. Gale is inoculating freely with stuff procured from Dow at Kensington. I this day looked at his Brother Benj's arm who was inoculated 4 days ago, he had the symptoms the next day after the insertion. The arm is much inflamed and ulcerated discharging largely—but I judge he has not had a symptom of the true Kine Pox. I told him my opinion that it would not secure him from the Small pox, that the infection was nothing more than pus taken from any Phagedenic Ulcer.

Dr. Amos Gate has inserted this into about 20 persons at one dollar per head without any ceremony ∞ Knaves invent & Fools believe ∞ I doubt whether (Dow, who had his matter from Jacob Kittredge and he from Dwight) any of the matter is of the real Kine Pox, Tilton's, Manning's or any that did not come from Waterhouse. . . .

L. BARTLETT.

These letters speak for themselves on the conditions prevailing. In conclusion I desire to present one final document which is of interest. It will be recalled that the doctors, Spalding and the Bartletts were concerned about methods of controlling their patients and preventing other doctors from having access to the supply of vaccine matter. One method was to bond the patients and such a bond is here reproduced.

It will be noted that it consists of two parts. Part one is a contract among three doctors agreeing on a schedule of fees and the second part is the bond wherein the patients consider themselves bound to Dr. Josiah Bartlett in the sum of $1000, individually and severally, that they will not permit any other doctor to inoculate them or to procure lymph from the pustule.

This is a most interesting document and it would be interesting to know if this bond was ever forfeited and if so under what circumstances. The records of such a suit would make a fascinating bit of medico-legal history.

Although the exact relationship between the two documents is not clear, it would seem that the bond was originally made out by and for Dr. Josiah Bartlett. At a later date, not clear from the document, he was joined by his brother and Dr. Thomas Banning. They agreed on a schedule of fees and pasted this at the head of the bond. I have not been able to determine whether the other doctors and their patients were included in the bond. A transcript of the text follows and the facsimile is on the next page.

(B)   Transcript of Bartlett Kine-pox Contract.

Kine-Pox

As the Kine-pox is of very great advantage to mankind we the subscribers do agree to inoculate persons within the circle of our common practice for the following fees.

For one or two in the same house $2.50 per head

For three or more in the same house $2.00 per head

THOMAS S. BANNING[?]

LEVI BARTLETT

JOSIAH BARTLETT

KNOW ALL MEN BY THESE PRESENTS that we the subscribers do individually and severally acknowledge ourselves to stand firmly bound to Josiah Bartlett of Streatham in the county of Rockingham & State of Newhampshire, physician, in the penal sum of one thousand Dollars the which payment will and hereby to be made we bind ourselves our heirs, executors, & administrators firmly by these present, — The condition of the above obligation is that the said Josiah Bartlett is to innoculate the subscribers or some of his or her family with kine-pox & is to attend the same through the disease for which we do covenant & engage to pay the fees as established above and we likewise do engage that no person or persons shall either directly or indirectly receive or procure the matter of said Kine-pox from us or our families excepting the said Josiah Bartlett. Now if we the signers hereof do severally & individually perform the aforesaid engagements then this obligation to be void and of no effect as to the performing person, otherwise to remain in full force and virtue.

IN WITNESS WHEREOF we have hereunto set our hands and seals in the year of our Lord 1800 & 1801

2

Fig. 1.

Facsimile of fee schedule and contract between physicians and patients regulating the practice of vaccination. [Recto]

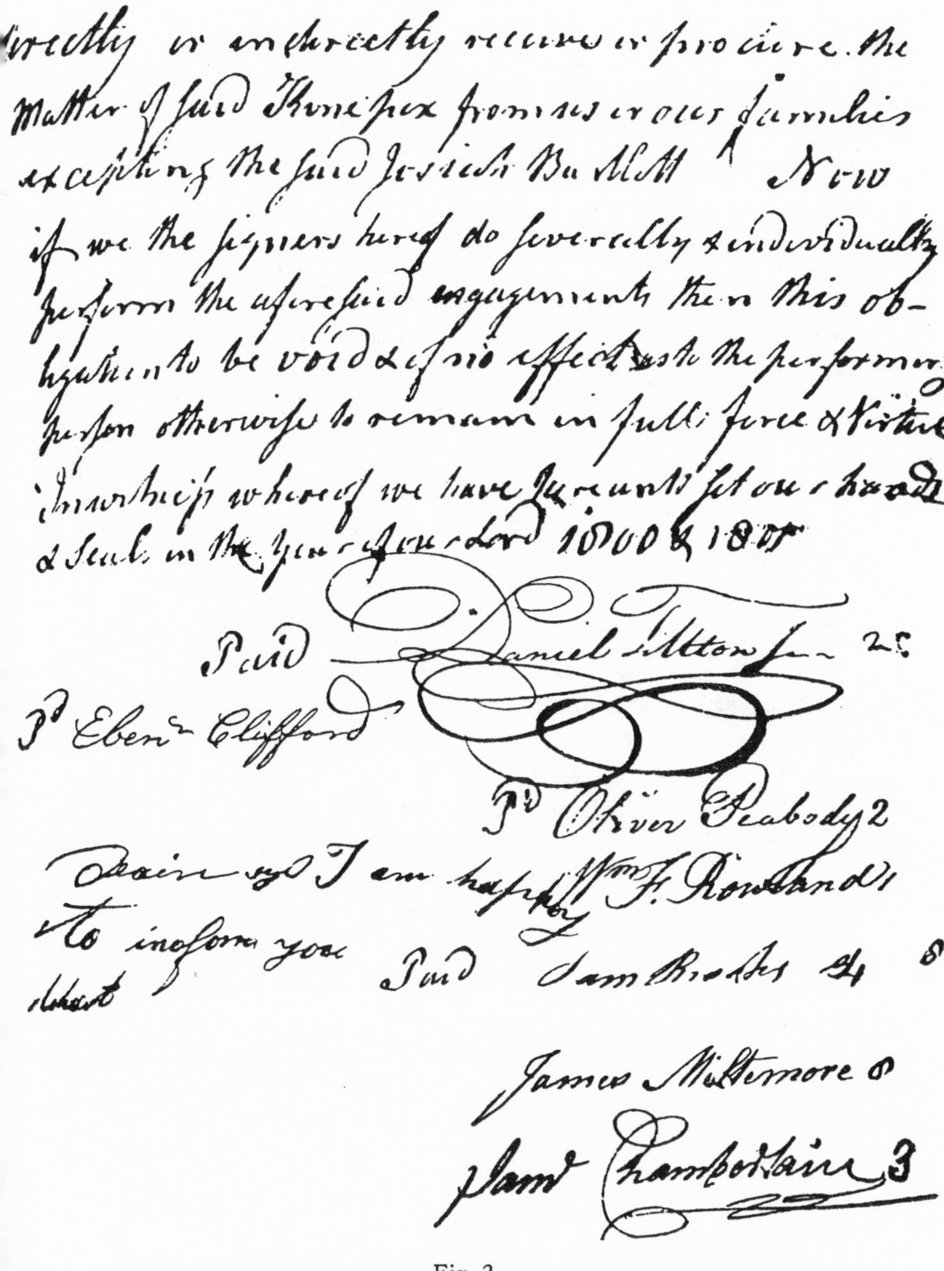

directly or indirectly receive or procure the
matter of said Kine pox from us or our families
excepting the said Josiah Bartlett ~ Now
if we the signers hereof do severally & individually
perform the aforesaid engagements then this obligation to be void & of no effect ~ to the performing
person otherwise to remain in full force & virtue
In witness whereof we have hereunto set our hands
& Seals in the Year of our Lord 1800 & 1801

Paid   Daniel Tilton Jun   2.$
P⁹ Ebenᶻ Clifford

                    P⁹ Oliver Peabody 2

Drain &c I am happy Wᵐ F. Rowland 1
to inform you   Paid   Sam Brooks 4   8
about

            James Wittemore 8

        Samᵈ Chamberlain 3

Fig. 2.

Facsimile of fee schedule and contract between physicians and patients regulating
the practice of vaccination. [Verso]

685

We see thus the difficulties under which the pioneer vaccinators in New England labored. The experiences recounted here were not in my opinion confined to New Hampshire. Waterhouse in his writings cites similar instances in Rhode Island. The discovery of new manuscript material from other localities will in all probability confirm the story here recounted. The stabilization of the supply of vaccine lymph did not come until late in the nineteenth century with the introduction of "animal vaccine." In 1842 Negri in Naples began to use lymph from cows and to propagate the matter in these animals. The practice first introduced in Italy spread to France in 1866, Germany and other parts of Europe. A strain of vaccine virus secured from France was introduced into a herd of cows near Boston in 1870 and this was the beginning of the use of calf lymph in the United States.

Acknowledgments

I wish to express my thanks to Mr. W. A. Fletcher of the Historical Records Survey of the Works Progress Administration, who first called my attention to the material in the Bartlett Collection. It is also a pleasure to record my thanks to Dr. St. George L. Sioussat, Chief of the Manuscripts Division of the Library of Congress, and to the members of his staff, for their many courtesies and the manner in which they facilitated my study of this material.

"A JOURNAL OF A YOUNG MAN OF
MASSACHUSETTS...WRITTEN BY HIMSELF."
BOSTON: 1816,
AND A NOTE ON THE AUTHOR

Henry R. Viets

A

JOURNAL,

OF

A YOUNG MAN OF MASSACHUSETTS,

LATE

A SURGEON ON BOARD AN AMERICAN PRIVATEER,

WHO WAS CAPTURED AT SEA BY THE BRITISH, IN MAY, EIGHTEEN HUNDRED AND THIRTEEN, AND WAS CONFINED FIRST,

AT MELVILLE ISLAND, HALIFAX, THEN AT CHATHAM, IN ENGLAND,

AND LAST, AT DARTMOOR PRISON.

INTERSPERSED WITH

OBSERVATIONS, ANECDOTES AND REMARKS,

TENDING TO

ILLUSTRATE THE MORAL AND POLITICAL CHARACTERS OF THREE NATIONS.

TO WHICH IS ADDED,

A CORRECT ENGRAVING OF DARTMOOR PRISON,

REPRESENTING THE MASSACRE OF AMERICAN PRISONERS.

WRITTEN BY HIMSELF.

" Nothing extenuate, or set down aught in malice."
SHAKESPEARE.

BOSTON:
PRINTED BY ROWE AND HOOPER.
1816.

A

JOURNAL,

OF

A YOUNG MAN OF MASSACHUSETTS,

LATE

A SURGEON ON BOARD AN AMERICAN PRIVATEER,

WHO WAS CAPTURED AT SEA BY THE BRITISH, IN MAY, EIGHTEEN HUNDRED AND THIRTEEN, AND WAS CONFINED FIRST,

AT MELVILLE ISLAND, HALIFAX, THEN AT CHATHAM, IN ENGLAND,

AND LAST, AT DARTMOOR PRISON.

INTERSPERSED WITH

OBSERVATIONS, ANECDOTES AND REMARKS,

TENDING TO

ILLUSTRATE THE MORAL AND POLITICAL CHARACTERS OF THREE NATIONS.

TO WHICH IS ADDED,

A CORRECT ENGRAVING OF DARTMOOR PRISON,

REPRESENTING THE MASSACRE OF AMERICAN PRISONERS.

WRITTEN BY HIMSELF.

" Nothing extenuate, or set down aught in malice."...SHAKESPEARE.

Printed by Rowe & Hooper....Boston.

MILLEDGEVILLE, (GEO.)
RE-PRINTED BY S. & F. GRANTLAND.
1816.

A

JOURNAL,

OF

A YOUNG MAN OF MASSACHUSETTS,

LATE

A SURGEON ON BOARD AN AMERICAN PRIVATEER,

WHO WAS CAPTURED AT SEA BY THE BRITISH, IN MAY, EIGHTEEN HUNDRED AND THIRTEEN, AND WAS CONFINED FIRST,

AT MELVILLE ISLAND, HALIFAX, THEN AT CHATHAM, IN ENGLAND,—AND LAST,

AT DARTMOOR PRISON.

INTERSPERSED WITH

OBSERVATIONS, ANECDOTES AND REMARKS,

TENDING TO ILLUSTRATE THE MORAL AND POLITICAL CHARACTERS OF THREE NATIONS.

TO WHICH IS ADDED,

A CORRECT ENGRAVING OF DARTMOOR PRISON,

REPRESENTING THE MASSACRE OF AMERICAN PRISONERS.

WRITTEN BY HIMSELF.

" Nothing extenuate, or set down aught in malice."...SHAKESPEARE.

THE SECOND EDITION,
With considerable Additions and Improvements.

BOSTON:
PRINTED BY ROWE & HOOPER...78 STATE-STREET.
1816.

A

JOURNAL,

OF

A YOUNG MAN OF MASSACHUSETTS,

LATE

A SURGEON ON BOARD AN AMERICAN PRIVATEER,

WHO WAS CAPTURED AT SEA BY THE BRITISH, IN MAY, EIGHTEEN HUNDRED AND THIRTEEN, AND WAS CONFINED FIRST,

AT MELVILLE ISLAND, HALIFAX, THEN AT CHATHAM, IN ENGLAND—AND LAST,

AT DARTMOOR PRISON.

INTERSPERSED WITH

OBSERVATIONS, ANECDOTES AND REMARKS,

TENDING TO ILLUSTRATE THE MORAL AND POLITICAL CHARACTERS OF THREE NATIONS.

TO WHICH IS ADDED,

A CORRECT ENGRAVING OF DARTMOOR PRISON,

REPRESENTING THE MASSACRE OF AMERICAN PRISONERS.

WRITTEN BY HIMSELF.

" Nothing extenuate, or set down aught in malice."...SHAKESPEARE.

LEXINGTON, (KY.)
RE-PRINTED BY WORSLEY & SMITH.
1816.

Title-pages of the four editions of
"A Journal, of a Young Man of Massachusetts, . . ."

"A JOURNAL, OF A YOUNG MAN OF MASSACHU-SETTS, . . . WRITTEN BY HIMSELF." BOSTON: 1816, AND A NOTE ON THE AUTHOR*

HENRY R. VIETS

Some time in the winter of 1815-1816, when the youthful Beaumont, for whom this lectureship is named, had finished his service as a surgeon's mate in the War of 1812 and had retired to practice in Plattsburg, another young man, a ship-surgeon, brought to the study of an old man in Cambridge a manuscript narrating a very different kind of service on an American privateer during the same war. The story was timely, for in spite of the fact that the Treaty of Ghent was signed December 24, 1814, the war had continued into the next year, the *Constitution* was capturing British ships off Madeira as late as February and March 1815, and American prisoners were confined in British prisons in the spring of that year. Tales of capture and the loss of "sailor's rights" still rankled in the American breast and the horrors of the prison at Dartmoor were told and re-told in American homes. Here, thought the oldish man, in reading over the manuscript, is a first-hand account, of unquestioned authenticity.

The manuscript was re-written, or at least re-edited, during the winter by the older man and published, anonymously, in the spring or early summer of 1816† in Boston, by Rowe and Hooper. The title, to give it in full, *A journal, of a young man of Massachusetts, late a surgeon on board an American Privateer, who was captured at sea by the British, in May, eighteen hundred and thirteen, and was confined first, at Melville Island, Halifax, then at Chatham, in England, and last, at Dartmoor Prison. Interspersed with observations, anecdotes and remarks, tending to illustrate the moral and*

---

* The Beaumont Lecture presented under the auspices of The Beaumont Medical Club, New Haven, March 8, 1940.

† *A journal* is dedicated, "To the common sense, and humane feelings of the people of America, this journal is inscribed, by a late Prisoner of War with the British." Massachusetts, County of Hampshire, 1815. It was copyrighted in the District Clerk's Office of Massachusetts, by Rowe and Hooper, March 6, 1816. A dedication, "To the Public," by "The author," in the second edition, is dated August, 1816.

political characters of three nations. To which is added, a correct engraving of Dartmoor Prison, representing the massacre of American prisoners. Written by Himself, is an epitome of the young man's adventures. So popular was this little book that a second edition was called for the same year, "with considerable additions and improvements," re-set by the same publisher, but with a new title-page. Before the year was out, moreover, the book was reprinted by S. and F. Grantland in Milledgeville, Georgia,* and by Worsley and Smith in Lexington, Kentucky. There is no clue in any of the editions to either the "Young man of Massachusetts" or to anyone who might have helped him in getting the book published. The problem might appear to be insoluble, but gradually in the course of time, evidence pointing to the senior author has been found and one can be reasonably certain also as to the identity of the "Young man."

The "Young Man of Massachusetts"

From the book one learns that a schooner was fitted out as a privateer in Salem in December, 1812. She was equipped with four carriage guns and carried ninety men. The "Young man" sailed on her as a surgeon, January 5, 1813. By the first of February the ship reached the coast of Brazil, where a landing was made, sixty miles below Cape St. Roque, to replenish the water supply. The schooner flew the English flag and passed as a British vessel. After filling the casks with water, it sailed north to Pernambuco. On the way the privateer had a brush with a British frigate and was nearly captured. Finally, it came up into Buzzard's Bay and sighted Gay Head on May 20, 1813. There a brig and a frigate, both British, were encountered. The American colors were hoisted, but the next morning, after a hard chase, the privateer was overcome by the larger British ship and was taken by the *Tenedos*. The members of the crew were put on board the *Curlew*, the smaller vessel, and landed at Halifax on May 29th. From Halifax they were marched to Melville Island and imprisoned.

At Melville Island they found the prison in a bad state. Most of the 900 prisoners were lousy. They were much tormented by the

---

* Milledgeville, named after John Milledge, Governor of Georgia, was the State capital from 1807 until after the Civil War. It was a center of wealth and culture and presumably Milledge, who gave the land for the University of Georgia, had a hand in seeing that there was a press in this small town.

agent and the turnkey. The author expresses a good deal of bitterness in regard to the treatment of American boys in this Nova Scotia prison. On September 3, 1813, he and about one hundred other prisoners were sent to England on the *Regulus,* arriving at Portsmouth on October 5th. There they were put into the hold of the *Malabar* with about 150 other prisoners, where they suffered extreme discomfort. Finally, they were transferred, along with many others, to the *Crown Prince,* which was used as a prison ship, at Chatham, on the bank of the Medway, 35 miles from London. There the young surgeon remained nearly a year, with 800 other prisoners, packed tightly into the boat. A number of boys died during epidemics of smallpox and typhus. Some of the prisoners escaped and the author gives amusing accounts of the escapades of these lively young men, who succeeded in making life miserable for the British in charge of them. It was not, however, until September 1814, that the British decided to transfer most of the unruly prisoners to Dartmoor Prison. They left in various groups, going to Plymouth and being marched over land to Princetown and then into the prison. In the prison there were nearly 9000 men, somewhat over 2000 of them being Americans who had been impressed into the British navy. The impressment of captured American seamen was one of the things that was most protested against by the unfortunate group confined at Dartmoor. The conditions at Dartmoor Prison, however, were not extremely bad. The chief difficulty lay in the way in which the men were handled by the director of the prison, Captain Shortland. The young surgeon can say nothing good about his supervision of the men. On the other hand, he is high in the praise of Dr. Magrath, the surgeon, who looked out for the men with great care.

By April 4, 1815, the Treaty of Ghent having been ratified, they were ready to go home. Just before they left, however, occurred an incident which was widely advertised as "the Dartmoor massacre." The latter part of the book tells the story in great detail. As a frontispiece the book carries an engraving of Dartmoor Prison, showing what were supposed to be the events of the massacre of April 6th, and appended to the account are numerous affidavits from the various prisoners and correspondence between the officials concerned. The prisoners were fired upon by British troops on very slight provocation; five or six were killed and a number of others wounded.

The account given in the *A journal, of a young man of Massachusetts* appears to be accurate and his statements are borne out by the diaries of other prisoners, such as Joseph Valpey, Jr.* of Salem, Benjamin F. Palmer† of Stonington, Connecticut, and others.‡

Shortly after this the author was given his freedom. He spent some time in Plymouth, where he was well received, as were all the other American prisoners, by the English populace. He left Plymouth on April 23, 1815, and arrived in New York on June 7th.

It is not easy to separate what was actually written by the "Young man" and the material that must have been added later by the senior author. The "Young man" was a good observer and describes in great detail, presumably with historical accuracy, the conditions he saw. Interspersed with it are paragraphs of a political and moral nature, probably added later by the other author. The book is, therefore, factual as well as interpretative. There is every appearance that the narrative was an actual account, written at the time the events occurred, or shortly after. There is a freshness about the style which makes the story live. The rest of the book is dull moralizing, but throws, no doubt, some light upon the political feelings of the time.

Who was the "Young man?" A clue is found in the date of capture of his ship off Gay Head on May 21, 1813. It is recorded in *Marine Notes, from a News Book kept in Salem, Mass., 1812-1815,* under the date of May 28, 1813, that the privateer schooner *Enterprise,* "returning from a cruize was captured on Soundings by the Curlew after a hard chase."‖ In the *Records of the Vice-Admiralty Court at Halifax, Nova Scotia,* moreover, one notes: "the *Enterprise,* schr., 225 tons, T. A. Morgan, master, 4 guns and 100 men, from Salem, cruising, captured May 21, 1813 by *Tenedos* and *Curlew.*"§ Furthermore, George F. Emmons, in his history, *The Navy of the United States,* writes: "the *Enterprise,* Sch. 4 guns, 91 men, Capt. J. Morgan. Salem. Capt. by the *Tenedos* Frigate & company

---

* *Journal of Joseph Valpey, Jr., of Salem. November, 1813-April, 1815.* Michigan Society of Colonial Wars, 1922.

† *The Diary of Benjamin F. Palmer.* New Haven, Conn.: The Acorn Club, 1914.

‡ The report of R. G. Beasley, the American agent in London, so much hated by the prisoners and hung in effigy a short time before the "massacre," will be found in *American State papers* (Gales and Seaton ed.), Foreign relations, v. 4, pp. 52-54, 1834. A recent and fair account is contained in *The story of Dartmoor Prison,* by Basil Thomson, London, 1907.

‖ *Essex Institute Hist. Coll.,* 1903, *39,* 299.

§ *Ibid.,* 1910, *46,* 159.

at sea, May 25, 1813, on her return from a 4 months' cruise to Brazil."*

Finally, William Bentley, D.D., in his *Diary*, on September 17, 1814, records: "news of the d. of my good friend Capt. John Morgan in a prison ship in England."† Bentley, always interested in all marine affairs, followed the building of the *Enterprise* from the time her keel was laid down, November 13, 1812, to the launching in December, "at the entrance to the neck,"‡ outside of Salem. Later, he noted the recruiting in the town in December, when the "Young man" joined, and had great expectations of the captain, John R. Morgan, then only thirty years of age.‖ That the schooner should have been captured so soon after leaving port must have been a keen disappointment to Bentley and to the other worthies of Salem.

In the Essex Institute, in Salem, among the manuscript Leavitt papers, there is a list§ of the officers and men of the *Enterprise*, many of them, no doubt, young Salem boys. The surgeon was Amos G. Babcock. Unfortunately, we know nothing about young Dr. Babcock. Local histories and accounts of the Babcock family give no clue to his identity. It seems probable, however, that he, freshly back from his experiences as a prisoner, wrote the manuscript which fell into the hands of the older man in Cambridge during the winter of 1815-1816. Of the "older man" we know much more, but before telling *his* story we must connect him with the anonymous book published in 1816.

The Co-author of "The Young Man of Massachusetts"

The book has long been attributed to Benjamin Waterhouse, without definite evidence proving his authorship. It is so unlike anything Waterhouse had previously written that I, in outlining the life of Waterhouse for the *Dictionary of American Biography* in 1936,¶ cast some doubt on this point, but left the question open. To be

---

* Emmons, George F.: *The Navy of the United States*. Washington, 1853, p. 176.

† *The Diary of William Bentley, D.D.*, Salem, Mass., 1914, v. 4, Jan., 1811-Dec. 1819, p. 283.

‡ *Idem.* p. 139.

‖ *Idem.* p. 144 and p. 146.

§ Crew list of the Schooner *Enterprise*. Received through the courtesy of Harriet S. Tapley, Librarian, Essex Institute, Salem, Mass. (See *Appendix* 6.)

¶ Viets, Henry R.: Benjamin Waterhouse. [In] *Dict. Amer. Biog.*, 1936, *19*, 529-32.

sure, John Adams had written to Benjamin Waterhouse from Quincy, on June 25, 1816 (*Appendix* 1), thanking Waterhouse for a copy of the book, but this was no proof that Waterhouse was the author. This letter was published in 1927* from the original in the Massachusetts Historical Society. It implied authorship, but something more was needed to make us feel sure in the matter. The "something more" has only recently come to light.

In the Library of Congress are two letters, one from Waterhouse to Thomas Jefferson, the other Jefferson's reply. Waterhouse communicated with Jefferson from Cambridge, June 18, 1816 (*Appendix* 2), probably soon after the book was issued, stating that Rowe and Hooper, the publisher, was sending a copy to him. Waterhouse wrote:

> I cannot refrain, because I think it is proper, giving *you* more information relative to its publication than what appears on the face of the book.
> This smart young man put his manuscript Journal into my hands, when I question him on each and every part of it, and felt satisfied of its authenticity. At his request, and at the request of the printers, I undertook to prepare this narrative for the eye of the American and British public. The raw material is here worked up into one uniform warp, woof and coloring; making, I hope, no bad specimen of American manufacture. Or, to change the figure, the young surgeon brought me all the stones and the bricks, while I designed, and built up the structure, finding the mortar or connecting material. Alexander Selkirk, who resided several years on a desert island, put his manuscript into the hands of the famous Dan'l DeFoe who out of it made the renowned *history of Robinson Crusoe*; this book may in some measure resemble it, provided DeFoe never suppressed or added any important facts. I believe every representation in this little book to be true; but the painter, aiming to make a general picture, has used a free and rapid brush, which, now and then betray marks of an incorrect *manner*, without ever once violating the truth of the story.
> This production was the amusement of my lonesome evenings the past winter; and was sent to the press without ever reviewing a paragraph or line of it.†

Jefferson, in a reply dated July 20, 1816 (*Appendix* 3) wrote:

> I have read it with avidity; for a more attaching narrative I have not met with; and it may be truly said of the whole edifice, that the bricks and the

---

* *Statesman and Friend. Correspondence of John Adams with Benjamin Waterhouse*, 1784-1822. Ed. by W. C. Ford. Boston, 1927. (See *Appendix* 1.)
† Original in Library of Congress. Received through the courtesy of Alice W. Lerch, Assistant Curator, Rare Book Collection, Library of Congress, and Willard O. Waters, Henry E. Huntington Library, San Marino, California.

mortar are worthy of each other, and promise to be a lasting monument to British Character. . . .*

Furthermore, in the Massachusetts Historical Society are two more letters, one from Benjamin Waterhouse to Jacob Brown, dated Cambridge, August 5, 1816 (*Appendix* 4), as follows:

I consider while writing it that it was a sort of an appendix to our military history, at least as far as the American character of its soldiers and seamen was implicated.†

Waterhouse had sent a copy of a book to General Jacob Brown and one can justifiably believe that the item was none other than the first edition of *A journal, of a young man of Massachusetts*. A second letter from Waterhouse to General Brown clears all doubt from our minds of the authorship. Waterhouse writes on November 21, 1816 (*Appendix 5*):

Another edition of the *Journal of the Dartmoor Prisoner* is just completed in Boston. This makes eight thousand copies of that popular book. The high Federalists dare not attack its authenticity; so only condemn its tendency as it regards the character of England and their own. This second edition has about 15 more pages in *addition* than the first. Matthew Cary is about publishing the *8th* edition of his *Olive Branch*. This book and the *Journal* have had a greater run, in a given period, than any works that have appeared amongst us.†

Thus, after more than one hundred years, Waterhouse is identified as the senior author, who took the manuscript from the "Young man," added to the raw material, and prepared the work of the surgeon of the *Enterprise* for publication. That he, an oldish man, should have taken an interest in a young man is, perhaps, not so surprising as it first seems, when we look at his life from the historical point of view.

Some Notes on the Life and Writings of Benjamin Waterhouse

While the fame of Waterhouse rests safely on his pioneer work as the American proponent of Jennerian vaccination, an achievement which makes him one of the great physicians of this country, his other work must not be neglected. A few points may well be brought out at this time, for my introductory remarks about the "Young man

---

* Original in Library of Congress. Received through the courtesy of Alice W. Larch, Assistant Curator, Rare Book Collection, Library of Congress, and Willard O. Waters, Henry E. Huntington Library, San Marino, California.

† Original in Massachusetts Historical Society. Received through the courtesy of Allyn B. Forbes, Librarian.

of Massachusetts" only serve to lead to a better evaluation of his remarkable personality. Born in Newport, Rhode Island, March 4, 1754, Waterhouse came from English stock settled in the American colonies soon after the middle of the seventeenth century. His mother was actually Quaker-born in Yorkshire, England, a cousin of Dr. John Fothergill, the eminent London practitioner. Newport, just before the Revolution, was a center of learning and Abraham Redwood's library must have been a frequent browsing-place of the young Waterhouse, a scholarly youth, soon drawn to medicine by Dr. John Halliburton and Judge Robert Lightfoot, two well-known Newport figures of their time. Quaker trained, an objector to war, he escaped to England on what is said to have been the last boat leaving the port of Boston in 1775. His Quaker upbringing made active participation in the War impossible, but Waterhouse was no Loyalist, as we shall see later. He must have left his boyhood friend, Gilbert Stuart, with some misgivings, but a prospect of work with his mother's cousin, John Fothergill, did much to overcome his reluctance to leave home and his close friend. Stuart, a year younger than Waterhouse, went to the same school in Trinity Church, founded by the collector of customs under Queen Anne, and lived in the next house to Abraham Redwood. Years later Waterhouse wrote of Stuart's early talent for drawing and states that when but thirteen years of age he could draw portraits.* Stuart went to Edinburgh at the age of seventeen, with a Scotch artist of mediocre caliber, but made his way back to this country two years later, penniless, on a collier. In the meantime we must think of Waterhouse, studying physic and the classics with Halliburton, Dr. William Hunter, and Judge Lightfoot. Stuart, too, escaped to England in 1775 and began painting portraits.† We know of at least one portrait, that of his friend, Benjamin Waterhouse, that hangs in the Redwood Library at Newport. It was probably painted in London in 1776, where Waterhouse was living with Dr. John Fothergill, and Stuart had moved from lodgings on the Strand to Gracechurch Street to be near him. The boys are said to have devoted one day a week to rambling about London and visiting its sights and picture galleries. Stuart soon became a pupil of Benjamin West and with West we must leave him to return to Waterhouse and his life with Fothergill.

---

* *Monthly Anthology*, November, 1805.

† Morgan, John Hill: Gilbert Stuart. [In] *Dict. Amer. Biog.*, 1936, *18*, 164-68.

When Waterhouse went to England in 1775, he first spent nine months in Edinburgh as a student of medicine. Then followed three years in Fothergill's house in London, attending lectures at various London hospitals and, as we have noted, seeing London with his friend Stuart. In 1778 we find him in Leyden and for a time he lived with John Adams, the American minister, and his two sons. His intense patriotism caused him to matriculate as a student of the *Free Republican American Federated States*, although the colonies were still at war with England and the British Ambassador was all powerful at the Hague. The Dutch were a little cautious and when his thesis was submitted, on April 19, 1780, Waterhouse added only *Americanus* after his name. The essay, dedicated to Fothergill, deals with sympathy and antipathy in the body and is based, in large part, on the work of Robert Whytt, whose book was so popular in Edinburgh, where Waterhouse had studied.

In June, 1782, after seven years in Europe, Waterhouse returned to Newport, perhaps the best educated physician in America at that time. Edinburgh, London, and Leyden had all contributed to his store of knowledge and the once Quaker boy, now twenty-eight, had become a scholarly physician. Harvard called him, the next year, to take the newly founded chair of Theory and Practice of Physic; they could hardly have chosen a better trained man. The opening of the medical school in 1783 was a festive occasion, with all the college buildings illuminated, and Waterhouse delivered his inaugural oration in Latin. It is interesting to note that he stressed the importance of the fundamental sciences in the medical course and, in a thoroughly modern manner, made an appeal for a study of "the mind diseased" and the erection of a hospital for mental patients.

While the school was in Cambridge and before the building of the Massachusetts General Hospital, Waterhouse was closely associated with John Warren, the Professor of Anatomy and Surgery. Warren, living in Boston, found it a long trip around Boston "Neck" to Cambridge; Waterhouse lived in Cambridge and must have given most of the lecture courses in the early years. Some idea of the teaching given by Waterhouse can be gained by a study of his *Synopsis*, published in 1786, three years after his first lecture. The notes are really headings for lectures, based largely on Fordyce, Haller, Boerhaave, Sydenham, and Cullen. Waterhouse brought the best of European medicine to his pupils in a day when there was no American medicine of a type that might be used in a medical school. He could teach only the doctrines and rules; practice was not part of the medical curriculum. His basis, however, was broad, for he added natural philosophy to anatomy, botany, and chemistry in his discourses on the theory of medicine. Natural history, too, formed a not inconsiderable part of his series of lectures; nothing in nature was foreign to his eyes.

Apart from the medical school, the wide range of Waterhouse's thought had its best expression in a discourse given at Concord, July 6, 1791, before the Middlesex Medical Association on *The Rise, Progress, and Present State of Medicine*. He traced the history of medicine from ancient times to the period of Boerhaave, Cullen, and Haller, ending with a laudation of the great names of the past. He insisted, however, that the American Revolution had given America her great opportunity to establish her own medical schools and that America should no longer be dependent on foreign schools for the education of her physicians. He urged his contemporaries, moreover, to "leave the flowery path of speculation for the more arduous one of experiment." Surely he, above all others, took his own words to heart in his vaccination experiments which followed a few years later. There was no "flowery path of speculation" about that accomplishment, and a more "arduous one of experiment," as you all know, was hardly possible. With his trials and tribulations from 1800 to 1810 we are not concerned; at the moment we are more interested in other matters.

With his vaccination experiments concluded and the two reports duly recorded in scientific form, Waterhouse continued his lectures at the medical school. He not only taught his young men, but he took an active interest in their health, their social life, and their morals. About the year 1805 he noticed a certain deterioration in their health, with an increase in acute diseases and nervous disorders. These he considered as due to the sedentary life of the scholars, plus intemperance in the use of wine, ardent spirits, and tobacco. "Unruly wine and ardent spirits," he wrote, "have supplanted sober cider." Chewing and smoking tobacco, too, were condemned. "I have been a Professor in this University twenty-three years," he continued, "and can say, as a physician, that I never observed so many palid faces, and so many marks of declining health; nor ever knew so many hectical habits and consumptive affections, as of late years; and I trace this alarming inroad on your young constitutions principally to the pernicious custom of smoking cigarrs." It sounds a little strange, moreover, to our ears to hear him say: "A physician should never use tobacco in any form, as some weak patients will faint at the smell."

Think what you will of the moralizing of Waterhouse in 1805, the salutary warning may have been needed. It certainly was appreciated, not only in Cambridge but throughout the country and even in Europe. This little pamphlet was the most popular of any of the writings of Waterhouse. Two editions ran off the presses in America, one edition was issued in London, another in Geneva (in French), and one in Vienna (in German). Benjamin Rush and Thomas Jefferson praised the book and I have no doubt that *Cautions to Young Persons Concerning Health* brought Waterhouse as much immediate fame as anything that he did in his lifetime. Few writings of the time had as wide an audience; Waterhouse, already known to the medical profession, became a national and even an international figure.

The interests of Benjamin Waterhouse, however, were not confined to his students at Harvard. He lectured at the Rhode Island College (later Brown University) on natural history, mineralogy, and botany. In 1782 he suggested the formation of a humane society, similar to those already established in Europe. He was much perturbed by the drowning of young men and, in 1785, drew up the plans of a society in Massachusetts. Five years later he gave a discourse, *On the Principle of Vitality*, before the Humane Society. This is a wordy paper, semi-religious in character, and of no medical value. Scant mention is made of artificial respiration, although the application of heat is considered an important form of treatment. Waterhouse must be given credit, however, for seeing that a Humane Society *was* established in Boston as early as 1790.

Brief notes on his natural history lectures were published in 1810, and his lectures on botany, first printed separately in the *Monthly Anthology* between 1804 and 1808, were issued in book form in 1811. With them was reprinted *The Principal of Vitality*. These works indicate his trend away from the Medical School and perhaps it is not surprising that he resigned his professorship in 1812. He had, moreover, long been at odds with his colleagues, especially with John Warren. The younger men, John Collins Warren and James Jackson, rapidly coming to the front, sided with the elder Warren. They saw the value of clinical instruction as Waterhouse was never able to see it; the Massachusetts General Hospital, with the Medical

School an integral part of it, was foremost in their minds. Water-house endeavored to establish a rival school in Boston; when this failed, he turned to invectives against his former colleagues. This unpleasant chapter ended in what must be considered as a forced resignation from his high post in the Medical School.

Still living in Cambridge, Waterhouse turned to the Army. His connection with the United States Marine Hospital since 1808, when he wrote the first *Rules and Orders*, led to an appointment by Madison, in 1813, as Medical Superintendent of all the military posts in New England, a position which he held until 1820. One published work during this period, on dysentery, indicates the high character of his services. From then on, except for a review of his cases of whooping-cough, his efforts were literary. This is the period of *A journal, of a young man of Massachusetts* and his *Essay on Junius*, in which he attributed the letters to William Pitt. Finally, he took the notes of a young adventurer, John B. Wyeth, a Cambridge boy, who had just returned from a journey to Oregon and, with additions of his own, published *Oregon: or a short history of a long journey*. Wyeth went with his uncle, Nathaniel B. Wyeth, on an ill-starred trip, which ended in misfortune. Only the boy returned home. In this narrative, Waterhouse saw an opportunity to moralize and, using it as a base, made an effort to prevent young men from going on western expeditions. He felt that the farmers and mechanics of New England should stay at home. The book, in spite of Waterhouse, is a stirring story and contains a good description of the hardships of overland travel in the early nineteenth century, as well as important notes on cholera and yellow fever.

Waterhouse lived on in Cambridge to a very old age, a broken figure towards the end, robbed of much of the honor he deserved by his unfortunate antagonism to his contemporaries. Only outside of his immediate circle was his fame secure, but posterity, sound in its estimation of the man and his work, has given him a high place in the annals of American medicine. His fame, moreover, as time has passed, has become greater, for, although his pioneer work in vaccination is enough to give him high rank, his other work is now being appreciated. To the young men of his generation his services were outstanding and few men can claim a longer and more continuous interest in youth and their problems than Benjamin Waterhouse, the scholarly, unlovable, irritating, but none-the-less human, Professor of the Theory and Practice of Physic at the Harvard Medical School.*

APPENDICES

-1-

Letter from John Adams to Benjamin Waterhouse

Quincy, June 25, 1816. In the Style of John and Jonathan Bull I give you a thousand thanks for your Letter of the 18th and the Journal of the Surgeon.

The great James Otis, whose Style was hasty, tough and coarse, and who hated and despised Correction, often gave some of his Compositions to Sam Adams, whose language was harmonious Soft and oily, as Otis expressed himself, "To quicu Yeuhicu it." Who "quicu Yeuhicued" this little Book?

Aut Erasmus aut Diabolus.

It has so much of the Air of Romance, and the American Character is so perfectly sustained, as far as I have read, or heard in it, that I wish 40,000 Copies were sold. I never laughed so much in reading Don Quixote, or McFingal. . .

-2-

Letter from Benjamin Waterhouse to Thomas Jefferson

Cambridge, 18th June, 1816. Finding that Mesrs. Rowe & Hooper are about sending you a copy of *a Journal of a young man of Massachusetts*, who was captured by the British, and confined during the war, at Halifax, at Chatham, and at Dartmoor, I cannot refrain, because I think it is proper, giving *you* more information relative to its publication than what appears on the face of the book.

This smart young man put his manuscript Journal into my hands, when I question him on each and every part of it, and felt satisfied of its authenticity. At his request, and at the request of the printers, I undertook to prepare this narrative for the eye of the American and British public. The raw material is here worked up into one uniform warp, woof and coloring; making, I hope, no bad specimen of American manufacture. Or, to change the figure, the young surgeon brought me all the stones and the bricks, while I designed, and built up the structure, finding the mortar or connecting material. Alexander Selkirk, who resided several years on a desert island, put his manuscript into the hands of the famous Dan'l DeFoe who out of it made the renowned *history of Robinson Crusoe*; this book may in some measure resemble it, provided DeFoe never suppressed or added any important facts. I believe every representation in this little book to be true; but the painter, aiming to make a general picture, has used a free and rapid brush, which, now and then betray marks of an incorrect *manner*, without ever once violating the truth of the story.

This production was the amusement of my lonesome evenings the past winter; and was sent to the press without ever reviewing a paragraph or line of it.

---

*There is no biography of Waterhouse. The most extensive account of his life occurs in the *Dictionary of American Biography*, with references to the important literature about him. His letters, of which there are many, are widely scattered in libraries and considerable material remains in the private family papers.

Sentiments of respect, and ideas of propriety forbad me to allow the book to be presented to *you*, without this explanation; although the public have [!] no idea of the painter.

—3—

Letter from Thomas Jefferson to Benjamin Waterhouse

Monticello, July 20, 1816. I thank you, dear Sir, for the new Robinson Crusoe you have been so good [as] to send me. The name of its' hero like that of the old, merits to be known as should that also of the new DeFoe. I have read it with avidity; for a more attaching narrative I have not met with; and it may be truly said of the whole edifice, that the bricks and the mortar are worthy of each other, and promise to be a lasting monument to British Character. . .

—4—

Letter from Benjamin Waterhouse to Jacob Brown

Cambridge, August 5, 1816. I hope you received safely the little book I sent you directed to the Adjutant-General. I considered while writing it that it was a sort of an appendix to our military history, at least as far as the American character of its soldiers and seamen was implicated.

—5—

Letter from Benjamin Waterhouse to Jacob Brown

November 21, 1816. Another edition of the *Journal of the Dartmoor Prisoner* is just completed in Boston. This makes eight thousand copies of that popular book. The high Federalists dare not attack its authenticity; so only condemn its tendency as it regards the character of England and their own. This second edition has about 15 more pages in *addition* than the first. Matthew Cary is about publishing the *8th* edition of his *Olive Branch*. This book and the *Journal* have had a greater run, in a given period, than any works that have appeared amongst us.

—6—

Crew List of the Schooner Enterprise

John R. Morgan	Captain	William Abbot	Steward
John Reith	1st Lieut.	Ephraim G. Kinder ...	Seaman
Joseph Harris	2nd "	Thomas West	"
Thomas Smith	3rd "	Joseph Camp	"
John H. Downie	Master's Mate	Joseph Pettingill	"
John Price	2nd " "	William Lufkin	"
William Richards	3rd " "	William Molloy	"
Thomas Trask	Captain's Clerk	John T. Saunders	"
John Simon	Boatswain	Joseph Peabody	"
James Lyons	Gunner	William Clothes	"
John Webster	Carpenter	William Tucker	"
John Orne	Cook	Robert Seldon	"

John Millet	Seaman		George Morse	Seaman
Jacob Prince	"		John Peach	"
D. Symonds	"		David Symonds	"
Thomas Turkey	"		George Johnson	"
John Thornton	Cooper		Thomas Lamson	"
Michael Barnes	Seaman		Peter McBread	"
William Hanson	"		Nathaniel Symonds ...	"
John Taylor	"		Amos Proctor	"
J. H. Hall	"		John Webb	"
S. Silver	"		James Gunnison	Gunner's Mate
James Cheever	"		Michael Grush	Seaman
Joseph Millet	"		Nathan Treadwell	"
Benjamin Peach	"		Nathaniel Fuller	"
R. W. Russell	"		Walter Phillips	"
John Clothes	"		John Widgan	"
John Bossel	"		Samuel Walker	"
Henry Walton	"		Stephen Blaney	"
Francis Williams	"		Edmund Brown	"
Isaac Fowler	"		Philip Wells	"
John Kelley	"		John Christian	"
Joseph Goss	"		George Oakes	"
William Robinson	"		John Bates	"
Asa Webster	"		Benjamin Blair	"
John Thomson	"		David Blair	"
Joseph Cloutman	"		Hiram Giddings	"
Charles Gage	"		Roderick Williams	"
Nathan Paul	"		John Wright	"
John McIntire	"		Samuel Moss	"
Amos Gandy	"		Francis Fortune	"
John Robinson	"		John Peach	"
Edmund Porter	"		Isaac Clark	"
Thomas Dunkin	"		Henry Torrey	"

Amos G. Babcock .... Surgeon

–7–

The Principal Writings of Benjamin Waterhouse

(1) Dissertatio medica de sympathia partium corporis humani, ejusque, in explicandis et curandis morbis, necessaria consideratione. 4°. pp. [4], 38, [2]. *Lugduni Batavorum: Th. Koet*, 1780.

> *Notes*: Addressed to Ewald Hollebeek, the rector of Leyden University, and dedicated to John Fothergill. The dissertation was given April 19, 1780. There are two lines of *errata* on the last leaf.

(2) A synopsis of a course of lectures, on the theory and practice of medicine. In four parts. Part the first. 4°. pp. x, 44. *Boston: Printed by Adams and Nourse*, 1786.

> *Notes*: The other parts were not published. The introduction is dated, Boston, May, 1786. *Errata* at end, p. 44.

(3) On the principle of vitality. A discourse delivered in the First Church in Boston, Tuesday, June 8th, 1790. Before the Humane Society of the Commonwealth of Massachusetts. 4°. pp. [4], 24, [4].
Boston: Printed by Thomas and John Fleet, 1790.

> Notes: Dedicated to James Bowdoin. The *appendix* contains a report of the semi-annual meeting of the Humane Society, June 8, 1790, the Treasurer's accounts (1786-1790), and a list of members and officers for 1790.

(4) The rise, progress, and present state of medicine. A discourse, delivered at Concord, July 6th, 1791, before the Middlesex Medical Association. 4°. pp. xii, 31, [1].
Boston: Thomas and John Fleet, 1792.

> Notes: The *preface* contains a brief description of Middlesex County, the constitution of the Medical Association, and there is a list of members on p. 31.

(5) A prospect of exterminating the small-pox; being the history of the variolæ vaccinæ, or kine-pox, commonly called the cow-pox; as it has appeared in England; with an account of a series of inoculations performed for the kine-pox, in Massachusetts. 4°. pp. 40.
[Cambridge]: Printed for the author, at the Cambridge Press, by William Hilliard, 1800.

(5a) A prospect of exterminating the small pox: Part II, being a continuation of a narrative of facts concerning the progress of the new inoculation in America; together with practical observations on the local appearance, symptoms, and mode of treating the variola vaccina, or kine pock; including some letters to the author, from distinguished characters, on the subject of this benign remedy, now passing with a rapid step through all ranks of society in Europe and America. 4°. pp. 139, [1].
Cambridge: Printed for the author, at the University Press by William Hilliard, 1802.

> Notes: Dedicated to John Coakley Lettsom and Edward Jenner, Cambridge, New England, November 1802. The *appendix* contains a biographical account of Dr. Jenner. *Errata*, p. 139.

(6) Cautions to young persons concerning health in a public lecture delivered at the close of the medical course in the chapel at Cambridge Nov. 20, 1804; containing the general doctrine of chronic diseases; shewing the evil tendency of the use of tobacco upon young persons; more especially the pernicious effects of smoking cigarrs; with observations on the use of ardent and vinous spirits in general. 4°. pp. 32.
[Cambridge]: Printed at the University Press by W. Hilliard, 1805.

> Notes: Colored, marbled paper cover, with label, *Doctor Waterhouse's lecture on the evil tendency of tobacco, and the pernicious effects of ardent & vinous spirits on young persons.* Dedicated, To the medical students, resident graduates, and scholars of every class, Cambridge, January 1805.

(6a) ———— 2 ed. *London.*

(6b) ———— 3 ed. *Geneva* (in French).

(6c) Vorsichtsregeln zur Erhaltung der Gesundheit der Jünglinge. Betreffend die allgemeinen Grundsatze der kronischen Krankheiten die durch den Missbrauch des Tabacks und vorzüglich des Rauchens der gerolten Tabacksblätter bey jungen Personen entstehen . . . 8°. pp. 62.
Wien, 1808.

(6d) Cautions to young persons concerning health, in a public lecture delivered at the close of the medical course in the chapel at Cambridge, November 20, 1804; containing the general doctrine of dyspepsia and chronic diseases; shewing the evil tendency of the use of tobacco upon young persons; more especially the pernicious effects of smoking cigars. With observations on the use of ardent and vinous spirits. Fifth edition with additional notes. 4°. pp. 40.

Cambridge: Printed at the University Press by Hilliard & Metcalf, 1822.

Notes: The *Introduction* states that this is the second American edition, although listed as the fifth edition in the title-page. The London, Geneva, and Vienna editions, noted above, were probably considered the second, third, and fourth editions, respectively (see *Introduction* to this edition). Note is also made in the *Introduction* to a reprinting, "in detached portions in South Carolina, with comments by the late eminent historian and physician Dr. Ramsay." Blue or brown paper cover with title, *Dr. Waterhouse's public lecture, on the pernicious effects of smoking cigars. Fifth edition.*

(7) Information respecting the origin, progress, and efficacy of the kine pock inoculation, in effectually and forever securing a person from the small-pox, extracted from a treatise entitled "A prospect of exterminating the small-pox," written in the year 1802.   4°.   pp. 53, [1].
Cambridge: Printed by Hilliard and Metcalf, 1810.

(8) Heads of a course of lectures on natural history.   4°.   pp. 13, [1].
Cambridge: Printed by Hilliard & Metcalf, 1810.

Note: Paper cover with title, *Heads of Waterhouse's lectures.*

(9) The botanist.   Being the botanical part of a course of lectures on natural history, delivered in the University at Cambridge.   Together with a discourse on the principle of vitality.   4°.   pp. 263, [1].
Boston: Published by Joseph T. Buckingham, 1811.

Notes: Dedicated to John Adams, Cambridge, July, 1811. *The botanist* first appeared in the *Monthly Anthology*, 1804 to 1808. There are some autobiographical references in the *Advertisement* and the *Preface*. *The principle of vitality* is reprinted from the issue of 1790 (see No. 3), with a new *Preface*, giving an account of the origin of the Humane Society. The *Appendix* contains two letters from George Washington. *Errata*, p. 263.

(10) A journal,* of a young man of Massachusetts, late a surgeon on board an American privateer, who was captured at sea by the British, in May, eighteen hundred and thirteen, and was confined first, at Melville Island, Halifax, then at Chatham, in England, and last, at Dartmoor Prison. Interspersed with observations, anecdotes and remarks, tending to illustrate the moral and political characters of three nations.   To which is added, a correct engraving of Dartmoor Prison, representing the massacre of American prisoners.   Written by himself.   12°.   pp. 228, 1 pl.
Boston: Printed by Rowe and Hooper, 1816.
(10a) ————
Milledgeville, (Geo.): Re-printed by S. & F. Grantland, 1816.
(10b) ———— 2 ed. 12°. pp. 240, 1 pl.
Boston: Printed by Rowe & Hooper, 1816.
(10c) ————
Lexington, (Ky.): Re-printed by Worsley & Smith, 1816.

(11) A circular letter, from Dr. Benjamin Waterhouse, to the surgeons of the different posts, in the second military department of the United States Army.   4°.   pp. 24. [Cambridge: 1817].

(12) An essay concerning tussis convulsiva, or whooping-cough.   With observations on the diseases of children.   4°.   pp. 152.
Boston: Published by Munroe and Francis, 1822.

---

* The essentials of this story were used as the basis for a novel, *The Lively Lady*, by Kenneth Roberts, New York: Doubleday, Doran & Co., 1931. One end-paper consists of a drawing of Dartmoor Prison, similar to that found in the original editions of *A journal*.

(13) Oratio inauguralis, quam in Academia Harvardiana, Cantabrigiæ Novanglorum, nonis Octobribus, A.D. MDCCLXXXIII. 4°. pp. iv, 8.
Cantabrigiæ: Typis Hilliard, Metcalf, et soc. 1829.
Note: Delivered in 1783 but not published until 1829.

(14) An essay on Junius and his letters; embracing a sketch of the life and character of William Pitt, Earl of Chatham, and memoirs of certain other distinguished individuals; with reflections historical, personal, and political, relating to the affairs of Great Britain and America, from 1763 to 1785. 4°. xvi, 449, [1].
Boston: Gray and Bowen, 1831.
Notes: The *Preface* contains autobiographical material, dated Cambridge, New England, 1830. *Errata,* p. xvi.

(15) Oregon; or a short history of a long journey from the Atlantic Ocean to the region of the Pacific, by land; drawn up from the notes and oral information of John B. Wyeth, one of the party who left Mr. Nathaniel J. Wyeth, July 28th, 1832, four days' march beyond the ridge of the Rocky Mountains, and the only one who has returned to New England. 4°. pp. [4], 87, [1].
Cambridge: Printed for John B. Wyeth, 1833.
Notes: John B. Wyeth, a boy of twenty, went with his uncle, Nathaniel J. Wyeth, the leader of the party. Dr. Jacob Wyeth, brother of Nathaniel, was the surgeon. There is a half-title with the word, *Oregon* and the gray, paper cover has the title, *Wyeth's Oregon Expedition.*
See *Rare Americana at Goodspeed's,* catalogue 321, 1940, item 219. This fine, uncut copy measures 19.5 x 13 cm.

–8–

Order of Waterhouse Publications

1.	Dissertatio medica de sympathia.	1780.
2.	A synopsis of a course of lectures, on . . . medicine.	1786.
3.	On the principle of vitality.	1790.
4.	The rise, progress, and present state of medicine.	1792.
5.	A prospect of exterminating the small-pox.	1800.
5a.	———— Part II.	1802.
6.	Cautions to young persons concerning health.	1805.
6a.	———— London.	
6b.	———— Geneva (in French).	
6c.	———— Vienna (in German).	1808.
6d.	———— Fifth edition with additional notes.	1822.
7.	Information respecting . . . kine pock inoculation.	1810.
8.	Heads of a course of lectures on natural history.	1810.
9.	The botanist.	1811.
10.	A journal of a young man of Massachusetts.	1816.
10a.	———— Re-printed. Milledgeville, Geo.	1816.
10b.	———— 2 ed.	1816.
10c.	———— Re-printed. Lexington, Ky.	1816.
11.	A circular letter.	[1817].
12.	An essay concerning tussis convulsiva.	1822.
13.	Oratio inauguralis.	1829.
14.	An essay on Junius.	1831.
15.	Oregon: or a short history of a long journey.	1833.

THE INTRODUCTION OF VACCINATION
INTO
THE UNITED STATES

Morris C. Leikind

THE INTRODUCTION OF VACCINATION INTO THE UNITED STATES

MORRIS C. LEIKIND, M. Sc.

Benjamin Waterhouse (1754-1846). Courtesy of the Library of Congress.

IN 1799, Dr. Benjamin Waterhouse, Professor of the Theory and Practice of Physic, at the Harvard Medical School, received from his friend, Dr. Lettsom of London, a copy of Jenner's *Inquiry in the Causes and Effects of the Variolae Vaccinae. . : .* How this publication affected and interested him is best told in the words of Waterhouse himself. In 1800 he published a pamphlet, now very rare, entitled *A Prospect for Exterminating the Small-Pox.* . . . There he wrote: " . . . On perusing this work (Jenner's *Inquiry*), I was struck with the unspeakable advantages that might accrue to this country and indeed to the human race at large from the diffusion of a mild distemper that would ever after secure the constitution from that terrible scourge the smallpox. . . . As the ordinary mode of communicating even medical discoveries in this country is by newspapers, I drew up the following account of the cowpox, which was printed in the *Columbian Sentinel,* March 12, 1799, under the title: *Something Curious in the Medical Line.*" This article was essentially a review of Jenner's book. Now Waterhouse continues, telling of the reception of this notice. He wrote: "This publication shared the fate of most others on new discoveries. A few received it as a very important discovery, highly interesting to humanity, some doubted it; others observed that wise and prudent conduct which allows them to condemn or applaud as the event might prove: while the greater number resolutely ridiculed it as one of those medical whims which arise today and tomorrow are no more." But this ridicule and indifference did not dismay or deter Waterhouse. He was determined to try the new protection against the dreaded smallpox and see its action for himself. In July, 1800, having secured some of the vaccine matter from England, he proceeded forthwith to vaccinate his children and several domestics, seven persons in all. Soon after they recovered from the effects of the vaccination they were sent to a licensed smallpox hospital in Boston where they were inoculated with smallpox virus as a test of the protection afforded by the kine-pox. All proved resistant. These first experiments of Waterhouse were a complete and triumphant vindication of Jenner's claims.

This successful experiment encouraged patients of Dr. Waterhouse to try the treatment. Some fifty persons were inoculated in a short time, there were no ill-effects and the word began to spread that vaccination was indeed all it claimed to be. Waterhouse now found himself deluged by demands from patients to be vaccinated and also by requests from physicians for supplies of the virus.

At that time Waterhouse seemed to have the only supply of matter available. It must be remembered that this was long before the days when purified lymph in sterile tubes was distributed through drugstores on every corner. Waterhouse understandably wished to control the use of his supplies and so he furnished it on threads, which were sold to physicians for a fixed fee plus a percentage of the profits for a stipulated period. Among those who wrote to Waterhouse for virus was Dr. Lyman Spalding, best known as the father of the U. S. Pharmacopoeia. Some of the correspondence between these two men has been preserved and is here reproduced.

In answer to a letter from Spalding, Waterhouse wrote:

"Cambridge, September 6, 1800. Dear Sir. I have only time to say that I have received your second letter and that I will accommodate you with the 'matter,' etc., at the same pay which has been offered to me, but I declined, namely for One Quarter of the profit arising from the inoculation, and the contract to remain for 14 months from this time. Abandon the idea of inoculating for the small pox and throw all your attention to the Kine-pox. If this idea suits you and Dr. Cutter you shall be accommodated at once, for half a dozen practitioners stand ready to jump at that offer, and two of them are not a very great distance from you. In haste, I am Yours, etc. "BENJAMIN WATERHOUSE."

Spalding's reply to this letter is as follows:

"Portsmouth, September 10, 1800. Dear Sir. The terms are accepted, and I promise that you shall have One Quarter part of the next profit arising from my inoculation with the kine pox for the space of 14 months, provided it be not made public before that term expires, and then the contract to remain in full force only to the time of its becoming public. However, on your part it is expected that the like privilege will not be granted to others in my vicinity. Yours, etc., L. SPALDING."

In the words of Spalding's biographer, "we have here a 'Vaccination Trust.'" But not only is there evidence of attempted monopolistic practice in connection with the new discovery. We even find evidences of "muscling in on a good racket." On September 12, 1800, Waterhouse again writes to Spalding:

"Cambridge, September 12, 1800. Yours of the 19th informs me that you accede to my proposal

Holden Chapel at Harvard where Waterhouse lectured. Courtesy of the Library of Congress.

'provided it be not made public before that time expires.' Now that is too vague to proceed on. Sam Brown may steal it before a month expires, and then in six months it may be diffused all over Boston, or it may not. I therefore propose that shall be for twelve months and that will leave you to yourself during the three autumn months of 1801. You however will have got the start of all others, so much that no one can rival you entirely; besides it will fix you in business. My fee is Five Dollars. You must engage not to supply any other practitioner. Your acceding to this will fetch the infection next post. If you wish to come and see the disease, and my practice, you shall have that in the bargain. Yours, B. WATER-HOUSE.

"P. S. I have a similar application from Amherst in your state and another from a young doctor going to settle at Hampton. But, if Dr. Cutter and you and I make the contract proposed, this gentleman will not be supplied. I will supply none within twenty or thirty miles of you and perhaps further."

Letters were shuttled back and forth, Waterhouse holding out for more pay and insisting that Spalding take an older man as a partner, thus further increasing the royalties; Spalding holding out for an individual contract in order to be the first in Portsmouth, thus giving him a monopoly of the practice. In an undated letter, Spalding writes to Waterhouse as follows:

"Dear Sir: . . . I applaud your policy of making a few guineas for yourself considering what pains you have taken in procuring and experimenting upon the Kine-pox. Now Sir, far from inoculating gratis or endeavoring to procure the infection by stealth, if you will permit me to inoculate I will give you ten per cent upon the fees received for it, till you shall, or by other means, and not through my carelessness, it shall be made public. If these terms coincide with your ideas, you will forward the infection IMMEDIATELY, for 'Now is the appointed time' and I promise you shall receive your premium without the least shadow of fraud.

"With fidelity

"LYMAN SPALDING.

"P. S. How do you obligate your patients to prevent the infection being taken from their pustules! !

"N. B. I expect the same privilege will not be granted to any other person in this vicinity!"

Waterhouse finally yields to Spalding. He writes on September 18th that he is enclosing a bond to be executed whereupon he will send the virus. This bond, if it could be found, would be a most interesting document. Another type of bond, however, has

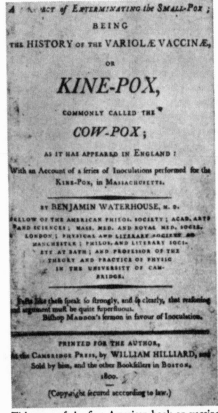

Title-page of the first American book on vaccination. From the Henry Barton Jacobs Collection. Courtesy of the Welch Medical Library.

been found. In the letter above, Spalding asks Waterhouse how he obligates his patients to prevent the infection being taken from their pustules. We do not have the reply of Waterhouse to this query but several New Hampshire doctors who also had received virus from him did execute a bond which bound the patients, individually and collectively in the sum of $1000 to allow only their physicians and no others to vaccinate them or to collect lymph for further vaccinations. The original bond is in the Library of Congress and since it has been recently reproduced it is not again illustrated here.

The above correspondence is only an illustrative sample of Waterhouse's activity in his crusade to establish vaccination in the United States. He was a prolific and voluminous writer and he sent many notices to the newspapers and finally summarized his experiences in book form. His first book was a 40-page pamphlet published in 1800, and entitled *A Prospect of Exterminating the Small-pox; Being the History of the Variolae Vaccinae or Kine-pox, Commonly Called the Cow-pox As It Has Appeared in England: With An Account of a Series of Inoculations Performed for the Kine-pox in Massachusetts.*" This was followed in 1802 by a second part considerably larger, in which Waterhouse includes additional observations on the local appearance, symptoms and mode of treatment of the kine-pox, together with many letters which had been sent to him by Jenner, Thomas Jefferson and other celebrities. Waterhouse carried on a long correspondence with Jenner who sent him a silver box as a token of appreciation of his work in behalf of vaccination. Waterhouse, in writing of this to Lettson, said: "Dr. Jenner has been to me what the sun is to the moon—Dr. Jenner has just sent to me a present I highly value, a silver box

inlaid with gold of exquisite taste and workmanship, bearing the inscription: 'Edward Jenner to Benjamin Waterhouse.' But Mr. Ring (a friend and disciple of Jenner) annexed the superscription in rather an hyperbolical style: 'From the Jenner of the Old World to the Jenner of the New World.' "

And, indeed, Waterhouse richly deserves this title. Fighting public and professional indifference, blamed for all the mishaps and failures which resulted from the use of vaccine virus by inexperienced physicians and lay vaccinators, Waterhouse when he died at 92 had lived to see the practice of vaccination established in the United States.

Among the most active of the supporters of Waterhouse was one who, in general histories of this country, has not been depicted as a proponent of new medical ideas. I refer to President Thomas Jefferson, author of the Declaration of Independence. The rôle which Jefferson played in establishing vaccination as a public health procedure doubtless comes as a surprise to many persons, but it was only very recently that the facts have been made known with any degree of completeness through the discovery of the letters which Waterhouse wrote to Jeffer-

Sheet of directions which accompanied sample of vaccine virus sent by James Smith to Dr. Josiah Bartlett in Stratham, New Hampshire. Courtesy of the Library of Congress.

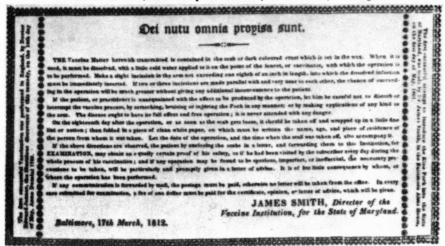

son and which are now preserved in the Library of Congress. The correspondence was uncovered by Dr. Robert H. Halsey of New York who published it in a most illuminating pamphlet.

Waterhouse had attempted to interest President John Adams but he was rebuffed with sympathetic indifference. But like Jenner, Waterhouse was fanatically devoted to the cause of vaccination and so he wrote to Thomas Jefferson, then a candidate for the Presidency. This letter was written on December 1, 1800, and Waterhouse enclosed a copy of his book, *A Prospect of Exterminating the Small-pox.* . . . Jefferson immediately replied as follows:

"Washington, Dec. 25, 1800.
"Sir:

"I received last night, and have read with great satisfaction, your pamphlet on the subject of the kine-pock, and pray you to accept my thanks for the communication of it.

"I had before attended to your publications on the subject in the newspapers, and took much interest in the result of the experiments you were making. Every friend of humanity must look with pleasure on this discovery, by which one more evil is withdrawn from the condition of man; and must contemplate the possibility, that future improvements and discoveries may still more and more lessen the catalogue of evils. In this line of proceeding you deserve well of your country; and I pray you accept my portion of the tribute due to you, and assurances of high consideration and respect, with which I am, Sir,

"Your most obedient and humble servant,
"THOMAS JEFFERSON."

The correspondence thus initiated continued for several years. During this time Waterhouse sent vaccine virus to Jefferson. Several of the first batches failed to take because the virus had lost its potency in transit. But on August 28, 1801, Waterhouse

General vaccination day at the Paris Academy of Medicine in 1870. *Harper's Weekly,* 1870.

The heifer from which the vaccine matter is taken. *Harper's Weekly*, 1870.

writes to Jefferson expressing his relief and joy that Jefferson had at last received some active material. Jefferson had sent matter to Dr. Wardlaw who used it successfully at Monticello.

Jefferson, in true scientific fashion, tested the protective power of the cowpox by having the patients inoculated with the smallpox. Having thus satisfied himself of its efficacy he began to spread the knowledge and the virus through Virginia and other parts of the United States. It was from Jefferson that John Redman Coxe of Philadelphia received his first supply of vaccinia, thus initiating vaccination in Philadelphia. Finally, Jefferson was instrumental in beginning the practice of vaccination among the Indians. In a letter to Jenner, too long to reproduce here, Waterhouse wrote on April 8th, 1802, that "last December" an embassy of Indian tribes visited Washington and that while there Jefferson sent for the chief, *Little Turtle,* to whom he communicated the fact that the GREAT SPIRIT had recently made a gift to the white men in showing them how to preserve themselves from the smallpox. This he now wished to communicate to the Indians and the chief asked that he be the first to be inoculated. The Rev. Dr. Gannt, Chaplain of Congress, performed the operation on the chief and several of his warriors and they were supplied with virus and a

copy of directions which had been drawn up by Jenner and reprinted for American use.

But not only was "true vaccine virus planted" as Waterhouse put it, in Massachusetts, Virginia and among the Indians. It was also spread to Maine, Vermont, Rhode Island, Connecticut, New York, South Carolina, Kentucky, Tennessee and Georgia.

Despite the response which Jefferson had made to his pleas and the satisfaction derived from the latter's results in the South, Waterhouse was still complaining about the indifference to his work in his native state. Finally, he made a plea to the Boston Board of Health to appoint a committee to investigate the subject of kine-pock inoculation. Six physicians comprised the committee who performed the tests upon nineteen boys. The results were completely in favor of Waterhouse. After this official recognition, vaccination made more rapid progress throughout Massachusetts. Although Waterhouse re-

Furnishing vaccine matter to French country doctors. *Harper's Weekly*, 1870.

ceived many honors both here and abroad, his personal traits prevented him from reaping the full reward of his labors. In 1812, described as an all-round pest and obstructionist, he was dismissed from his professorship at Harvard. Being an educated controversialist (few of his colleagues could match his scientific training obtained in Europe), and also a religious dissenter and a Jeffersonian Republican to boot, it is easy to understand how Waterhouse got into difficulties with his professional brethren and also the university and the public. These were some of the factors which interfered with the ready acceptance of vaccination.

But Waterhouse was not alone in his efforts to spread the benefits of vaccination throughout the United States.

In Connecticut it was Dr. Elisha North who began vaccinating in the year 1800. He obtained his first vaccine virus from a patient in New Haven who had been vaccinated with lymph obtained from Waterhouse some six or seven days earlier. With this lymph North vaccinated three persons, an adult and two children who lived in his home town of Goshen. The children had good takes although the adult did not. The youngsters were later tested by variolization but proved resistant to the smallpox. Although he was encouraged by the results, North felt that his results were due to chance. He did not feel sure that he had taken the lymph at the proper time. Waterhouse at that time was also not certain of the proper time for taking the virus. However, with additional

Vaccination from the calf (1). Taking lymph from the calf. *The Graphic* (London), 1883.

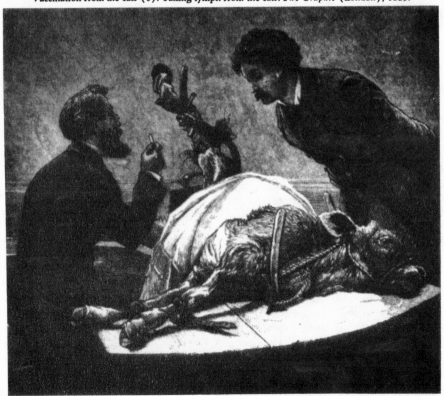

experience and information obtained from Jenner via Waterhouse, North learned to know the proper time to take virus so as to get uniformly successful results. The dictum set down by Jenner to take the virus on or before the eighth day, North called a "golden rule."

In May, 1801, North saw a patient whose complaint he was able to diagnose as cowpox which had been contracted while milking an infected cow. From this patient, North vaccinated a little girl and from her the virus was transferred to a man named Hunt. Mr. Hunt went to New York on a business trip immediately after he was vaccinated and at the request of North he called upon Dr. Edward Miller, who obtained lymph from Hunt's vaccine pustule. Thus, claimed North, the first genuine cowpox introduced into New York came from an American source.

Vaccination, however, reached New York from another source at about the same time. Dr. Valentine Seaman of that city was the first advocate of the new practice there. He had read a review of Jenner's book and immediately became interested. His attempts to use virus obtained from England were unsuccessful and finally, in the spring of 1801, he was able to vaccinate a number of persons with lymph obtained from a patient who had been freshly vaccinated by Waterhouse in Boston. Eighteen of these persons were later tested by variolization and all proved resistant. As was common in every center where vaccination was begun, Seaman immediately met with opposition and obstruction. Despite this, Seaman was able to organize an Institution for the Inoculation of the Kine Pox in 1802. Its purpose was to inoculate the poor free of charge. There Seaman vaccinated more than 200 persons,

Vaccination from the calf (2). Vaccinating infants. *The Graphic* (London), 1883.

a number of whom were later proved to be immune to the smallpox.

Although the title of the Jenner of America is generally awarded to Waterhouse it has also been claimed for Dr. James Smith of Baltimore who began vaccination in that city just about the same time as Waterhouse with virus received directly from England. The question as to who merits the honor of being the first to vaccinate in America is, however, somewhat academic since the important fact is that vaccination was begun and established here in two separate localities thus insuring and hastening the spread of this beneficent practice throughout the United States.

Dr. James Smith who was a native of Maryland studied medicine in Philadelphia under Dr. Benjamin Rush. Smith early in his career displayed an interest in matters of public health and in his frequent clashes with medical and public opinion there is a similarity to the character and experiences of Waterhouse.

Smith received his first sample of vaccine virus in a sort of roundabout way from Mr. Ring of London who was a friend of Jenner's. Virus had in fact been received earlier in Baltimore by Dr. John Crawford but his attempts at vaccination were unsuccessful, probably because his material had lost its potency. Smith tested his virus on May 1, 1801, on a little girl in the Baltimore Almshouse. With lymph obtained from her he proceeded to vaccinate a number of other babies there, and at last convinced of the efficacy of this treatment, Smith began to agitate for its acceptance by the medical profession and the public. The usual opposition and indifference greeted him. However, in 1802, the Medical and Chirurgical Faculty of Maryland endorsed vaccination. Encouraged by this, Smith proposed the establishment of a free vaccine clinic. He had recognized the fact that the ultimate success of vaccination depended upon a constant supply of virus whose authenticity and potency could be controlled. On March 25,

1802, having obtained the approval of the Mayor of Baltimore and the backing of a number of medical colleagues, Smith opened a vaccine institute in his own home, the first institution of its kind in America. Very soon after, similar institutes were opened in other cities of America.

After seven years Smith felt that the benefits of his institution ought to become more widely distributed. He therefore petitioned the legislature of Maryland to take over his Institute and make it a state agency, distributing virus free of charge to all doctors and other citizens who might ask for it. Smith wanted $1000 a year for his services as Vaccine Agent. The Institute was established with Smith at its head but he was required to obtain the money for operating it from the proceeds of a lottery. This might have netted sufficient funds except for the fact that simultaneously the state was running a lottery to obtain funds for a monument to George Washington. Smith's project received the short end of the deal but he did realize enough money to get a start in 1812. In the meantime, Smith had petitioned the Congress of the United States to be allowed to vaccinate in the District of Columbia. Congress passed the necessary legislation and he was appointed by the President as Federal Vaccine Agent. He was given authority to send virus anywhere in the United States, post-free and to retain the fees which he charged. His usual price was five dollars, although he sent out large quantities of virus with no charge whatever. Each sample of virus was wrapped in a sheet on which were printed directions for use. A copy of this direction sheet which Smith had sent to Dr. Josiah Bartlett of New Hampshire is herewith reproduced from the original preserved in the Library of Congress (see page 1117).

In addition to his activities of National and Maryland Vaccine Agent, Smith also was appointed to a similar post in Virginia at a salary of $600 per year.

He sent out agents to various parts of the country to spread the method and in 1816

The district vaccinator. A sketch at the East End of London. *The Graphic* (London), 1871.

when a smallpox epidemic threatened some localities he sent supplies of virus there free of charge. He encountered considerable opposition in his career as National Vaccine Agent. Part of this arose from the fact that although he was a public agent he collected fees for the virus (Congress paid him no salary). But in addition he had been granted a franking privilege so that he could send virus post free. In those days of high postage, this was quite a privilege and it was not available to other vaccinators. This naturally antagonized many, who, in addition, were jealous of Smith's success and he was accused of operating a monopoly. This was a charge with little foundation since he was most generous with his supplies of virus.

But a second charge was more serious. Smith claimed that any intelligent person could learn to perform the operation, that in fact the services of a physician were not necessary. A number of accidents resulting from vaccinations performed by inexperienced persons did not help his cause along.

It is not possible to detail the history of the National Vaccine Institute *in extenso* and so this account must close with a mention of certain events which led finally to Smith's discharge and abolition of the Institute.

In 1821 smallpox had come again to Baltimore, arriving on a ship from Liverpool. Vaccination was immediately resorted to but among the victims of the smallpox was a girl who had been vaccinated by Smith. This was a most unexpected fact since Smith had continuously preached as one of the virtues of cowpox the fact that it afforded permanent protection against the smallpox. Smith, confronted by this situation, now publicly reversed his opinions and cast doubt upon the protection afforded by vaccination. This, of course, was aggravated by the fact that he opposed the principle of re-vaccination. Public confidence was badly shaken but the epidemic continued and the city authorities appointed a number of public vaccinators to inoculate the poor. Smith by this time had recovered his earlier confidence and he directed the work. Over 1000 persons were vaccinated thereby suppressing the epidemic. But while Smith was still under a cloud, the final blow fell. Smith had sent some vaccine virus to a Dr. Ward of Tarborough, North Carolina. But Ward's patients instead of coming down with cowpox, showed the symptoms of smallpox. A national scandal was provoked, thus ending Smith's career. The fact that it was later discovered that some smallpox scabs had inadvertently been sent to Ward did not, of course, mitigate the affair. Congress refused to extend Smith's term of office and the Institute was discontinued. However, Smith's basic thesis that there must be governmental control of the purity and distribution of vaccine virus was ultimately accepted and it is in this that Smith's great contribution to preventive medicine lay.

In America, as in Europe, vaccination had to fight its way into general acceptance against an opposition resulting from public and professional apathy, ignorance, personal jealousies, fear of the unknown among the uninformed and the antagonism of vested interests from those who were established as inoculators. Other vested interests were represented by medical faddists and cultists while, finally, there was the opposition coming from those who opposed compulsory vaccination as an unwarranted infringement of personal liberty and an entering wedge for state medicine.

One of the most serious objections to vaccination, however, has been eliminated. This is the danger of transmitting other disease, such as syphilis. The transmission of other infections was an ever present danger as long as humanized virus was used. In 1845 Negri, of Naples, began to propagate virus in cows, thus inaugurating a new era in vaccination. The practice spread from Italy to France in 1866 and then to Germany and other parts of Europe. Virus obtained from France was introduced into a herd of cows near Boston in 1870 and this was the beginning of the use of calf lymph in the United States.

It is a pleasure to acknowledge with many thanks the gracious permission granted by Professor Henry E. Sigerist and Dr. Sanford Larkey to reproduce materials in the Henry Barton Jacobs Collection in the Welch Medical Library in Baltimore. My thanks go also to Mr. Archibald MacLeish, Librarian of Congress, and Dr. St. George Sioussat, for allowing me to use materials from the Library of Congress Collections.

SOMETHING CURIOUS
IN
THE MEDICAL LINE

Reginald Fitz

BULLETIN OF THE
HISTORY OF MEDICINE

ORGAN OF THE AMERICAN ASSOCIATION OF THE HISTORY OF MEDICINE
AND THE JOHNS HOPKINS INSTITUTE OF THE HISTORY OF MEDICINE

Editor—HENRY E. SIGERIST

| VOLUME XI | MARCH, 1942 | NUMBER 3 |

"SOMETHING CURIOUS IN THE MEDICAL LINE"

REGINALD FITZ

In the early days of 1799, Dr. Benjamin Waterhouse of Cambridge, Massachusetts, received a present from Dr. John C. Lettsom, an acquaintance of his in London. Dr. Waterhouse, as everyone knows, was the first Hersean Professor of the Theory and Practice of Physic in the Harvard Medical School, a Quaker from Rhode Island and an individual fairly bristling with peculiarities. He was a man of strong character, a properly cantankerous soul such as Harvard likes to develop from time to time, by no means the kind of a person whom the students could ornament with an affectionate, friendly nickname like "Kitty"[1] or "Copey" or "Frisky" but rather the sort of professor who was held in great awe. Certain mischievous undergraduates once announced that he was prepared to offer a series of public lectures on "Oudenology,"[2] which suggests that a number of them considered him unduly diffused and long-winded. On the other hand, one can be sure that after having heard him speak on the evils of tobacco no undergraduates would wish to be caught by him near the College while they were taking a surreptitious pull at a cigar or when they were at all under the influence of ardent spirits.

[1] To non-Harvard men, Professors G. L. Kittredge, C. T. Copeland, and R. B. Merriman.

[2] Liddell and Scott: οὐδενέια, *nothingness*.

239

Dr. Waterhouse had been educated abroad and had many more friends in England than in America. He kept up his British affiliations by correspondence, for he was a great letter-writer and in the habit of exchanging all manner of ideas with transatlantic friends. Perhaps this year, therefore, Dr. Lettsom meant this particular gift to reach Cambridge in time for Christmas. In any event it arrived at Dr. Waterhouse's home shortly after New Year's Day and was an interesting present for any doctor to receive—a copy of Dr. Edward Jenner's [3] " An Inquiry into the Causes and Effects of the Variolae Vaccinae," fresh from the press, as interesting to read now as it was a hundred and forty years ago. It tells for the first time that ' what renders the cow-pox virus so extremely singular is, that the person who has been thus affected is for ever secure from the infection of the Small Pox ' and how the latter unpleasant disease can be prevented by the simple expedient of vaccination.

Dr. Waterhouse studied this article with the greatest zeal. He was familiar with smallpox and its ravages, he knew about Zabdiel Boylston and inoculation, but here seemed something vastly more promising. After reading and re-reading it he soon determined that it should be publicized. So in the Columbian Sentinel for March 16, 1799 there appeared from his pen a short newsletter under the caption " Something curious in the Medical Line," [4] describing Jenner's work as simply and clearly as possible. Dr. Waterhouse says that this article shared the fate of most articles dealing with medical discoveries. A few of his friends read it carefully and were prepared to accept Jenner's work as an important scientific contribution, highly interesting to humanity; more, being conservative Bostonians, said nothing: they observed that wise and prudent conduct which would allow them to condemn or applaud the discovery as events might later prove; most of those who glanced through the article, however, openly ridiculed the thought of producing cowpox to prevent smallpox and considered the idea one of Professor

[3] This tract quickly achieved great popularity and was soon translated into German, Latin, and French. The copy sent to Dr. Waterhouse was the first to cross the Atlantic Ocean.

[4] His enemies called this the first of a series of advertisements and claimed that Waterhouse was unethical to use the public press for medical writings.

AN

INQUIRY

INTO

THE CAUSES AND EFFECTS

OF

THE VARIOLÆ VACCINÆ,

A DISEASE

DISCOVERED IN SOME OF THE WESTERN COUNTIES OF ENGLAND,

PARTICULARLY

GLOUCESTERSHIRE,

AND KNOWN BY THE NAME OF

THE COW POX.

BY EDWARD JENNER, M. D. F. R. S. &c.

——— QUID NOBIS CERTIUS IPSIS
SENSIBUS ESSE POTEST, QUO VERA AC FALSA NOTEMUS.

LUCRETIUS.

London:

PRINTED, FOR THE AUTHOR,

BY SAMPSON LOW, N°. 7, BERWICK STREET, SOHO:

AND SOLD BY LAW, AVE-MARIA LANE; AND MURRAY AND HIGHLEY, FLEET STREET.

1798.

Fig. 1.

Title page of Jenner's original publication on Vaccination. 1798.

241

Waterhouse's medical whims which might arrive today and to-morrow would be no more.

Public interest in this trial balloon was anything but impressive. So next Dr. Waterhouse determined to approach a more discerning audience. At one of the meetings of the American Academy of Arts and Sciences held in the Philosophy Chamber of Harvard Hall during the ensuing winter, he says that he told the members present what he had read of the kine pock as a preventive against smallpox, and that he exhibited Dr. Jenner's publication. By this time, too, Dr. Pearson's [5] book had come to his hand. This amply supported Jenner's views on the importance of vaccination and is the second significant article in the English language on vaccination. Dr. Water-house confesses that he was forced to recapitulate from memory all that he could tell the Academicians of Pearson's views because, apparently, in his enthusiasm to promote the cause of vaccination he had lent his own copy of Pearson's book to one of his friends, and like so many books that are loaned, it had departed forever from his library.

The members of the Academy of Arts and Sciences appeared dubiously interested in the matter. On the one hand, Dr. Waterhouse says that the reception to his communication was entirely satisfactory and that it provoked so much discussion and questioning as to make him promise to prepare a memoir on the topic of vaccination for a future meeting. On the other hand, the minutes of the Academy make no mention of any remarks by Dr. Waterhouse on the subject of vaccination during that season. Perhaps he spoke privately of this new procedure to the President [6] of the Academy, and to a few other members who seemed so much interested as to encourage him to go ahead. In any event, before he had time to prepare any paper, Woodville's [7] book arrived in Cambridge—the third pioneer article in the field of English vaccination literature. Waterhouse modestly said that this was so perfect a piece of work that there was no sense

[5] Pearson, G., An inquiry concerning the history of the cowpox, 1798.

[6] Lest this should ever be read beyond the bounds of New England, it will not be superfluous to add here that the President of the American Academy of Arts and Sciences was Mr. John Adams, President of the United States.

[7] Woodville, W., Reports of a series of inoculations for the variolae vaccinae, or cow-pox, 1799.

in his trying to write anything better for the Academy, that it contained a chain of facts in favor of vaccination stronger than any that
he could possibly assemble, and also—and this lent weight—that

Fig. 2.

BENJAMIN WATERHOUSE.

(Portrait by Frothingham in Harvard Medical School Library.
The book which the Doctor holds is entitled, " Jenner ").

everything that Woodville said was backed up by his old friend Dr.
Haygarth of Bath whom Waterhouse regarded as the one man then
alive most thoroughly acquainted with the laws of contagious diseases.

Dr. Waterhouse by now was convinced that vaccination was of fundamental importance but still he moved carefully. He wrote to a number of his friends in England, asking that new articles dealing with vaccination be forwarded to him as quickly as possible, and he took pains to obtain opinions from those of his British friends whom he knew to be most conservative, from men, he said, who always were in the habit of objecting much to new ideas and of acting upon them slowly.

So at last it happened that in the early spring of 1800 Dr. Waterhouse was as well read as anyone in America on the subject of vaccination. He knew Jenner's original article almost by heart and was thoroughly familiar with what was going on in England regarding the new method. His mind was made up; hoping to effect a public benefit and conceiving it a duty to do so if he could in his official situation in Harvard University, he determined to attempt the *experimentum crucis*.

To obtain potent vaccine virus in Boston was no easy task. No one in New England professed to know anything about the cow-pox so that the disease had to be introduced there, and how best to do this was largely a matter of conjecture. Various suggestions were offered: perhaps the most original was that of vaccinating a suitable sailor just before a ship sailed for Boston from a British port, and when his arm grew sore, of transmitting the cow-pox from him to another non-immune sailor and so on all the way across the sea. The proponents of this idea said it had a double advantage: there would arrive in Boston a man with a nicely ripened case of cow-pox who could be used as a donor for the New World, and a lot of other sailors who landed there would henceforward be protected from acquiring the smallpox—which would be a great blessing to all of them.

Knowledge about cow-pox in the meantime was developing steadily in England. That the virus in many ways was tough and difficult to kill yet at the same time fragile and easy to lose, had already become apparent. Even Dr. Jenner himself on occasion had lost his virus strain and had been forced to borrow a new planting from one of his friends. This experience led him to formulate what he termed the golden rule in vaccine inoculation: [8] never to use the virus from a donor after the formation of an efflorescence around the pustule or when the fluid of the pustule had lost its limpid quality.

It became apparent, too, that vaccine virus taken on a lancet soon corroded the metal and was quickly decomposed. On the other hand, various methods were being successfully adopted for conveying the vaccine fluid to distant parts of Europe in a state of activity; a piece of cotton thread might be well moistened with fluid obtained from a recent vaccination blister, allowed to dry in the open air, and not by the heat of a fire—for the virus was not particularly heat resistant— and then rolled up in a scroll of writing paper or put in an envelope or enclosed in a glass bottle. Or the matter might be kept between flat glasses sealed with wax or gold-beater's skin, eventually to be taken up in a drop of water and used several weeks later with complete success. All these facts led Dr. Jenner to surmise that viable material might easily be sent his transatlantic coadjutor, as he termed Dr. Waterhouse, and he was fully as eager as Waterhouse to see the experiment tried.

The exact deliberations that occurred in England concerning the project are not known. Jenner and Lettsom undoubtedly had a hand in them, among others, along with Dr. Haygarth of Bath and a young surgeon there named Thomas Creaser who was an early vaccinator, having been taught the tricks of the trade by Jenner himself. The general idea seems to have been to have sent to Dr. Waterhouse by the quickest possible route some properly prepared material. With this thought in mind, young Creaser in Bath was directed to prepare some threads frestly coated with virus, to place them in a tightly stoppered glass bottle, to put them aboard a Boston-bound boat just before she sailed from Bristol, and to instruct whomsoever was made custodian of this precious bottle to deliver it to Dr. Waterhouse as quickly as possible upon arrival. Presumably Creaser was selected because of his known technical ability to prepare the vaccine virus properly, and Bristol was chosen as the port of departure because a package placed on a ship there would have quicker sea passage to

[8] I am told by modern vaccinators that when the efflorescence forms and the pustule fluid becomes cloudy, enough antibodies are present so as to make a " take " from such fluid unlikely.

Boston than would a package shipped from London and thus have less time in which to disintegrate from the rigors of a long ocean voyage.

Fig. 3.

EDWARD JENNER.

The " Foxwell " left Bristol on the 3rd of May 1800, arriving in Boston on July 4th. As she came to anchor off Long Wharf she fired a grand federal salute, perhaps thus celebrating the arrival of the first vaccine virus to be brought to New England. The " Foxwell " was the only ship from Bristol to arrive in Boston around that time hence it is not unreasonable to credit her with carrying along with a cargo of paving stones, warming pans, pots and kettles, nails, some gun powder, a quantity of fine blown salt, and several barrels of Bristol Crown Glass, the precious bottle containing Dr. Waterhouse's threads impregnated with kine-pock virus. He hardly would have kept the material around the house for long without using it, and on July 8th 1800, he performed his first vaccination. Exactly from whose hands he received the bottle is not known: possibly from Captain Henry Barnard's, of the " Foxwell " or from the hands of her solitary first class passenger, a Mr. Mardenbrough.

Suffice it to say that like Zabdiel Boylston before him, he began experimenting with his own family: [9] " The first of my children that I inoculated, was a boy of five years old, named Daniel Oliver Waterhouse. I made a slight incision in the usual place for inoculation in the arm, inserted a small portion of the infected thread, and covered it with a sticking-plaster. It exhibited no other appearance than what would have arisen from any other extraneous substance, until the 6th day, when an encreased redness called forth my attention. On the 8th, he complained of pain under the inoculated arm, and on the 9th, the inoculated part exhibited evident signs of virulency. The sore in the arm proceeded exactly as Dr. Jenner and Woodville describe, and appeared to the eye very like the second plate in Dr. Jenner's elegant publication. In short, the appearance and symptoms of this disease, in the *old* world, and in the *new*, were more completely alike than I expected."

A few days later he inoculated a younger son, Benjamin, Jr., with material from Daniel's arm, and from him a baby daughter, Mary, and her nursery maid. He inoculated also a servant boy with some of the infected thread from England, and, before long, a daughter Elizabeth and two other domestics. They all had good " takes " and were Waterhouse's first series of cases.

He was not satisfied with this result for next he felt it necessary to find out whether the persons so vaccinated in America were really immune to smallpox as in accordance with Dr. Jenner's experience in England. So he sent young Daniel to Dr. Aspinwall's smallpox

[9] This and the following quotations from Dr. Waterhouse are taken from his publications, from an autobiographical manuscript in his own handwriting, or from letters now in the Harvard Medical School Library.

hospital in Brookline and there watched Dr. Aspinwall inoculate
him with matter taken that moment from a patient who had the
inoculated smallpox " pretty full upon him," and to make doubly sure
with an infected thread. Finally, Daniel was placed in bed alongside
of a patient ill with ordinary smallpox. On the 4th day Daniel's arm
grew sore, but in a day or two it dried off, and grew well, without
producing the slightest trace of any disease. Daniel did not develop
smallpox and was dismissed from the hospital on the 12th day after
the experiment began none the worse from being such a Spartan
guinea-pig. Dr. Waterhouse, in no way inflated with parental pride,
merely remarked a trifle complacently that one such observation was
worth a thousand arguments. Dr. Aspinwall was less impersonal.
Instead of stating that this was no humbug, as Bostonians are expected to do when they observe something new and curious in the
medical line, he said almost the same thing in slightly different words,
perhaps a little wistfully, " This is no deception. I rejoice at the
discovery as a friend of humanity although it must deprive me of a
very handsome annual income."

In this fashion was vaccination introduced into America.

Dr. Waterhouse presently found himself tempted to build up a
new and lucrative medical business as the result of his experiments.
The news spread quickly. By the first of September, to quote Dr.
John Warren, the kine-pock was making good deal of noise around
Boston. A little later Dr. Waterhouse was assailed by practitioners
all over New England to supply them with vaccine virus—at very
generous terms—in order that they might take advantage of what
promised to become a veritable medical bonanza. He considered this
not the correct way to proceed, and yet in spite of all that he could
do there developed in no time at all " a singular traffic in the article
of vaccine matter by persons not in the least connected with the
profession as stage-drivers and peddlars. Vagrant quacks strolled
about the country inoculating for half a dollar a head and several for
a quarter that sum; this impudence was not confined to such characters; several young practitioners pursued the same disgraceful line."
His struggles against that sort of thing and his heroic fight to
establish vaccination on a proper basis in this country have been described by many pens more talented than mine. There are innumer-

able stories connected with it, one that I like particularly being his own version of the energetic [10] manner in which the situation in Rhode Island once was handled.[11] " They never did anything in vaccination when the smallpox was brought into Newport. They inoculated a few, but were much inclined to inoculate with *small pox*; and perhaps would have committed this mad and wicked act, had not my son Andrew, who resides there, prevented it by the strongest of arguments. He told them that should his father hear of it, he would come himself to stop it; and if he could not, would publish them to the world as fools or knaves or both. He told the men in authority there, that it would be a double disgrace to Newport, where the first promoter of the Kine Pock inoculation was born, to encourage such an unwise project. He soon gained men of the most influence on his side; and they arrested the contagion before it had done any very serious mischief, or allowed of such a disgraceful precedent."

One of the pleasant and important by-products of the vaccination struggle was the staunch friendship which grew up between Waterhouse and Jenner. Although actually they never saw one another, Dr. Waterhouse came to feel that Jenner to him was what the sun is to the moon, and Dr. Jenner to look on Waterhouse as an interesting and original character unlike any other of his immediate circle of acquaintanceship and a man of whom he grew very fond. Letters passed between the two for several years: the few that are known are interesting for the informal medical information they contain and for the manner in which they are written. They are models of urbanity making any reader agree with Sam Weller that the great art of letter writing is to make the recipient wish there were more.

This friendship began entirely by accident. In the fall of 1800 Dr. Waterhouse found himself in trouble: " This autumn a serious

[10] From a letter to his son John while a student at Andover Academy, " I love to see *energy* in everything even in quarreling. Alexander conquered the world by *energy*. Caesar attained the height of power and glory by *energy*. Bonaparte holds the reins of Europe by *energy*. Nothing can be attained worth acceptance without *energy*; everything within the circumference of human power can be acquired by *energy*. It is the *will*; the *desire* that raises one man above another. It is not good luck but *energy*." (Harvard Medical School Library.)

[11] From a letter to Dr. Sylvanus Fansher, June 8th, 1827. (Harvard Medical School Library.)

occurrence at Marblehead attracted the attention of the public; a practitioner inoculated his children with smallpox matter, which he supposed to be the vaccine matter. This spread the smallpox through that seaport, and forty persons who had been inoculated with spurious

KINE POCK INSTITUTION
BY DR. WATERHOUSE.

BY applying at this institution in the EXCHANGE BUILDING, Boston, *Sailors* may be inoculated agreeably to an arrangement made for their particular benefit.

All other persons may, by applying to the same place, be inoculated at a reasonable fee.

The room is at the top of the stairs leading up to the District Court, from the front door, or post office entry ; where Dr. Waterhouse or his assistant, Mr. Fancher, will attend to all, who may either call, or send a line, expressing a wish to be visited at their own houses.

A branch of this Kine Pock Institution is kept at Dr. Waterhouse's dwelling house

where parents may send their children, with perhaps more conveniency than to the Exchange. Attendance will be given here *every hour* of *every day*.

It has been thought, that the peculiar nature of this extraordinary gift of Providence will justify the dispensation of this blessing on the morning and evening of every *sabbath ;* more especially to Seamen, and some others, who cannot attend on working days.

Vaccine matter, preserved and put up in a peculiar way, may be had at all times, at a fixed price (viz. five dolls.) in imitation of the *Vaccine Institution* of London.

Fig. 4.

Broadside of the Kine Pock Institution of Boston, a medical venture which failed.

kine-pock matter took the distemper, and a sudden downfall of the credit of Vaccination followed, together with not a few execrations on the original promoter of it." Naturally, Dr. Waterhouse was much disturbed, particularly when so sage an adviser as President Willard of Harvard University got wind of the matter and told him that he had collected the opinions of reliable doctors in Boston, Salem, and Beverly and had honestly come to believe that so much trouble had been stirred up by this outbreak in Marblehead and so much doubt had been cast on the usefulness of vaccination as to make it appear to him inexpedient for a Professor in the college to be mixed up in the business.

Dr. Waterhouse, however, was a stubborn soul. Moreover, there was one thing about the Marblehead outbreak which attracted his attention and gave him faith: those townspeople whom he himself had vaccinated escaped the smallpox although many of them slept with people ill with the disease.

He was in an awkward predicament and therefore moved cannily. " By the end of Novr spurious cases multiplied so fast upon me and everyone else that I was glad to wind up the business with the year. I therefore gave out that the winter would not be so favorable to the inoculation as the spring; and at this perplexed stage of the business I wrote to my correspondents in Eng^d."

First he wrote to Dr. Lettsom describing what had occurred, believing it in part due to deterioration of the virus, and suggesting that it would be nice if Dr. Jenner could be consulted. Thus on March 4th, 1801,[12] Dr. Jenner wrote his first letter to Waterhouse. It is a long letter, including some general rules regarding vaccination, a fugitive illustration from his next pamphlet, and a great deal of good advice. Parts of it are quoted because they show how sympathetic Jenner was to a struggling clinical investigator in far distant land and how glad to lend a helping hand.

" Previously to the transmission of your letter to me, by Dr. Lettsom, I had heard of the sad embarrassment you had fallen into from the loss of your vaccine matter, and most ardently do I hope that the efforts I have used with the view of your being resupplied, may long before this time have proved successful. . . .

" By the conveyance which brings you this, you will not only receive vaccine matter, such as I employ with my patients here, and among them I frequently find the offspring of some of the first families in our Realms, but such laws also for conducting the vaccine process, or if you please, such a map of the road you are to pursue, as will in future prevent forever your losing the way.

" I am about to publish a fourth Tract upon the cow pox, and am sorry that it is not yet in print, or with pleasure would I send it to you. . . . But although I am thus precluded from sending you the pamphlet, that infor-

---

[12] From Waterhouse's, A Prospect of exterminating the Small Pox. Part II, 110.

mation which may prove most satisfactory to you will lie in a small compass, and shall form the principal subject of this epistle.

" The vaccine fluid must be considered as especially delicate in its texture. . . . The perfect virus only can produce the perfect vaccine pustule, at least the fluid inserted must contain some particles of it in its perfect state.

" Now I conceive that at some period of your inoculation, which may now have escaped your recollection, an imperfect pustule arose, either from some peculiarity in the constitution of your patient, or some alteration in the qualities of your matter, and that from this stock you propagated. The consequence was, that continued degeneracy you complain of in the nature of the disease. . . .

" I am aware that it is the opinion of some, that the vaccine matter loses its properties after it has passed from the cow through a given number of human subjects. . . . I am now, almost daily, inoculating children in the metropolis; and producing with it the vaccine disease with all its characters. . . . In short there does not appear to be the least tendency toward change in the nature of the virus *from time*. . . .

" It is unnecessary for me to say that the vaccine virus I now convey to you is perfectly genuine, when you may be assured it is from that stock which I am using among all my patients here, and these are of every order from the Peer to the Porter; for all ranks of society readily embrace our new doctrine. . . .

" This letter ought certainly to be written over again, but Dr. Lettsom has just sent a message that forbids it. It is of no less magnitude than that the ship, which is to convey it across the Atlantic, is about to sail.

" It will afford me much pleasure and satisfaction to be favoured with your correspondence on this subject, or any others. Sincerely wishing you health and happiness, and complete success with your inoculation, I remain,

Dear Sir,

your obliged and very faithful

humble servant,

Edward Jenner.

" P. S. Some of the virus I have sent was taken from a pustule this morning by my friend Mr. Ring,[13] *Surgeon in New Street Hanover Square.* We

---

[13] John Ring who wrote " A Treatise on the Cow-Pox," the first volume of which was published in 1801. Of vaccination he says on page 443, " It has crossed the waves of the wide Atlantic, and been adopted by Dr. Waterhouse, the learned Professor of the Theory and Practice of Physic in the University of Cambridge.

This university is situated about three miles from Boston. Here the bright beam that was to illume the realms of Columbia, first dawned. Here the Jenner of America first appeared;

And a new sun in the new world arose.

occasionally assist each other with the fresh fluid. The whole is from my original stock. I have sent you one of the coloured plates, which will be published with my next pamphlet, to shew the progress of the perfect pustule.

E. J."

Dr. Waterhouse was both delighted and flattered when he received this. On April 22nd, 1801,[14] he wrote Dr. Lettsom:

"I received your parcel, containing the two publications on the cow-pox, and also a packet from Dr. Jenner with *fresh* matter, and a lengthy and most admirable letter. It was, like his publications, plain and lucid beyond his compeers; displaying that perspicuity and dignified simplicity which is the peculiar ornament of genius. His letter is (excuse my enthusiasm) a ray of light from the East, and oh! that the reflected ray might become more brilliant; and even generative at the point of repercussion! I shall write to this *primitive apostle* by the Galen; should you in the mean time see him, make my most cordial acknowledgment to him: tell him he receives not only my thanks, but the thanks of the American public; for the name of Jenner is familiar in every village in New England. . . .

"I should be grateful to know more of Jenner's [15] personal history. Is he not a son of Oxford, or Cambridge? I have never heard any particulars concerning him; but from his logic, I suspect he is a son of one of them, or else he is like Franklin, one of Nature's own pupils. Some men are destined to follow the rules of colleges, but with others, *rules follow them.*"

His letter to Jenner written on April 24th [16] is even more ebullient:

"Being just informed of a ship's sailing tomorrow for London I have only time to acknowledge the receipt of your most excellent letter. . . . With it I received a supply of vaccine matter, which came to hand thirty-eight days after the date of your letter, for which you have my most cordial thanks. I have inoculated with it, and found it good, and here send you the first crop from it. When my good friend Dr. Lettsom [17] has sent me curious melon

---

[14] From Pettigrew's, Memoirs of the Life and Writings of the late John Coakley Lettsom. Vol. III, 212.

[15] This was for a short biographical sketch which Waterhouse published later.

[16] From Baron's, The Life of Edward Jenner, M. D. Vol. I, 439.

[17] Dr. Waterhouse and Dr. Lettsom apparently reciprocated in the interchange of seeds as well as medical opinions. On March 9, 1801, Dr. Waterhouse sent Dr. Lettsom some pumpkin seeds which he found on the Island of Nantucket. He was told that whale-men had brought the original seeds from Cape Horn, and hence they were called locally, when they grew, Cape Horn Pumpkins. Dr. Waterhouse told Dr. Lettsom that to cultivate them properly, they should be planted like cucumbers and given plenty of manure; they made admirable puddings or bread, " when mixed with half flour or Indian meal." In September 1840, Dr. Waterhouse claimed to have one growing in his garden " almost as big round as a beer barrel." What luck Dr. Lettsom had with the seeds is not known.

seeds I have sent him as soon as possible some seed raised from them, that he might see whether our soil, atmosphere, and mode of culture effected any alteration from the original stock. The same I have now done with your Vaccine virus. . . . I took the patient into my own house that I might watch the progress of the local affection, which I did under the microscope. It is now the tenth day in the morning, and I expect the efflorescence will, in ten or twelve hours more, put on the appearance of your *tenth day representation* in the coloured engravings.

" It is impossible for me to express the great satisfaction your letter gave me. The subject was before involved in a mist: your letter was a ray of light, which ray must be reflected for the benefit of the western world. Oh! that it were possible for this ray to become still more brilliant and even generative at the point of repercussion.

" I entirely agree with you as to the cause of our late failure in inoculation. . . . You know not what it is to be perplexed in this business. That prince of physiologists, John Hunter, once told me that ' he loved to be puzzled, for then he was sure he should learn something valuable.' Burthensome as it was at the time I do not now regret my perplexity. When I had lost my way, and wandered into the wilds of conjecture, I stood still. . . . Now we [18] are going on again, but not with the faith and spirit of the last season. . . .

" Accept my thanks for the coloured plate. It is indeed a happy expedient, and honours the graphic art. It is thought here to be so important that I am anxious to know if I can with propriety procure some more of them. I should wish to possess a couple of dozen to be deposited in the hands of some of our leading practitioners, or clergymen, in different parts of the United States by way of standards. . . .

" I have been informed from a quarter not likely to be deceived, that cows [19] (contrary to my assertion in page 22 of my pamphlet) have been known to have the small-pox.

---

[18] Presumably this does not refer to Waterhouse himself but rather to New England physicians.

[19] Dr. Waterhouse puzzled over the relation between cow-pox and smallpox for many years. In 1827 he wrote Dr. Fansher: " I have believed from the beginning of my knowledge of vaccination that such an epizootic distemper was amongst our kine. I grounded my belief upon the origin of our cows, & the similarity of the country of *New* England with that of the old. . . . I have had three or four very strong *presumptive* evidences of milkers having taken the distemper from milking, one given me by Dr. Willard of Vermont, and another, still stronger, by a Mr. Nathan Adams now living in Charlestown, near Boston; but I never had that plenar of evidence which would satisfy a Judge in court of law on a trial of life & death. But the case you mention is of a nature to determine the question beyond all shadow of doubt, if you have seen the eruptions on the udders of the cows & the pustules on the hands of the milkers, and above all if *you have given the true disease to one of the human species.* And I am in hopes to hear from you that you have been confirmed in your opinion by *inequivocal experiment.*

"The account is this. At one of our periodical inoculations, which occurs in New England once in eight or nine years, several persons drove their cows to an hospital near a populous village, in order their families might have the daily benefit of their milk. These cows were milked by persons in all stages of the small-pox: the consequence was, the cows had an eruptive disorder on their teats and udders, so like the small-pox pustule, that every one in the hospital, as well as the physician who told me, declared the cows had the small-pox. Since the cow-pox has been talked of this account has been revived and credited. Have you found any thing like this in England?

"I inoculated one of my cows with the Vaccine virus, and obtained from her a crop of matter on the ninth day, which produced the disease in the human subjects to perfection. Is this experiment known among you? As I operated myself there was no avenue opened for deception in the whole experiment. . . .

"You very politely express a wish for more of my letters on the Vaccine or any other subject. In order to damp this desire and surfeit you at once, I have directed my book-seller to send you a whole volume of them, which the partiality of Dr. Lettsom has brought into light. . . .

"I need not, I think, say how highly I should prize the correspondence of Dr. Jenner on any subject; but more especially on that for which he is so deservedly celebrated; and who, according to my understanding, is the only *clear, consistent,* UNCONFUSED writer on the cow-pox that has yet appeared.

"I reiterate my thanks for your kindness, and beg you to accept the assurances of high consideration and esteem!

"P. S. As the library of this University is by far the largest in the United States, and is the grand deposit of rare and valuable books in this quarter of the world and will continue so, I cannot resist expressing my wish that a copy of your invaluable work may be deposited there by its author. I presume my motives for wishing this, and hinting it, stand in no need of an apology. By a law of the Commonwealth, an author to secure his copy-right must deposit a copy of his work in this library; and books sent to it come free from duty. This library, museum, and other public rooms are constantly visited by strangers as among the curiosities of the country. When I had the honour of waiting on the Duke of Kent through them, he expressed his surprise at such a collection of books and material productions in about thirty years, *for the small-pox destroyed the chief of what had been collected since* 1638: that is to say, it raged in Boston, and the legislature on that account occupied one of the public rooms in the hall, which contained the library; when it by some accident took fire and was, one alcove excepted, totally destroyed. Thanks be to Dr. Jenner, such an accident from *such a cause* can never happen again."

On the 30th [20] of May he wrote a follow-up letter to this, of chief

[20] From Baron's, The Life of Edward Jenner, M. D. Vol. I, 469.

interest as it so well illustrates his characteristic energy and some of his perplexities:

"I now send you a portion of your own virus, being a part of that *identical* thread which you, in conjunction with Mr. Ring, took from the arm of a patient on the *third day of last March* in London, that experiment may be

Fig. 5.

Cow Pox Virus in a fine female arm of about two-and-twenty years' standing. From a water-color painting found opposite the title-page of Waterhouse's own copy of Jenner's, "The Origin of the Vaccine Inoculation." 1801.

made respecting its activity at a still greater length of time. . . . It is now within four days of being *three months* old, and it had not lost its activity ten days ago. . . .

"You will doubtless rejoice with me that the vaccine inoculation is progressing here to my entire satisfaction. I began with the matter you sent me the 24th [21] of March, and have inoculated not quite a hundred, and have not had one dubious case among them all. I have given the virus to most of the

---

[21] Obviously a misprint. Jenner's letter was written on March 4th.

leading physicians in Boston and its vicinity. But, alas! poor human nature! thou art the same in *New*-England as in *Old*." . . .

What Waterhouse referred to in the last sentence is better explained in his own words. He did not like the Massachusetts Medical Society nor did its members like him. " Early in the spring of 1801, I was met by Dr. Isaac Rand in one of the streets of Boston, who told me that the Mass. Med. Society had just imported some vaccine matter from London; and that they had distributed it among two or three of their members, and that it had failed in their hands; and that he was fearful that what he himself had used would fail also; but of this he was not certain, he spoke as if he had as much to fear as to hope on the matter. On hearing this, without saying a word of my intention to Dr. Rand, I at once resolved to send a fresh supply of matter to the Medical Society, with a view to prevent their disappointment. I therefore on returning home, put up with great care vaccine matter of various ages, both recent matter, as well as some I had just received from England, and the next day I sent it to the Medical Society. . . . These gentlemen did not chuse to be under obligation to me for matter, nor to notice the offer I made them." Once he remarked that the natives of America were skilful in bushfighting and that had he not a kind of apostolic zeal he would at times feel a little discouraged!

On the whole, however, by virtue of the shipment of vaccine virus described above, Waterhouse now found himself able to carry on successfully. By following Jenner's rules he went ahead to spread the gospel of vaccination, not, however, without meeting other difficulties than an unfriendly attitude of the Massachusetts Medical Society. For example, in 1802, for a time, he found himself obliged to hire volunteers to be inoculated in Cambridge in order that he might maintain a certain continuous supply of fresh virus.

There is a very pleasant letter from Jenner to Waterhouse written on February 24th,[22] 1802.

---

[22] In Dr. Waterhouse's pamphlet of " Information respecting the origin, progress and efficacy of the Kine Pock Inoculation " published in 1810, there is a curious typographical error. Dr. Jenner's letter is quoted in full, beginning on page 49. It is dated " London, Bond Street, February 24, 1801." Actually it was written a year later. Dr. Jenner's extreme busyness at the time perhaps explains this slip of the pen.

" I believe, according to the laws of true politeness, I should begin this letter with an apology. Allow me then to request you to pardon my seeming inattention. I say *seeming*, for be assured you are frequently in my thoughts; and when I think of you, I foolishly long for powers that a mortal ought not to aspire to. Nothing less than a trumpet, not that *whispering* thing used by the mariner, but one that would carry my voice on the rapid wings of the wind across the wide ocean that divides us. . . .

" What a lamentable thing is distance? distance almost immeasurable between friend and friend!—Would I could say, will you dine with me? or take your coffee with me tomorrow, that we may talk over fully our vaccine affairs? But alas! so great is the space between us, you might as well receive my invitation in the moon, nay the georium sidus, as on the other side of the Atlantic. We must do the best we can under these disadvantages, and be thankful that the ingenuity of man has devised ships, and given speech to *feathers*.

" Of the vaccine subject I fear I shall have little new to offer you. Knowing that you are in possession of the writings of Mr. *Ring* upon the vaccine inoculation, I shall find it difficult to give you any thing worthy of observation. . . . His work will contain a fund of information, both for present times, and those which are to come. . . .

" The most arduous task that I have lately had to execute has been that of keeping practitioners in order; making them sensible of the absolute necessity of attending to the *quality* of the virus employed. You will receive with this some rules, compressed in a small space. I have sent you also some virus from a new stock, the history of which you shall hear. . . . A medical gentleman at Milan, Dr. *Sacco*, who informed me he has inoculated 8000 persons in that city, has lately sent me vaccine virus, taken from a dairy on the plains of Lombardy. It has produced again and again the perfect pustule here. I always ventured to predict, that the cow pox was not confined to this island only. . . .

" And now, my good Doctor, I would fain proceed further, and *settle my epistolary account* with you; but our friend *Spalding*[23] tells me that if I do not make haste, the ship, intended to convey this, will be gone. Spare then *my life* a little longer.—I have not said half I wish to say, nor taken that

---

[23] Matthias Spalding, a graduate of Harvard College in 1798 and a protégé of Waterhouse, to whom Jenner took a great fancy. When he went to England in the fall of 1801, Waterhouse gave him proper letters of introduction and presently wrote, " I was grateful at hearing of the polite attention of Dr. Lettsom to you. . . . I was pleased to hear that you had conversed with the man I so much admire, I mean Jenner. Present my best regards to him and tell him that although I sought his life with eagerness, and failed in the attempt, I have nevertheless (instigated by the same spirit) been a little consoled in *hanging him up, in effigy*, in my parlour."

notice of your excellent epistles so fully as I ought. But I am this moment fifty letters behind hand with my correspondents—a distressing idea."

Dr. Waterhouse lost no time in answering this for on April 8th,[24] he replied:

"Four hours ago I received your polite and very interesting letter dated 24th. February. The ship had but thirty-two days passage. I have just put your Lombardy virus into a fine female arm of about two-and-twenty years' standing, and shall give you the result by the return of the ship which brought it. . . .

"Dr. Rush has come out full and strong in praise of the new inoculation and has sent me a copy of an eloquent lecture of his on the blessings of the Jennerian discovery. . . .

"Last December a grand embassy of certain tribes of the Indians came to the city of Washington while the Congress was sitting. . . . The chief of this embassy was named *Little Turtle*. The President one day sent for the warrior and his interpreter. . . . He then told him that the Great Spirit had lately made a precious donation to the enlightened white men over the great water, first to a single person, and from him to another on this side the waters, and then explained to him the history of the cow or kine-pock as a gift from Heaven to preserve them from the small-pox, and even to banish it from the earth. The chief heard him with marked attention, and desired first to receive the benefits of it himself. . . .

"When the Minerva returns I may possibly write you a *letter* instead of this *receipt* for your valuable favours; as it is you will receive the cordial wishes of an affectionate friend."

The year of 1802, was not without interest to the friendship between Waterhouse and Jenner in other ways than by correspondence. It was in the autumn of this year that Waterhouse added the finishing touches to his book on Vaccination, the preparation of which he said represented the labor of more than six months and an investment of more than 50 guineas. He felt bitterly over the way in which it was received: there were scarcely more than half a dozen copies bought by Boston physicians and the critics [25] of the Massachusetts Medical Society humiliated him by terming his book "obscure"

[24] From Baron's, The Life of Edward Jenner, M. D. Vol. I, 593.

[25] In 1808, the Massachusetts Medical Society appointed a committee to report on vaccination. The committee rendered a lengthy report in which Waterhouse's name does not appear nor is any reference made to his efforts towards introducing vaccination in America.

To JOHN COAKLEY LETTSOM;

AND

To EDWARD JENNER;

PHYSICIANS PREEMINENTLY DISTINGUISHED FOR

THEIR ACTIVE BENEVOLENCE

AND

PROFESSIONAL SKILL,

THIS ESSAY

IS INSCRIBED,

AS A MARK OF ESTEEM AND RESPECT,

BY THEIR TRANSATLANTIC FRIEND

BENJAMIN WATERHOUSE.

CAMBRIDGE *New England,*
November 1801.

Fig. 6.

Dedication of the book by Dr. Waterhouse, "A Prospect of exterminating
the Small Pox." 1802.

and not worth looking at. He would have been badly hurt had not his British friends helped out and had not the volume sold fairly well in the South.

To compensate for this, he received an unusual present from England in that same autumn. His letter [26] to Dr. Lettsom of November 16, 1802, describes this nicely:

" I have sent, by this opportunity, a few pages of my publication on the Kine-pock, to Mr. Ring. The whole will be printed within a month. Every body will approve of the absolute propriety of addressing it to yourself and to Dr. Jenner, when they know that the first intimation I ever had of the cow-pox came from Dr. Lettsom, and that Dr. Jenner has been to me what the *sun* is to the *moon*. Should any of you think this book of sufficient importance to admit of a London edition, I shall add to it an Epistle Dedicatory, expressive of these obligations. But more of this hereafter. I shall bear in mind the LL. D. for Dr. Jenner next July. We give degrees but once a year. Dr. Jenner has just sent me a present I highly prize, a silver box inlaid with gold of exquisite taste and workmanship, bearing the inscription " Edward Jenner to Benjamin Waterhouse." But Mr. Ring annexed the superscription in rather an hyperbolic style, " From the Jenner of the Old World tó the Jenner of the New World." Long will it remain among the sacrae relictae of my family."

The silver box is fully as attractive as Dr. Waterhouse described it and now is in the Harvard Medical School Library, a living token of affection between two unusual friends.

At Commencement in 1803, Dr. Jenner was duly made an Honorary alumnus of Harvard University with the degree of Doctor of Laws, and Waterhouse had the pleasure of sending the diploma to his friend in England. The citation,[27] which seems to have a Waterhouse touch to it, is as follows:

" A profound scholar of medicine, anatomy, and physiology, endowed with discerning originality and pre-eminent now because of his brilliant investigations on inoculation with cow-pox through which smallpox, a disease destructive to the human race, may be outrooted; a wise clinician, master, too, of other arts and sciences which add beauty and usefulness to human endeavor."

---

[26] From Pettigrew's, Memoirs of the Life and Writings of the late John Coakley Lettsom, Vol. II, 481.

[27] From the Harvard Archives. The original citation was in Latin. This translation has the sanction of Professor E. K. Rand.

After this year letters between the two are more difficult to un-
cover. In 1807, when Dr. Waterhouse appealed to the Massachusetts
legislature for financial compensation because of his vaccination

Fig. 7.

The Silver Box: "From the Jenner of the Old World to the
Jenner of the New World." 1802.

efforts, Jenner [28] wrote rather perfunctorily that "the granting of
favors to the man whom I have the satisfaction to rank among the
earliest, the most active, and the most successful of my transmarine
disciples, I shall ever feel as an honor conferred upon myself." Jenner

[28] From Waterhouse's, Information respecting the origin, progress and efficacy
of the Kine Pock Inoculation, 48.

seemingly wrote this for publication, or so that Waterhouse might use it as he saw fit and hence it lacks all personal warmth.

By 1810, with the threat of war in the offing, all friendly correspondence between England and New England seems to have dwindled. Waterhouse wrote Lettsom [29] in May " what a tedious length of time has elapsed since I had a line from you, or indeed, any of my old friends and correspondents in England! . . . Where is Jenner? and where is Ring? There is, I hope, no embargo on their friendship." In December [30] of the same year he wrote, " I believe it is near upon two years since I have received a line from Dr. Lettsom; and more than a year since I had one from Dr. Jenner. Has our Act of Congress occasioned this *non*-intercourse between old friends?" On the other hand, some degree of friendship between Jenner and Waterhous managed to survive the ordeals of war for in 1812, Jenner [31] mentions having received recently some political news from Waterhouse, ". . . a man of correct habits. For the first seven years of vaccination I corresponded with him regularly. He upbraids me justly for late irregularities." And in 1817, Mr. John Adams [32] wrote to Waterhouse, " The Calamity of your friend Jenner affects me very Sensibly." From which one may assume that the Cambridge physician knew of the illness which prostrated his friend six years before his death.

The Metropolitan [33] Life Insurance Company has published recently an interesting account of the decreasing incidence of smallpox in the United States. The writer of this article concludes with the statement that the disease is now a public health anachronism. Methods for its control are well known and measures for its prevention are at hand: in the near future it should be completely wiped off the public health slate of this country.

The medical knowledge on which such a statement depends originated in England more than a hundred and forty years ago by virtue

[29] From Pettigrew's, Memoirs of the Life and Writings of the late John Coakley Lettsom. Vol. II, 484.

[30] From *Ibid.* Vol. II, 491.

[31] From Baron's, The Life of Edward Jenner, M. D. Vol. II, 382.

[32] From W. C. Ford's, Statesman and Friend, 134.

[33] Statistical Bulletin, Metropolitan Life Insurance Company, 22: 6 (June) 1941.

of the accurate observations and deductions of a keen clinician. It was transmitted to New England and spread through the New World largely by the persevering efforts of a well-read and fearless clinical investigator on this side of the ocean. Friendship, in one way or another, had a good deal to do with making this possible. That friendship between two doctors who never met should have played an important part in the achievement of a result so vital to our national health as the prevention of smallpox is, indeed, something curious in the medical line.

THE FIRST NATURAL HISTORY LECTURES
AT BROWN UNIVERSITY, 1786,
BY DR. BENJAMIN WATERHOUSE

J. Walter Wilson

THE FIRST NATURAL HISTORY LECTURES AT BROWN UNIVERSITY, 1786, BY DR. BENJAMIN WATERHOUSE

By J. WALTER WILSON, Ph.D.

PROVIDENCE, RHODE ISLAND

WHEN, in 1783, the French soldiers left "the College Edifice" of the College of Rhode Island, now Brown University, it was in a sad state of repair, and the funds of the College were practically nonexistent. The only professor the College had ever had, David Howell, had given up hope that the College would survive as early as 1777, and entered the law. Apparently his success was great enough so that he had no interest in returning to his professorship. The problem of replacing him without funds was solved by the generous action of two members of the corporation who had scientific interests: Joseph Brown and Benjamin Waterhouse. They both volunteered to serve without pay, Brown as professor of experimental philosophy and Waterhouse as professor of natural history. Waterhouse thus became the first professor of natural history in New England, if not in any American college, and he claimed that his lectures comprised the first course of lectures in natural history given in any college in America.

Waterhouse was a Quaker, whose early life was spent in Newport, just before the Revolution, and Newport had been a center of intellectual activity at least from the days of Berkeley in the early part of the century. About 1752 William Hunter came from Edinburgh with a fine medical library and the best training in anatomy and surgery of any medical man in the colony. He gave the first public lectures in anatomy in America at Newport.[1] Thacher[2] says that they treated not merely of human anatomy, but the history of anatomy, and comparative anatomy, subjects indicating a much broader outlook, both historical and philosophical, than would be required in a purely descriptive course. The Redwood Library at Newport was so fine that the Rev. Ezra Stiles, who was later president of Yale and said to have been one of the most learned men in the colonies, owed much to its books. He was the pastor of the Second Congregational Church in Waterhouse's youth. There were fine gardens in Newport, some very famous, where Solomon Drowne in 1772 saw lemons on the trees, and orange and lime trees, sensitive plants, and pineapples growing.[3] Waterhouse did not have a college education; he began the study of medicine under Dr. Hunter and Dr. Halliburton in Newport.

With this background Waterhouse went to London, just before the Revolution, to live with Dr. Fothergill, his mother's cousin, and to continue his study of medicine. Here he met, among others, Jenner—who later discovered smallpox vaccination. How important smallpox must have seemed to medical men, and this young medical man in particular, can be readily understood from the accounts in Dr. Stiles' diary[4] of town meetings called in Newport in 1772 to permit inoculation, then to revoke the permission, and then to grant it again, while Dr. Stiles found it necessary to send his own son into Connecticut with a party who went there to be inoculated—all this when the inoculation was with the real disease itself rather than with cow-pox. Waterhouse later wrote a letter to Dr. Haygarth of London, about the laws and regulations concerning smallpox in America. This was printed in 1782.[5] In later years Waterhouse became known as the American Jenner, for he obtained from Jenner and imported to America the first cow-pox vaccine, and tried it first on his own five year old son. How, with the help of Thomas Jefferson, he introduced vaccination and established it as a regular public health practice has been adequately told.[6]

In addition to his study with Dr. Fothergill he studied also at Dublin and Edinburgh and finally in Leyden where he received his Doctor's degree. Leyden at this time was still the medical capital of the world. The influence of the great Boerhaave continued to be felt though he had died forty years before. In these centers of science Waterhouse acquired not only a medical training, but a grasp of the spirit of scientific adventure. He returned home at the close of the war and gained immediate recognition.

The Harvard Medical School was being organized, and in 1783 he became its first professor of medicine (Professor of the Theory and Practice of Physic). He was elected in 1782 to the Board of Fellows of the young College of Rhode Island, then struggling to re-establish itself after the blow that had almost killed it in infancy; and he generously served as professor of natural history without salary while it fought its way back to a healthy existence (1784-1791).[7]

Harvard is frequently credited with

the *first* professor of natural history: William D. Peck appointed in 1805; but Waterhouse was appointed at Brown twenty-two years earlier, and Smallwood points out[8] that, in 1757, Daniel Treadwell was appointed professor of mathematics and natural history at Columbia (then King's College) though no record that he actually taught natural history has been found. The information presented here was uncovered in an attempt to discover exactly what Waterhouse did as professor of natural history at the College of Rhode Island.

The professorship at Brown did not hinder Waterhouse's work at the Harvard Medical School, in spite of the lack of fast commuting trains. The daily teaching of the students at Brown was conducted by the tutors who heard regularly recitations from textbooks specified by the Fellows and Trustees in the "Laws" of the College.[9] Those who today decry the evils of the lecture system might well study the depths to which the tutorial system can sink and the reasons great efforts were made to substitute for it courses of lectures by scholarly men.

It appears that the services of Dr. Waterhouse consisted in giving a course of lectures just before commencement time of the years 1786 and 1787.[10] By opening them to the public, presumably for a fee, and by giving them in the court-house (now the old State House) which was more convenient to the public than the college edifice, he was apparently able to acquire a salary to defray at least part of his expenses in attending commencement as a member of the Board of Fellows. I have not been able to find any indication that he did anything else in his professorial rôle, but this alone was a highly significant event, for he himself asserts, in his book

H E A D S

O F A

COURSE of LECTURES,

INTENDED AS

An INTRODUCTION to NATURAL HISTORY.

By B. WATERHOUSE, M. D. *Professor of the Theory and Practice of Physic in the UNIVERSITY OF CAMBRIDGE, and of Natural History in the COLLEGE OF RHODE-ISLAND.*

METHOD is the Soul of Science: by it a confused Heap of Facts may be so ranged and disposed, that the Judgment may act with Freedom, and perform its Office with Advantage. After the Subject of an Enquiry is fixed on, it should be divided into particular Heads; then the Order of the Things themselves are to be ranged and digested into the Form of a regular Table, so that the Mind may act upon them in just Order and with Regularity; *the Whole to be so constructed as to admit of being transposed, added to, or corrected.* (See Novum Organa.)

It is difficult to ascertain the exact Order in which these Lectures may be delivered; and yet, as the Hearers may wish to have some Idea of what is intended, the following Sketch is given of the Matter, and of the Order in which these Lectures will most probably be given.

CURIOSITY, or the Desire of Knowledge, is as natural to us as Reason—exerts itself with particular Vivacity in Youth.—The Difference in the Minds of Men, not so much the Effect of Organization as Education. The *Aptitude* to Understanding is a dead Power in Man, when not vivified by Passions. What Form of Government, and at what Period most favourable to Learning.

How the Sciences were first taught by Signs and Symbols—Importance of a Clue to the Fables and Allegories of the Antients, they having *Nature* for their Basis.—How the Symbols of Ideas came to be taken for Ideas themselves;—Truth came mixed with Falshood,—human Things with Divine.

Distribution of Knowledge into particular Sciences—PHILOSOPHY divided into the Doctrine of the *Deity*—of *Nature*—and of *Man.*

An Account of some of the Grecian Philosophers—of the Inundation of the *Goths*—of *Mahomet's* Conquests, and their Consequences—of the Revival, or Resurrection of Letters.

Elogium on FRIAR BACON.

The Discovery of the ARS ARTIUM OMNIUM CONSERVATRIX, the *Art of Printing:*

Of the *two Systems* of PHILOSOPHY prevalent at this Period, viz. the Philosophy of *Aristotle,* and the Philosophy of *Plato.*

Concerning simple Matter—its astonishing Divisibility—the infinite Divisibility of Matter, a mathematical Truth, but a physical Falshood?—What led some Philosophers to believe that all Nature was animated. The imperceptible Translations of inert Matter to organized; from a vegetating Body to the lowest Order of Animals.

Of the ZOOPHYTES, or that Class of Beings which connects animated and insensible Nature.

On the SCALE of BEINGS. Do the two Tribes of organized Beings, viz. Animals and Vegetables, form (instead of two distinct Kingdoms) *one immense Family?*

The UNIVERSE—a System whose very Essence consists in *Subordination.*

SYSTEMA NATURÆ of LINNÆUS briefly explained.

The Animal produced by a Cutting, as in the *Zoophytes,* is but *one Degree* above a Vegetable—that produced from an Egg, is a *Step higher;* that Class of Animals, which is brought forth alive, *still more exalted;* and of these such as bring forth *One* at a Time the *most complete*—the foremost of which stands the great *Master of all*—MAN.

The *Universe* affords nothing so deserving our Consideration and Wonder as OURSELVES.

MAN includes within himself all the Powers and Qualities of Nature. The Knowledge of him reduced to six Heads—(1.) Physiologice, (2.) Dietetice, (3.) Pathologice, (4.) Naturaliter, (5.) Politice, and (6.) Theologice.—"*Hæc si noveris* HOMO *es, et a reliquis animalibus, distinstissimum genus.*" LINNÆUS.

The Doctrine of Man divided into the Doctrine of the *Body,* and of the *Mind*—and the Doctrine of the *Union.*

MAN is a Being compounded of *Body, Spirit* and *Soul;* or *Corpus, Vis attinens, et Mens.*

Wide Distinctions made in the Dignity and Perfection of Animals, little or none in their Happiness. Concerning the various Degrees of *Perfection, Beauty, Strength* and *Understanding.*

In all Animals, whose Individuals rise little above the Rest of their Species, Knowledge is *Instinctive;* in Man, whose Individuals are so widely different, it is acquired, by *Education.*

Of the VIS MEDICATRIX NATURÆ so famous in the Schools of Medicine.

The simplest Idea of a *Disease,* and the *natural* Method of its Cure.

A View of the Date and *Quæstio,* in the Art of Physic.

Where did *Hippocrates* and other *Princes* of the Art study?—Wherever there were Men, and the Concomitants of Humanity, Diseases and Death,—AIR, EARTH, and WATER, all that surrounded them were the Pages they studied.

Concerning the important Process of Digestion. All the Food used by Mankind consists of farinaceous, or mucilaginous vegetable Substances,—or native vegetable Acid,—or Sugar,—or expressed Oil—or animal Solids—or animal Fluids, containing a mucilaginous Matter—all traced ultimately to *Vegetables* and *Water.*

A View of the TERRAQUEOUS GLOBE. Of the *Circulation* between the *Ocean*—the *Atmosphere,* and *Earth.*—The whole terraqueous Globe, Sea as well as Land, together with the whole Region of the Atmosphere, happily contrived to afford us sweet and running Waters, all of which have a Reference to the original Food of Man, VEGETABLES.

VEGETATION traced from the *Sowing of the Seed* to the Formation of the Root—the TRUNK—the BRANCH—the FLOWER—the FRUIT—and last of all the Seed *again.*

Of the great Importance of AGRICULTURE to this Country at *this Period.* Agriculture gives the only Riches we can call our own; from the *upper Layer* of Earth all vital Blessings are continued with unceasing Circulation; from it Man receives a Reward of his honest Industry by a Kind of perpetual Miracle! Why the Antients adopted the Phrase MOTHER EARTH.

The Advantages of LABOUR—kindly imposed upon us by an indulgent CREATOR as the best Means of preserving our *Health*—our *Safety*—and our *Innocence.* On the superior Wisdom of the *Chinese* to any Nation yet known.

THE GREAT BOOK of NATURE comprehends the Objects of every Science—how construed by the ancient MAGI. Analogy between Things material and intellectual.

On that unceasing Change—that Renovation, and perpetual Series of Revolutions which all Things undergo! REASON and INSTINCT compared—Reason is a self-improving Power or Faculty of the Mind.

INSTINCT is that *Discretion,* which in different Degrees is diffused through every Animal, directing them to choose what is good, and to avoid what would be destructive to them. It attains its Perfections at once, and is most apparent when Reason is weakest.

HUMANITY TO BRUTES.—Concerning the uncivilized Tribes of Men, and Nations distinguished for polished Humanity.—The nearer Man approaches to a State of Nature, the more a cruel Disposition predominates—exemplified in *Savages* and *Children.*

All true *Dignity, Power* and *Pleasure,* derived from *superior Knowledge* or *Cultivation of the Mind.* TEACHERS of YOUTH held in the highest Estimation among the wise Antients—and why—

"Would you prevent CRIMES? let LIBERTY be attended with KNOWLEDGE." (*Beccaria.*)

CONCLUSION.

FIG. 2. BROADSIDE ANNOUNCING WATERHOUSE'S LECTURES AT HARVARD UNIVERSITY.
(In the Library of the Rhode Island Historical Society.)

HEADS

Of a Course of Lectures on NATURAL HISTORY, given annually (since 1788) in the University of Cambridge, by B. WATERHOUSE, M. D. Professor of the Theory and Practice of Physic, and Lecturer on Natural History.

A private man may love the seeds of Science, but public Benefactions must water them. LORD BACON.

UT SPARGAM.

I. INTRODUCTION. The difference between *talents*, and knowledge acquired by *education* ...

II. METHOD, the soul of Science ...

III. HISTORY or PHILOSOPHY from *Pythagoras* to the destruction of learning by the *Goths, Vandals*, and *Mahometans* ...

IV. On the PRIMARY MATTER; or that which is constantly changing *out* of and into all the various forms of Nature. Illustrations.

V. A *glance* of the UNIVERSE. Sketch of the most celebrated theories of the Earth, viz. *Burnet's, Woodward's, Whiston's* and *Buffon's*.

VI. View of the TERRAQUEOUS GLOBE ...

VII. On WATER, and the *circulation* of it between the *salt* Ocean, the ATMOSPHERE and the EARTH ...

VIII. BOTANY. The *anatomy* of a full grown plant ...

IX. On the GRAND PRINCIPLES or AGRICULTURE ...

X. The LINNÆAN SYSTEM or BOTANY, briefly explained ...

XI. The ANIMAL KINGDOM ...

XII. CLASSIFICATION of *Animals*, by *Aristotle, Gesner, Aldrovandus, Ray* and LINNÆUS. *Pennant, Latham* and *Shaw*, recommended.

XIII. On INSECTS; Their surprising structure ...

XIV. On the *relative perfection*, or SCALE OF BEINGS ...

XV. MAN; placed at the top of the *rear*; or *visible* series of creation ...

XVI. In all animals, whole individuals rise little above the rest of their species ...

XVII. MINERALOGY. The contents of the earth but little known ...

XVIII. The MINERALOGICAL SCHOOLS of *Sweden, Germany*, and *France*. Definition of a metal ...

XIX. ANALOGY between things *material*, and *intellectual* ...

XX. The French *System de la Nature* opposed by arguments drawn from *Newton, Clarke, Cicero* ...

* See Locke on Human Understanding.

[Printed at the UNIVERSITY PRESS in CAMBRIDGE, by W. HILLIARD.]

FIG. 2. BROADSIDE ANNOUNCING WATERHOUSE'S LECTURES AT HARVARD UNIVERSITY.
(In the John Hay Library, Brown University.)

"The Botanist" that this was the first course of lectures on natural history given in any college in America.

be evident to anyone familiar with the history of biology in the late eighteenth century.

FIG. 3. TICKET TO WATERHOUSE'S LECTURES AT BROWN UNIVERSITY.
(In the Library of the Rhode Island Historical Society.)

It is futile to claim "firsts" or to quibble about them. It has been pointed out to me that lectures on botany had previously been given in the College of Philadelphia.[11] While botany is obviously a phase of natural history, it would be absurd to compare lectures on materia medica, or on plant collecting and classification, with the comprehensive course of lectures outlined in Dr. Waterhouse's broadsides. A course of lectures given today with the same outline would be a liberal education in the natural sciences even for the modern student. That Dr. Waterhouse was familiar with the best thought in the biological sciences of the time, and was thoroughly aware of the significance of the advances that were being made will

There are two broadsides, the first in the possession of the Rhode Island Historical Society, the second in the John Hay Library at Brown University containing "Heads of a course of Lectures on Natural History." The one in the Historical Society Library was published in Providence and represents the outline of the course as presented here.

The other broadside says that the lectures were "given annually (since 1788) in the University of Cambridge." But our copy has written on it apparently in Dr. Waterhouse's own handwriting, "First delivered in Providence." The botanical parts of the lectures were later (1811) published as a book, "The Botanist," the Brown University Library copy of which is inscribed, "For the Library of Brown University from the author"—apparently in the same handwriting. In the close the day after commencement, and be delivered in the court-house as more convenient to the inhabitants than the college."

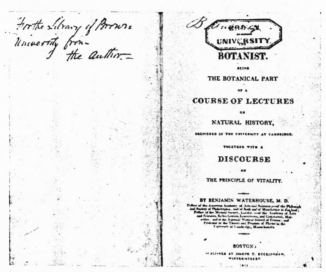

FIG. 4. TITLE PAGE OF THE COPY OF WATERHOUSE'S BOOK "THE BOTANIST." (In the John Hay Library, Brown University.)

preface of this book he says: "There had never been any lectures on Natural History in the United States prior to the course referred to. Neither had Botany nor Mineralogy been publickly taught in any part of the Union anterior to the year 1788; excepting, indeed, a short course of twelve lectures on Natural History in general, given by the author in the college at Providence, in the years 1786 and 1787; he being, at the same time, Professor of the Theory and Practice of Physic in the University at Cambridge."

In the *Providence Gazette* for August 19, 1786, the following announcement appeared:

"Dr. Waterhouse, Professor of Natural History of Rhode Island College, intends to open his lectures next Monday evening at seven o'clock. They will

In the issue of September 9, following the account of commencement, which was held September 6th, this item appears:

"Wednesday evening Dr. Waterhouse, Professor of Natural History in the College of Rhode Island, completed for the present season his course of pleasing and instructive lectures, which were attended by large and very respectable audiences."

In these "very respectable audiences" must have been some of the most substantial citizens, for the Rhode Island Historical Society possesses a ticket printed on the back of a playing card and issued to John Howland, who later was to play a leading part in the establishment of the public school system of Providence. The number 35 on the ticket may serve at least as a minimal basis from which to estimate the size of the audiences.

Parsons' comment on the broadsides

foreign plants. The latter is discussed in "The Botanist" (p. 165) which purports to be the botanical part of his lec-

FIG. 5. THE COURT HOUSE, NOW CALLED THE OLD STATE HOUSE, ON NORTH MAIN STREET IN PROVIDENCE, WHERE WATERHOUSE GAVE HIS LECTURES ON NATURAL HISTORY.

is as follows: [They indicate] "more study of books than of nature at first hand, and more disposition to wander over a sea of varied suggestions than to the condensed and systematic statement of facts and principles."[12] I am not sure that this criticism is justified. The nature of his audience, if made up of townspeople as well as of students, would demand a treatment that might seem superficial to us. The lecture on the Hortus Siccus and how to make one (i.e. an herbarium of dried plants) seems close enough to nature. Furthermore the accounts of the difficulties he encountered later in the use of the Philosophy Chamber of Harvard, as told by Lane,[13] indicate that his minerals and stuffed birds were a nuisance. He had known the Redwood Garden in Newport and Fothergill's Garden in London to which were imported many

tures. He himself started the first Botanical Garden in Cambridge and among other things imported the Lombardy poplar.[14] His extensive efforts in building the mineralogy collection are also told by Lane. He obviously had a knowledge of the natural history collections in Europe and at one time advised the Redwood Library people to start a museum.[15] So, in addition to the book-learning so obviously displayed in the broadsides, he must have had better than a passing acquaintance with nature herself.

Whether or not his own assertion that these were the first natural history lectures in America will stand, matters little. It does seem important that they were given, for they indicate a lively interest in science even in such a primarily commercial community as Providence.

There are, indeed, many other indications of this interest. Two years before Waterhouse's lectures a Dr. Moyes of Edinburgh gave a series of lectures on "Philosophical Chemistry, or rather on what may be called the philosophy of nature" in the Providence State House. This was a course of twenty-one lectures for which the audience paid one guinea. They were "illustrated and confirmed by a variety of experiments," and "may be deemed a complete introduction to the study of Natural History, and will exhibit an accurate view of all those astonishing discoveries which must forever distinguish the eighteenth century."[16] If the lecturer attempted to cover completely the topics outlined in the pamphlet "containing the Heads of the Lectures" in the John Carter Brown Library, his advertisement was no idle boast! These lectures were given about commencement time of 1784, that is, at about the time Waterhouse volunteered his services as professor of natural history, which were to eventuate only in a similar series of lectures in succeeding years. Waterhouse had been elected a fellow of the College in 1782 and would have been present at the corporation meeting which was always held at commencement time.[17] If the lectures of Dr. Moyes were much talked of he may even have attended one or more of them. At any rate, it seems possible that the lectures of Dr. Moyes, which "afforded the highest entertainment as well as pleasing instruction, to large and respectable assemblies"[18] and must therefore have given him a good income, may have served as an inspiration to the action of Dr. Waterhouse. That interest in such lectures did not wane after Dr. Waterhouse's time is shown by a broadside in the possession of the John Carter Brown Library. It is dated June 24, 1790, and announces "a course of Lectures upon Natural Philosophy and Astronomy" to be given by the Reverend Peres Fobes, Professor of Natural and Experimental Philosophy in Rhode Island College—the successor of Dr. Waterhouse.

REFERENCES

1. KRUMBHAAR, E. B. Doctor William Hunter of Newport. *Ann. Surg.*, 101: 506, 1935.
2. THACHER, J. American Medical Biography. Boston, 1828, p. 305.
3. DROWNE, S. Manuscript diary in John Hay Library, Brown University.
4. DEXTER, F. B. The Literary Diary of Ezra Stiles. New York, 1901, vol. I, p. 278.
5. PARSONS, C. W. Some Early Votaries of Natural Science in Rhode Island. Collections of the Rhode Island Historical Society, VII:241, 1885, p. 259.
6. HALSEY, R. H. How the President, Thomas Jefferson, and Doctor Benjamin Waterhouse Established Vaccination as a Public Health Procedure. History of Medicine Series, Library of the New York Acad. of Med. No. 5, 1936.
7. GUILD, R. The Early History of Brown University. Providence, 1897.
8. SMALLWOOD, W. M., and SMALLWOOD, M. S. C. Natural History and the American Mind. New York, 1941, p. 288.
9. The Laws of Rhode Island College enacted by the Fellows and Trustees. Providence, Printed by J. Carter, 1793, p. 6.
10. I have found actual records only for 1786, other than his own statements.
11. MULHERN, J. A History of Secondary Education in Pennsylvania. Philadelphia, 1933, p. 170.
12. PARSONS, C. W. *Loc. cit.*
13. LANE, W. C. Dr. Benjamin Waterhouse and Harvard University. The Cambridge Historical Society Publications, 1909, vol. 4, p. 5.

14. THAYER, W. R. Extracts from the Journal of Benjamin Waterhouse (p. 35). The Cambridge Historical Society Publications, 1909, vol. 4, p. 22.
15. PARSONS, C. W. *Loc cit.*, p. 261.
16. An advertisement in the *Providence Gazette*, Sept. 4, 1784.
17. On the same page of the *Providence Gazette*, Sept. 4, 1784, as the above advertisement, appears the notice of the corporation meeting, held Sept. 1st, and stating among other things that "Benjamin Waterhouse, M.D. of the University at Leyden, and Professor of the Theory and Practice of Physic in the University at Cambridge (in America) was elected Professor of Natural History."
18. News item in *Providence Gazette*, Sept. 11, 1784.

EDWARD JENNER
AND
HARVARD UNIVERSITY

I. Bernard Cohen

Edward Jenner and Harvard University

THIS year we celebrate the two-hundredth anniversary of the birth of Edward Jenner, famous in the annals of medical history for the introduction of smallpox vaccination. It is altogether fitting that a commemorative note should appear in this journal because Harvard University granted Jenner an honorary LL.D. in 1803 — the first honorary degree to be conferred on Jenner by an institution of higher learning anywhere in the world.[1] The text of Jenner's diploma and his letter acknowledging the degree are published below for the first time, and various memorabilia of Jenner at Harvard are described.

Thomas Jefferson's appraisal of Jenner's discovery still stands without need of revision after one hundred and fifty years and serves as a fitting introduction. In a letter to Jenner, Jefferson declared:

I have received the copy of the evidence at large respecting the discovery of the vaccine inoculation, which you have been pleased to send me, and for which I return you my thanks. Having been among the early converts in this part of the globe to its efficacy, I took an early part in recommending it to my countrymen. I avail myself of this occasion to render you my portion of the tribute of gratitude due to you from the whole human family. Medicine has never before produced any single improvement of such utility. Harvey's discovery of the circulation of the blood was a beautiful addition to our knowledge of the ancient economy; but on a review of the practice of medicine before and since that epoch, I do not see any great amelioration which has been derived from that discovery. You have erased from the calendar of human afflictions one of its greatest. Yours is the comfortable reflection that mankind can never forget that you have lived; future nations will know by history only that the loathsome small-pox has existed, and by you has been extirpated. Accept the most fervent wishes for your health and happiness, and assurances of the greatest respect and consideration.[2]

The award of an honorary degree to Jenner was voted by the President and Fellows of Harvard College on 29 April 1803. The vote was

[1] According to the 'Chronological List of Diplomas, Honours, Addresses and Various Communications from Public Bodies and Distinguished Individuals to Dr. Jenner, on the Discovery of Vaccination,' printed as Appendix No. I to John Baron, *The Life of Edward Jenner* (London, 1838), II, 449 ff.

[2] Letter dated 14 May 1806, printed in Baron, *op. cit.*, II, 94–95.

read at a meeting of the Overseers on 3 May, and on 28 July the latter body 'voted to concur.' The text of the degree in the original Latin and a translation follow:

Senatus Universitatis Harvardianae, Cantabrigiensis, in Republica Massachusettensi, ad quos literae praesentes pervenerint; salutem in Domino sempiternam.

Cum eum in finem Gradus Academici instituti fuerint ut viri disciplina, sapientia et virtute insignes et bene de republica meriti honoribus laureatis remunerentur, maxime decet quod huiusmodi honore afficiatur Edvardus Jenner, M.D., R.S.S. etc. Britannus, vir ingenio perspicaci indutus, artis medendi anatomiae et physiologiae jamdudum praeclarus, nuperrime vero Vaccinae Variolae insitionem sagacissime investigando, qua Variolarum morbus, iste generis humani perditor, exterminetur, celebratissimus; qui non solum medicinae cognitionem altam adeptus est, sed etiam literas scientiasque illas acquisivit, quae viros et exornant, et utiles reddunt.

Notum igitur esto quod Nos Praeses et Socii, consentientibus Honorandis admodum ac Reverendis Universitatis antedictae Inspectoribus, praefatum Edvardum Jenner M.D. R.S.S. etc. juris utriusque, tum naturae et gentium, tum civilis Doctorem creavimus et constituimus; eique dedimus et concessimus omnia privilegia, dignitates ac honores, quibus, ad istiusmodi Gradum ubicumque gentium evecti ornantur vel ornari debent.

In cujus rei testimonium literis hisce, nostro communi sigillo munits die Augusti XXXI. Anno Salutis humanae MDCCCIII Reique publicae Americanae XXVIII. apposuimus chirographa.

The Governing Body of the University of Harvard, in Cambridge, in the State of Massachusetts, [gives] eternal greeting in the Lord [to all] to whom the present letters may come.

Since Academic Degrees were instituted to the end that men distinguished for learning, wisdom, and virtue and deserving well of the state should be rewarded with laureled honors, it is especially fitting that Edward Jenner, D[octor of] M[edicine], F[ellow of the] R[oyal] S[ociety], etc., [a] British [subject], should be rewarded with an honor of this sort: a man endowed with a penetrating genius, long famous for the art of healing, for anatomy, and for physiology; recently also very well known for his most ingenious research into the implanting of the vaccine of smallpox, by which the disease of smallpox, that destroyer of the human race, may be wiped out; [a man also] who has not only acquired a deep knowledge of medicine but likewise has attained those letters and sciences which both adorn men and make them useful.

Be it known, therefore, that We, the President and Fellows, with the consent of the Honorable and Reverend Overseers of the said University, have created and constituted the afore-mentioned Edward Jenner, M.D., F.R.S., etc., Doctor of both laws, both that of nature and peoples and the civil; and we have given and granted to him all privileges, dignities and honors with which men raised to a Degree of this sort everywhere among peoples are adorned or ought to be adorned.

In evidence of which fact we have affixed [our] signatures to these letters, furnished with our common seal, on the thirty-first day of August in the eighteen-hundred-and-third year of the Salvation of mankind and the twenty-eighth of the American Republic.[3]

Jenner's letter acknowledging the receipt of the diploma is dated 17 March 1805, a year and a half after the degree was awarded. The reason for this delay is a mystery; it could be solved if we knew just how the diploma was sent. Perhaps it was taken to him personally by a courier, in which event there may have been a delay until the courier in question actually arrived in England and was able to meet Jenner.[4] Jenner's letter follows:

Gentlemen:

Your Diploma address'd to me arrived safe and is in my possession. I beg leave to return my sincerest acknowledgements for the high honor you have conferd upon me. The benefits which the Vaccine Inoculation has diffused among Mankind, have induced many public Societies to grant me marks of distinction, all which I value most highly; not only because they are grateful to my own feelings, but because they greatly contribute by the sanction attach'd to them to extend more widely the practice I had the happiness to announce to the World.

Much as I prize every honor which has been shewn me, yet I will acknowledge that yours was more than ordinarily gratifying, both on account of its rarity, and of the high reputation your Society enjoys of never acting from sentiments of favor and unmerited partiality.

I have the honor to be
Gentlemen
your obliged and very
faithful humble
servant
EDWD. JENNER.

Berkeley
  Glostershire
    March 17
      1805
To the Senate of the Harvardian
University of Cambridge
  &c   &c   &c[5]

[3] Both transcription and accompanying translation were made by Professor Mason Hammond of Harvard University. The text was transcribed from the draft of the diploma preserved in the Harvard University Archives in the volume entitled 'Harvard Degrees and Diplomas,' I, 161. Professor Hammond notes: 'In the

It will be noted that Jenner addressed his letter 'To the Senate of the Harvardian University of Cambridge,' a direct translation of the opening phrase of his diploma, 'Senatus Universitatis Harvardianae, Cantabrigiensis.'

Jenner was neither the first person to receive a Harvard honorary degree for scientific work nor the first British subject, after the Revolution, to receive such a degree *in absentia*. In 1803, when Jenner received his LL.D., four persons were awarded an honorary A.M. (Nathaniel Bowen, Elias Hasket Derby, John Sylvester John Gardiner, and Michael Walsh), William Symmes was awarded an honorary S.T.D., Charles Cotesworth Pinckney was awarded an honorary LL.D., as Jenner was, and James Welsh was awarded an A.B. *ad eundem gradum* in accordance with the prevailing custom, long since discontinued, of awarding graduates of other institutions (particularly Bachelors and Masters of Arts) the same degree (*ad eundem gradum*) in Harvard College.

It is questionable whether the honorary degrees awarded in 1692, 1703, 1709, 1710, 1712, 1714, 1720, and 1723 are honorary degrees in the modern sense, the sense in which Jenner was awarded his. Perhaps, therefore, the first true honorary degree awarded by Harvard was Benjamin Franklin's A.M. of 1753, a recognition of his extraordinary achievement in electrical research.[6] The next honorary degree seems to be the A.M. awarded to Justice William Parker in 1763. The first LL.D. in Harvard's history was awarded in 1774 to John Winthrop, Hollis Professor of Mathematics and Natural Philosophy,

---

above, the line divisions of the original are neglected and occasional accents omitted. "Munits" in the last paragraph for "munitis." I would read "omnibus" in the first paragraph before "ad quos," and a comma in paragraph two, after "medendi." '

[4] Possibly the diploma followed a more circuitous route; a courier may have taken it to London, then have given it to some one else to give to Jenner, who probably would not have been in London at the time. While I have not found any statement in the University Archives on this point, a more systematic search of the records might reveal further information. According to Baron 'the Diploma was transmitted by his friend Dr. Waterhouse, and it arrived in England during the spring of 1805' (*op cit.*, II, 33).

[5] Corporation Papers, 1804–1805, in the Harvard University Archives.

[6] For Franklin's degree see William Coolidge Lane, 'Harvard College and Franklin,' *Publications of the Colonial Society of Massachusetts*, X (1907), 229–239, with plates reproducing the diploma, its seal, and its tin box emblazoned with the College arms.

It may be noted that a list of all honorary degrees granted since the foundation of the College may be found in any issue of the *Quinquennial Catalogue*.

Fellow of Harvard College, and one of the most distinguished Harvard men of the eighteenth century. Harvard's second LL.D. was awarded to George Washington in 1776, the eighth to Lafayette in 1784, the thirteenth to Thomas Jefferson in 1787, the twenty-second to Nathaniel Bowditch in 1802, and the twenty-third to Jenner.

This is not the place to record the details of the spread of the practice of vaccination, the opposition to it, and the statistics that show the importance of the discovery: nor even to compare the new practice of vaccination with the slightly older practice of inoculation, or 'variolation,' introduced into America in 1721 by Zabdiel Boylston (aided by Cotton Mather) during Boston's sixth epidemic of smallpox. In vaccination, the patient was given a case of the mild disease, cowpox, which then prevented him from getting smallpox; while in variolation, the patient was given a 'mild' case of smallpox itself.[7] Variolation, while better than no precaution whatever, was a dangerous practice; and it may be recalled that one of the greatest thinkers produced in America during the eighteenth century, Jonathan Edwards, died soon after his election to the presidency of Princeton, following an unsuccessful variolation. By contrast, cowpox vaccination as introduced by Jenner was mild, safe, and sure, if performed with due precautions. Overnight, man was given the opportunity of eradicating from the face of the earth one of the dreadest scourges of the human race; no honor or praise was too great for Jenner.

Edward Jenner (1749–1823), son of a Gloucestershire clergyman, was a pupil and friend of the great London surgeon John Hunter. According to tradition, he made his momentous discovery after learning from a milkmaid of the countryside tradition that women who had contracted the disease cowpox through milking were no longer susceptible to smallpox. Supposedly, several decades of patient and accurate study elapsed before he was ready to put his discovery to the test. However, in actual fact hardly anything is known for certain about Jenner's activities during the early part of his career.[8]

In 1796 he vaccinated a young boy with pus from a human case of

[7] Cf. Arnold C. Klebs, *Die Variolation im achtzehnten Jahrhundert, ein historischer Beitrag zur Immunitätsforschung* (Zur historischen Biologie der Krankheitserreger, VII; Giessen, 1914); also R. H. Fitz, 'Zabdiel Boylston, Inoculator, and the Epidemic of Smallpox in Boston in 1721,' *Bulletin of The Johns Hopkins Hospital*, XXII (1911), 315–327.

[8] Cf. Edgar M. Crookshank, *History and Pathology of Vaccination* (Philadelphia, 1889), I, 131 ff.

cowpox and then tried to inoculate him with smallpox — unsuccess-fully. Convinced of the effect of cowpox vaccination in preventing smallpox, Jenner submitted an account of his work to the Royal Society of London for publication in the _Philosophical Transactions_, but publication was refused.[9] Jenner therefore embodied the results of his work in a small quarto volume published in London in 1798 and entitled _An Inquiry into the Causes and Effects of the Variolae Vaccinae_. Successive tracts recorded further observations and also improvements in technic. In 1802 and 1806, Parliament gave Jenner an official recognition by awarding him grants amounting to £30,000.

The merit of having made as important a discovery as Jenner's did not long go unrewarded. On 25 May 1802, he received his first American honor: a diploma of Fellow of the American Academy of Arts and Sciences signed by John Adams (President of the Academy), Joseph Willard (Vice-President of the Academy), John Davis and John Quincy Adams (Secretaries); and in the following year, he was awarded the honorary LL.D. from Harvard. The Harvard diploma, dated 31 August 1803, as already indicated, was again signed by Joseph Willard (President of Harvard as well as Vice-President of the Academy), and also by Oliver Wendell, Simeon Howard, John Lathrop, Eliphalet Pearson, John Davis, and Ebenezer Storer as members of the Corporation.[10]

The introduction of vaccination into the United States is largely the achievement of Dr Benjamin Waterhouse, 'stormy petrel' of the young Medical School. Waterhouse was one of the first two appointees to the School, his title being Professor of the Theory and Practice of Physic.[11] He had studied medicine in Holland and in

[9] Cf. Cecilia F. Mettler, _History of Medicine_ (Philadelphia, 1948), p. 422. Baron writes, _op. cit._, I, 140, that Jenner's intention was that his work 'should first have appeared before the public in the Transactions of the Royal Society; but this design was abandoned, and the work appeared as a separate publication.' The full story of the rejection of Jenner's paper by the Royal Society, suppressed by Baron and omitted in the account of Jenner in the _DNB_, may be found in Crookshank, _op. cit._, I, 137–138, 250–265.

[10] Baron, _op. cit._, I, 532; II, 450–451.

[11] Cf. Josiah C. Trent, 'Benjamin Waterhouse (1754–1846),' _Journal of the History of Medicine and Allied Sciences_, I (1946), 357–364; 'The London Years of Benjamin Waterhouse,' _idem_, I (1946), 25–40. (At the time of his recent death Dr Trent was writing a full-length biography of Waterhouse; this is being completed and will be published posthumously by Henry Schuman Inc. in the 'Life of Science' series.) A most valuable bibliography of Waterhouse will be found in

England; through his mother's cousin, the famous Quaker physician John Fothergill, he had met a number of the leading British men of medicine, of whom one — John Coakley Lettsom — was to play a most important part in Waterhouse's life and in the development of science and medicine in the United States.

While in London, Waterhouse, under the influence of Fothergill, became interested in the general topic of Natural History. Soon after his return to America, in 1786 and again in 1787, he delivered a series of lectures on Natural History at Brown.[12] He began a similar course at Harvard in 1788 and continued to offer instruction in this subject at Harvard for some two decades, developing his 'interest in Natural History at the expense of his lectures on health and disease.'[13] Indeed, 'the fact is,' Waterhouse wrote to Lettsom on 25 November 1794, 'I have no taste for the practice of physic as it is conducted in this country.'[14] Lettsom not only sent Waterhouse specimens for his Natural History collection, but also fossils and later a collection of minerals which Waterhouse gave to Harvard and which mark the beginning of the present Mineralogical Museum.[15] Waterhouse was soon lecturing on Mineralogy and Geology, the first such instruction to be given in an American college. Harvard acknowledged Lettsom's welcome gifts by awarding him an honorary M.D. in 1790.[16]

The history of vaccination in America begins when Waterhouse received from Lettsom in 1799 a copy of Jenner's book on vaccina-

---

Henry R. Viets: ' "A Journal of a Young Man of Massachusetts, . . . Written by Himself." Boston: 1816, and a Note on the Author,' *Yale Journal of Biology and Medicine*, XII (1940), 605–622. Cf. also Dr Viets's account of Waterhouse in the *Dictionary of American Biography*, and Thomas F. Harrington, *The Harvard Medical School* (New York, 1905), I, *passim*.

[12] Cf. J. Walter Wilson, 'The First Natural History Lectures at Brown University, 1786, by Dr. Benjamin Waterhouse,' *Annals of Medical History*, 3rd ser., IV (1942), 390–398.

[13] S. E. Morison, *Three Centuries of Harvard* (Cambridge, 1936), p. 171.

[14] T. J. Pettigrew, *Memoirs of the Life and Writings of the Late John Coakley Lettsom* (London, 1817), II, 464. The three-volume set of this work in the Harvard College Library formerly belonged to Waterhouse, who has corrected errors in transcription by Pettigrew in the Waterhouse-Lettsom correspondence.

[15] Cf. [John Eliot Wolff], 'The Mineralogical Museum,' *Harvard Alumni Bulletin*, XV (1913), 440–442; also William Coolidge Lane, 'Benjamin Waterhouse and Harvard University,' *Cambridge Historical Society Publications*, IV (1909), 5–22.

[16] Further details on Waterhouse's instruction in Natural History and Mineralogy and the collections begun under his direction will be found in the writer's *Tools of Early Harvard Science* (Harvard University Press, to appear in autumn 1949).

tion. Waterhouse was quick to appreciate its merit and published in the *Columbian Sentinel* of 16 March 1799 a short account of Jenner's work under the title, 'Something Curious in the Medical Line.'[17] In time this was followed by a forty-page quarto work, *A Prospect of Exterminating the Small-Pox . . . with an Account of a Series of Inoculations Performed for the Kine-Pox, in Massachusetts* (Cambridge, Mass., 1800). A supplement was published in 1802, and an abridgment in the same year.[18]

Waterhouse's first 'cow-pox matter' had been obtained from Dr Haygarth of Bristol and derived from Jenner's own stock;[19] it arrived on 4 July 1800. With it he vaccinated his own children and then, in order to demonstrate the success of the vaccination, he had one of them (aged twelve) publicly inoculated with 'small-pox matter' to show that the child would not become infected.[20]

Apparently the new practice received a setback when a sailor aboard a vessel arriving in Marblehead from London, who was thought to be ill with cowpox, had matter taken from him and used extensively; it turned out that the sailor had smallpox, not cowpox, and the disease spread rapidly. Waterhouse felt the need of a surer supply and wrote to Lettsom, urging him to get some fresh 'matter' from Jenner himself, adding: 'a letter from him, should he allow me to publish it or any part of it, might set this benevolent business a-going again next spring. Could I likewise say to the American public that I received matter from Dr. Jenner himself, it would have a very good effect indeed.'[21] Jenner complied with both requests and the 'matter' arrived in the spring of 1801, together with a letter (dated 4 March 1801) containing an explanation of the 'deviations from the regular course of the disease' and rules for the successful practice of vaccination. This letter marked the beginning of the Jenner-Waterhouse correspondence.

In a letter to Lettsom of 22 April 1801, Waterhouse acknowledged 'a packet from Dr. Jenner with *fresh* matter, and a lengthy and most

---

[17] Baron, *op. cit.*, II, 386.

[18] Viets, *Yale Journal of Biology and Medicine*, XII (1940), 620–621, items 5, 5a, 7.

[19] Baron, *op. cit.*, II, 386. Cf. Reginald Fitz, '"Something Curious in the Medical Line,"' *Bulletin of the History of Medicine*, XI (1942), 239–264. According to Fitz, Dr Haygarth came from Bath, and it was a Bath surgeon named Thomas Creaser who prepared threads coated with virus for Waterhouse to use.

[20] Baron, *op. cit.*, II, 386.   [21] *Idem*, II, 388–389.

admirable letter. It was, like his publications, plain and lucid beyond his compeers; displaying that perspicacity and dignified simplicity which is the peculiar ornament of genius. His letter is (excuse my enthusiasm) a ray of light from the East, and oh! that the reflected ray might become more brilliant, and even generative at the point of repercussion . . .' [22] Waterhouse printed Jenner's letter in his second publication on cowpox (1802).[23]

Waterhouse's interest in Jenner's educational background is manifested in another part of his letter of 22 April 1801 to Lettsom: 'I would be gratified to know more of Jenner's personal history. Is he not a son of Oxford, or Cambridge? I have never heard any particulars concerning him; but from his logic, I suspect he is a son of one of them, or else he is like Franklin, one of Nature's own pupils. Some men are destined to follow the rules of colleges, but with others, *rules follow them.*' [24] Waterhouse's alternative suspicion was correct; Jenner was neither a son of Oxford nor of Cambridge.

Waterhouse brought Jenner's achievement to the attention of the American Academy of Arts and Sciences, the organization which gave Jenner his first formal American recognition. That Waterhouse was also instrumental in the conferring of the degree by Harvard may be seen in the following letter sent by Waterhouse to Lettsom on 16 November 1802:

. . . I have sent, by this opportunity, a few pages of my publication on the Kine-pock, to Mr. Ring. The whole will be printed within a month. Every body will approve of the absolute propriety of addressing it to yourself and to Dr. Jenner, when they know that the first intimation I ever had of the cow-pox came from Dr. Lettsom, and that Dr. Jenner has been to me what the *sun* is to the *moon* . . . I shall bear in mind the LL.D. for Dr. Jenner next July. We give degrees but once a year. Dr. Jenner has just sent me a present I highly prize, a silver box inlaid with gold of exquisite taste and workmanship, bearing this inscription "Edward Jenner to Benjamin Waterhouse." But Mr. Ring annexed the superscription in rather an hyperbolical style, "From the Jenner of the Old World to the Jenner of the New World." [25] Long will it remain among the sacrae relictae of my family.[26]

[22] Pettigrew, *op. cit.*, III, 212–213.

[23] Waterhouse's reply to Jenner, acknowledging the gift, is printed in Baron, *op. cit.*, II, 439–443.

[24] Pettigrew, *op. cit.*, III, 213.

[25] John Ring, a surgeon and a collaborator of Jenner's, referred to Waterhouse in his *Treatise on the Cow-Pox* (1801) as 'the Jenner of America.' Cf. Fitz, *Bulletin of the History of Medicine*, XI (1942), 252.

[26] Pettigrew, *op. cit.*, II, 481. Miss Genevieve Miller informs me that Waterhouse

Two years before Jenner received his LL.D. from Harvard, Waterhouse wrote a letter (dated 24 April 1801) to Jenner containing the following postscript:

As the library of this University is by far the largest in the United States, and is the grand deposit of rare and valuable books in this quarter of the world and will long continue so, I cannot resist expressing my wish that a copy of your invaluable book may be deposited there by its author. I presume my motives for wishing this, and hinting it, stand in no need of an apology. By a law of the Commonwealth, an author to secure his copy-right must deposit a copy of his work in this library; and books sent to it come free from duty. This library, museum, and other public rooms are constantly visited by strangers as among the curiosities of the country. When I had the honour of waiting on the Duke of Kent through them, he expressed his surprise at such a collection of books and natural productions in about thirty years, for the small-pox destroyed the chief of what had been collected since 1638: that is to say, it raged in Boston, and the legislature on that account occupied one of the public rooms in the hall, which contained the library; when it by some accident took fire and was, one alcove excepted, totally destroyed. Thanks be to Dr. Jenner, such an accident from such a cause can never happen again.[27]

Did Jenner comply with this request and send to the Harvard College Library a copy of one or more of his works? The silver snuffbox engraved 'Edwd. Jenner to Bn. Waterhouse' is preserved in the Library of the Harvard Medical School, together with a set of Lowestoft china presented by Jenner to Waterhouse, each piece of which has a circular medallion, over which appears a gold script 'W,' with a landscape featuring cows (in token of the discovery and spread of vaccination).[28] But there is no inscribed copy of a book by Jenner in any of the Harvard libraries today, nor any record that Jenner ever sent one.

---

was not the only one of Jenner's followers to receive a snuffbox. Jean de Carro, for example, a Swish physician resident in Vienna who was chiefly responsible for propagating vaccination on the Continent (cf. Baron, *op. cit.*, both vols., *passim*) was also a recipient. A letter from De Carro, addressed to his London friend Dr Alexander Marcet, and describing his joy in receiving the gift from Jenner, may be found in The Johns Hopkins Institute of the History of Medicine.

[27] Baron, *op. cit.*, I, 443.

[28] Both snuffbox and china were given to the Medical School by the Waterhouse family. The china was included in the Tercentenary Exhibition of Furniture, Silver, Pewter, Glass, Ceramics, Paintings, and Prints, and is listed in the *Catalogue* (Cambridge, Mass., 1936) of this exhibition as item 423, with reproduction in plate 66. The Medical School Library also possesses a lock of Jenner's hair, presented by Dr Arthur T. Davies, enclosed in a locket given jointly by Dr Davies and Sir William Osler.

This is surely surprising when one considers the high regard in which Waterhouse was held by Jenner (witness the silver box and the 'vaccination' china, and the fact that Jenner received an honorary degree from Harvard). Furthermore, we know of the general respect for Harvard on the part of Jenner and his close associate Ring (who called Waterhouse the Jenner of America). The latter, in his *Treatise on the Cow-Pox* (volume one, published in 1801), recounted the work of Waterhouse, 'the learned Professor of the Theory and Practice of Physic in the University of Cambridge. This university is situated about three miles from Boston. Here the bright beam that was to illume the realms of Columbia, first dawned. Here the Jenner of America first appeared;

And a new sun in the new world arose.'[29]

According to the old printed catalogues of the Harvard College Library and the available records, no work by Jenner was to be found at Harvard until 1858, when Waterhouse's widow donated a number of works from her late husband's collection. Among these, there is a copy of Jenner's *Origin of the Vaccine Inoculation* (1801) that is of exceptional interest. This work is bound with a copy of the third edition of Jenner's *Inquiry*, and the two *may* have been bound together in Waterhouse's time. Unfortunately, the present binding is of recent date.

One may safely assume that this copy of the *Origin* was a presentation copy from Jenner himself. Facing the title-page there is a watercolor painting of a female arm, holding a rose. On the biceps there was formerly a small piece of sealing wax which must have given the picture a realistic aspect, portraying the arm of a recently vaccinated woman, complete with scab. A banner above the arm, in gold leaf, bears the inscription: '*VACCINE INOCULATION*,' words which also form a portion of the title-page.[30] The book contains no autograph; hence one can not determine whether Jenner sent it (if indeed he did so) to Waterhouse as a personal gift, in the manner of the snuffbox and the china, or to the University which had honored him. Perhaps a discovery of further Jenner-Waterhouse correspondence will cast light on this question.

Among the manuscripts in the Harvard Library, there are two

[29] Quoted in Fitz, *Bulletin of the History of Medicine*, XI (1942), 252.
[30] This water-color is reproduced by Fitz as fig. 5.

further unpublished Jenner letters. One of these (undated) is addressed to his sister Ann, Mrs William Davies, and discusses family matters, chiefly the health of his sister's husband. The other, dated 21 February 1809, is a letter of introduction to an unidentified correspondent, and was written for J. (or I.?) Green, 'a young Man of amiable character' who had 'solicited an introduction . . . to a *Friend* of mine in Calcutta.' The letter reads in part:

Bombay has been good enough to follow the example of my Benefactors in Calcutta, & Madras is about to do the same; at least I hear so, & indeed have seen a List containing some respectable names which open the Contribution. So that the Seed which you so kindly planted, has ramified luxuriantly, & produc'd abundantly.

Our Friend Dr Saunders told me we might ere long expect the pleasure of seeing you in England, a pleasure I should much enjoy. I live as much in retirement in my native Village, Berkeley in Glostershire, as Circumstances will permit. When you return, I should be most happy with a visit from you. Here you may shut out as much of the artificial World as you please, and enjoy it more in the State in which Nature fashioned it.

It will be no news to you to hear that Vaccination goes on most charmingly all the World over. The information I derive from all Quarters allows me to say that wherever it is universally adopted, the Smallpox ceases to exist.[31]

I. BERNARD COHEN

[31] Both letters are preserved in the Autograph File in the Houghton Library. The letter to Mrs Davies was received in 1914 as a part of the Norton autograph collection, while the letter for Green was presented in 1935 by Mayo Tolman.

EDWARD JENNER, BENJAMIN WATERHOUSE,
AND
THE INTRODUCTION OF VACCINATION
INTO THE UNITED STATES

E. Ashworth Underwood

EDWARD JENNER, BENJAMIN WATERHOUSE, AND THE INTRODUCTION OF VACCINATION INTO THE UNITED STATES

By Dr. E. ASHWORTH UNDERWOOD

The Wellcome Historical Medical Museum

THE two-hundredth anniversary of the birth of Edward Jenner, the discoverer of vaccination, was celebrated on Tuesday, May 17, by functions in many places, but notably at Berkeley, Glos, his birthplace, at the Royal College of Physicians, the Royal College of Surgeons—where Sir Edward Mellanby gave an address—and the Wellcome Historical Medical Museum. Much of what can be said—within the limits of an article—on Jenner's life and work has already been said. This present tribute to a man to whom mankind owes so much will therefore be concerned mainly with those aspects of his life and work which have some bearing on the introduction of vaccination into the United States. Although these events are well known in America, the important work which Benjamin Waterhouse did is not fully appreciated in Britain. In this brief article, it is impossible to avoid ground which has already been covered in certain American journals.

Jenner's Early Life

Edward Jenner was born at the Old Vicarage, Berkeley, on May 17, 1749. His father was vicar of Berkeley, and his elder brother Stephen was also in Holy Orders. Edward was apprenticed to a surgeon at Sodbury when he was thirteen, and for the next eight years he had excellent practical experience. When he was twenty-one he became a resident housepupil in the London house of John Hunter, and during the two years while he was a pupil, a friendship developed between Jenner and Hunter, twentyone years his senior. In 1772, when Jenner seemed set for a London career, he succumbed to the lure of his native county—he was essentially a countryman—and returned to practise at Berkeley. There, with brief interludes, he remained the rest of his life. Until Hunter's death in 1793, he and Jenner corresponded regularly, and the elder man constantly encouraged the younger in natural history pursuits, and as constantly requested specimens of the most varied kind. It was early in this correspondence that Hunter gave the famous advice : "But why think, why not try the experiment ?"[1]. This encouragement resulted ultimately in Jenner's admirable paper on the habits of the cuckoo[2], in which he described the method whereby the young cuckoo clears the nest of its foster-parent. Often discredited, this work has been completely vindicated in recent years.

Jenner and the Concept of Vaccination

Baron says[3]—probably with truth—that the idea that cowpox could confer protection against subsequent infection with smallpox first entered Jenner's mind when, as an apprentice at Sodbury, he heard a young countrywoman say when smallpox was mentioned in her presence : "I cannot take that disease, for I have had cow-pox". He certainly reflected on this statement, and in later years he was impressed by the fact that, when he was inoculating smallpox matter for 'protective' purposes, the operation was unsuccessful in those who had previously had cowpox.

The principle of inoculation was that the individual was given what was hoped would be a mild attack at a convenient time, and was thereby protected against a natural attack of the disease, which was often severe and loathsome, and fatal in as many as 50 per cent of the cases. This practice was introduced by Timoni (1714) and Pylarini (1715) ; but the effective agent in popularizing it was Lady Mary Wortley Montagu (1721). By Jenner's day it was a common practice. It was a bad method, since the resulting disease was often not mild, and sometimes caused death. · Further, each inoculated person acted as a focus for the dissemination of true smallpox.

To return to Jenner. He was well aware of the fact that cowpox was found only in certain counties in Britain, and moreover was present only at intervals. Smallpox, on the other hand, was possibly worst in London, where at that time it was causing a rough average of two thousand deaths annually. Natural cowpox would therefore not be very effective in preventing smallpox in a crowded city where only a few people handled cows. On the other hand, if he could show that cowpox occurring naturally in man could then be transmitted from one individual to another without losing its power to protect against smallpox, there would be no limit to the number of individuals who could be protected. These were the two propositions which Jenner set out to test experimentally, and the results were set out in his "Inquiry into the Causes and Effects of the Variolæ Vaccinæ, a disease discovered in some of the Western Counties of England . . . and known by the name of the Cow Pox". This small book was published in the summer of 1798, and two further editions were published later. I have given elsewhere[4] a critical statement of the genesis and reasoning of this book, and it must suffice to state here that, though the cases were few, they did form a prima facie case.

Events Following Publication

After publication of the "Inquiry", Jenner went to London to seek volunteers for vaccination ; but though he stayed there three months he was unsuccessful. Vaccination in London was popularized by Henry Cline, who started with some lymph which Jenner gave him ; by Dr. Woodville, of the Smallpox Hospital, and by Dr. George Pearson. It was soon evident that Woodville and Pearson were planning to take the whole credit for the introduction of vaccination ; but Jenner's equanimity enabled him to stem the tide. Vaccination was soon widely practised in Britain. Various contretemps occurred, many of which Jenner had foreseen. In May 1799, De Carro introduced vaccination to Vienna, and German cities soon followed. In January 1800, the "Inquiry" was translated into French, and was published in Paris soon afterwards[5]. It should be remembered that Britain was then at war with France—which explains the delay. Vaccination spread from France to Spain during the latter part of 1800, and it was soon widely practised in most European countries. From the very time when the announcement of the discovery was first made, the emphasis was always on *free* vaccination. By the end of 1799 various attempts had been made in provincial cities to form "institutions for gratuitous inoculation", that is, vaccination'. In London, Pearson formed a vaccine board, which was to carry out free vaccination. As early as September 1798, Jenner had been pressed by Henry Cline and Sir Walter Farquhar to take a house in Grosvenor Square ; they promised him £10,000 per annum. He declined, and in a letter to a friend at this time he wrote :

"Shall I, who even in the morning of my days sought the lowly and sequestered paths of life, the valley, and not the mountain ; shall I, now my evening is fast approaching, hold myself up as an object for fortune and for fame ?—Admitting it as a certainty that I obtain both, what stock should I add to my little fund of happiness ?

"My fortune, with what flows in from my profession, is sufficient to gratify my wishes ; indeed so limited is my ambition and that of my nearest connexions, that were I precluded from future practice I should be enabled to obtain all I want. And as for fame what is it ? a gilded butt, for ever pierced with the arrows of malignancy"[8].

Introduction of Vaccination to the United States

The fact that vaccination was introduced into the United States by Benjamin Waterhouse is stated briefly in all works dealing with the history of vaccination. Baron, writing in 1838, had quite a lot to say about the event. But though the. work of Waterhouse was recognized in most parts of America and abroad, in Boston, where he spent all his active life, he was half-forgotten. This was due to the fact that he was never popular with the other members of the profession at Boston and Harvard. He was a Quaker, an active controversialist, an opponent of the political party in power, and at heart a scientific man who had perforce to practise medicine. It was the publication of the paper "Waterhouse, the Jenner of America", by William H. Welch, in 1885, that really placed him in his proper place[9]. Welch gives all the relative facts, but for a true appreciation of the various difficulties encountered we must go to Waterhouse's own publications on vaccination[10,11]. These, like other early vaccination tracts, are now very rare. First let us look at the man.

Dr. Benjamin Waterhouse

Benjamin Waterhouse was born in Newport, Rhode Island, on March 4, 1754. His mother was a niece of John Fothergill, the famous London physician, and in due course Waterhouse studied under Fothergill. He also took courses at Edinburgh and for four years at Leyden, where he graduated in 1781. After assisting his uncle for a time he returned to practise in Newport, Rhode Island, in June 1782. A medical college was then being inaugurated in association with Harvard College, and Waterhouse was invited to take the chair of the theory and practice of medicine. He was the first in America to give a systematic course of instruction in botany and mineralogy, and he founded the Botanical Gardens at Cambridge, Mass.. and the collection of mineralogy at Harvard. Despite these advances, his unpopularity and the acrimonious disputes in which he was involved led to him being deprived of his chair in 1812. He died at Cambridge. on October 2, 1846.

Benjamin Waterhouse
From Lettsom's "Hints", vol. 3 (1801)

In the beginning of 1799 Waterhouse received from his friend John Coakley Lettsom. in London a copy of Jenner's "Inquiry". Waterhouse says that the disease cowpox was totally unknown in that part of the world. He goes on : "On perusing this work, I was struck with the unspeakable advantages that might accrue to this country, and indeed to the human race at large, from the discovery of a mild distemper that would ever after secure the constitution from that terrible scourge, the small-pox"[10]. Soon after, he received a copy of George Pearson's book on vaccination, and he sent to the *Columbian Centinel* of March 12, 1799, a short account of the method under the title "Something Curious in the Medical Line". He reprints this article in the first part of his "Prospect"[10]. He says that he wrote the article to direct the attention of the dairy farmers to the existence of cowpox. A few weeks later he showed Jenner's book at a meeting of the American Academy of Arts and Sciences. The president of the United States, John Adams, was at the meeting and was much interested[12]. Waterhouse conceived it his duty. considering his official position in the University, to give the matter a trial. After several unsuccessful attempts to obtain cowpox matter from England. Waterhouse succeeded in getting some from Dr. Haygarth of Bath—this lymph having come from Jenner's stock. With this matter he vaccinated seven members of his own family, and thereafter he invited Dr. Aspinwall, the physician to the smallpox hospital. to inoculate them with smallpox virus. The test was quite successful, though all were not inoculated. He then says that he had laboured to collect all the evidence on this subject, and to lay it "before the American public, in so plain and simple a manner, as to require no other preparation for its admission than common sense and an unprejudiced mind"[10]. Waterhouse had obviously been receiving requests for vaccine matter from professional men. and in an

Lyman Spalding
From J. A. Spalding

appendix to the first part of his "Prospect", which is dated from Cambridge, August 18, 1800, he writes : "To those of the faculty who have applied to him by letter *to supply them with matter for inoculation* —He would just observe, that as he has taken much pains in this business, run no small risk of reputation, as well as of personal feelings, there are *few* he trusts, that will wonder he is anxious to have the matter under his own eye until the practice is more firmly established by the public opinion. Some unsuccessful cases at the beginning, deprived Scotland of the blessing of inoculation for the small-pox for more than 20 years. He hopes this idea will operate as an excuse at present, even in the minds of his *ci-devant* pupils.

"Dr. Waterhouse informs those who have applied to him out of Cambridge, to inoculate their families, that he declined it only until the disorder had gone fairly through his own family, and until some of them had been inoculated by Dr. Aspinwall, and otherwise exposed to the small-pox. But having now confirmed his assertion, *that the kine-pox protects the constitution from the infection of the small-pox*, by a fair experiment, he is ready to attend them whenever they choose. Those who live in Boston, may rest assured, that from the proximity of his residence to the capital, he shall make such arrangements as to be able to attend them as punctually as if he resided there."

In Part 2 of his "Prospect", published in 1802, Waterhouse says that by September 1, 1800, he had vaccinated about fifty persons. The public attention was now fairly excited, and he was embarrassed by numerous applications for vaccine. But soon everybody believed that the operation of arm-to-arm vaccination was a simple matter and could be performed by anyone. Gone was Jenner's advice on the correct stage of the vesicle for the withdrawal of

lymph ; gone also were Waterhouse's own injunctions. Women and children were encouraged to inoculate each other, and by the autumn of 1800 there was a traffic in cowpox matter by non-professional persons. Waterhouse says : "I have known the shirt sleeve of a patient, stiff with the purulent discharge from a foul ulcer, made so by unskillful management, and full three weeks after vaccination, and in which there could have been none of the specific virus ; I have known this cut up into small strips, and sold about the country as genuine kine-pock matter, and coming directly from me. Several hundred people were inoculated with this caustic morbid poison, which produced great inflammation, sickness, fever, and in several cases *eruptions*, with a greater disturbance of the system than what occurs in the true disease. It is worthy of remark, that I could not influence these people to believe that they had *not* passed through the true disease, and that they were *not* secure from the small-pox."

At Marblehead a vessel arrived from London having aboard a sailor supposed to have cowpox. Matter was taken from him and distributed widely, and many cases of smallpox resulted. However, in the winter of 1801, Waterhouse obtained new matter from England, and advice from Jenner. As a result, the practice of vaccination was successfully established in Massachusetts.

Waterhouse always regarded Jenner with the greatest admiration and respect. It is worthy of note that, in a letter which he wrote to Jenner on April 24, 1801 [13], Waterhouse tells of the transmission of smallpox to cows. At one of the inoculation hospitals—where smallpox matter was used—several persons drove their cows to the neighbourhood, so that they could be milked for their families in the hospital. The milking was done by persons in all stages of the smallpox. The cows developed eruptions on their teats and udders, "so like the small-pox pustule, that every one in the hospital, as well as the physician who told me, declared the cows had the small-pox".

Dr. Lyman Spalding

During the early stages, when Waterhouse was receiving many requests for vaccine lymph, he had correspondence with Dr. Lyman Spalding. Most of this correspondence was published in a biography of Spalding by his grandson [14]. Some of it has also been re-published, notably by Leikind [15]. As the originals of two of these letters are now in the Wellcome Collection, and as this story is virtually unknown in Britain, they are re-printed here in facsimile. They illustrate an amusing incident, which was perhaps unavoidable in the social atmosphere of that time, but which is not at all representative of Waterhouse's character and of the great work which he did for vaccination and American medicine.

Lyman Spalding [16,17], the originator of the United States Pharmacopœia, was born in Cornish, New Hampshire, on June 5, 1775. As a boy he attracted the attention of Dr. Nathan Smith, who finally had him sent to the Harvard Medical School. He was a pupil of Waterhouse, and graduated in 1797. He assisted Smith in the foundation of the Dartmouth Medical School in 1797, and he gave the first course of chemical lectures when the school was opened. He then studied medicine and practised at Portsmouth, New Hampshire. There he printed yearly bills of mortality, and sent them to the leaders of the profession in America and in Europe. He was well known

(a) Letter from Waterhouse to Spalding
Original in the Wellcome Historical Medical Museum (39826·1)

as an anatomist and a surgeon, and he was the first in America to inject the lymphatics. In 1810 he was invited to lecture at the Fairfield Medical School in New York State, and in 1813 he became president of the institution. He now established himself in New York City. Even in 1815 he had the idea of a national pharmacopœia ; but it was not until 1820 that he was able to reconcile conflicting interests, and the first edition was published in that year. Spalding died as the result of an accident on October 21, 1821.

Letters in the Wellcome Collection

The two letters to which I referred are reproduced here in facsimile. The texts are as follows :

(b) Letter from Spalding to Waterhouse
Original in the Wellcome Historical Medical Museum (39826·2)

(a) Waterhouse to Lyman Spalding, at Portsmouth (W.H.M.M. (39826·1)) :

"Cambridge, Sept. 6th, 1800.

Dear Sir,
I have only time to say that I have received your second letter, and that I will accomodate you with the matter &c at the same lay which has been offered to me but I declined, namely for *one quarter of the profits arising from* the inoculation & the contract to remain for 14 months from this time. Abandon the idea of inoculating for small-pox & throw all your attention to the kine-pox. If this idea suits you & Dr Cutter you shall be accomodated at once, for half a dozen practitioners stand ready to jump at that offer and two of them are not at very great distance from you.

  I haste I am Yours &c
      Benjn. Waterhouse
Sam B.— is in a fair way of being hooted out of Boston."

(b) Spalding to Waterhouse (W.H.M.M. (39826·2)) :

"Portsmouth 10 Sept 1800
The terms are accepted, & I promise that you shall have one quarter part of the neat profit arising from my inoculation with the kine pox for the space of 14 months, provided it be not made public before that term expires—& then the contract to remain in full force only to the time of its becoming public : however on your part it is expected, that the like priviledge will not be granted to others in my vicinity.
        L. Spalding.
Dr. Waterhouse"

Additional Material of J. A. Spalding

James Alfred Spalding was the grandson of Lyman Spalding. He was born in 1842. In 1908 he was given Lyman Spalding's papers to look over, and this biography[14] was published in 1916. This book is very little known and there is probably only one copy in the libraries of London. It is not in the British Museum.

Since the biographer had all the papers, he was able to give much additional information on this interesting subject. The correspondence opened on August 25, 1800, when Spalding heard that Waterhouse had vaccinated his household successfully, and he asked for a supply of lymph. Waterhouse replied *on September* 6, 1800, advising Spalding not to vaccinate in a smallpox hospital. It is not clear whether Spalding had meanwhile written again ; but, though there is confusion of dates, this must be the case. Waterhouse then wrote the letter which is reproduced here as letter (a). J. A. Spalding says that Lyman's reply had not been preserved ; but that there was a copy of it. This must be letter (b). It is apparently written and signed by Lyman Spalding, and bears the name of Waterhouse on the reverse —as if it had been given to some friend to deliver.

The Dr. Cutter mentioned in letter (a) may have been either the father or the son—both being well-known physicians at Portsmouth. "Sam B." was Sam Brown, who had been a friend of Lyman Spalding at Harvard. Lyman Spalding was the youngest physician in the town, and Waterhouse was evidently disinclined to give his cowpox matter to him alone, to the exclusion of an older physician.

Sam Brown had been following up the patients vaccinated by Waterhouse, to see whether the scabs could not be used to vaccinate his own patients. In his next letter—September 12—Waterhouse says that the time factor proposed is too vague, as Sam Brown may steal the method within a month. He therefore proposed that the term should be for twelve months. "You, however, will have got the start of all the others, so much that no one can rival you entirely ; besides it will fix you in business. My fee is Five Dollars." Each man stuck to his guns—Spalding for monopoly, Waterhouse for Cutter and a higher figure. On September 18, Waterhouse informed Spalding that he had divided New Hampshire into three vaccination districts, with the exception of certain specified towns.

At this time the method was generally in use of transmitting the vaccine matter on pieces of linen thread, and it was for one of these threads that the bargaining was taking place. From a bond which existed when the book was written, it would appear that Waterhouse sometimes let one of these go for 150 dollars. On September 25, however, Waterhouse did send Spalding a thread ; but he did so under protest that older men should have been included in partnership, and declared that he hoped that Lyman would take them in with him, so that vaccination could be extended everywhere as rapidly as possible. Spalding acted at once on receipt of the thread, and in one day vaccinated thirty persons. Shortly after this it was found that the virus could be passed from arm to arm, and linen threads and bonds immediately became valueless.

The two letters reproduced here in facsimile were presented to the Wellcome Historical Museum by Sir William Osler on January 31, 1919, eleven months before his death. In the note accompanying the two documents, Osler said that from them it would be seen that "they tried to make it a commercial affair ; this I did not know". Item 6814 in the "Bibliotheca Osleriana"—the printed catalogue of Osler's library —is this biography by J. A. Spalding, and it seems strange that Osler had not at least glanced at it.

The manner in which these two letters came into Osler's hands is unknown. One can only assume that these two items were given to someone from the Spalding collection. If they had been given to Osler direct by the owner of that collection, Osler would have known a lot about the subject. Further, if the Spalding collection had been broken up, he would almost certainly have heard the fact. Would he not also have picked up many more letters, for was he not "William the Fowler, Guillaume l'Oiseleur", who kept all that was taken in his net ?[17]. It would be of interest to know what has happened to the Spalding letters as a whole.

On March 4, 1801, Jenner wrote his first letter to Waterhouse. It is a long letter full of sound advice, and is published by Waterhouse in full in the second part of his "Prospect". In 1802 Waterhouse was for a time forced to hire volunteers in Cambridge to keep up the strain of fresh virus. The correspondence with Jenner continued. This second part of the "Prospect" was criticized by the Massachusetts Medical Society as being obscure and not worth looking at. But he was much helped by British friends, and the book sold fairly well in the South. Meanwhile, vaccination was spreading to other parts of the United States, and this is too large a subject to deal with here.

A Third Letter in the Wellcome Collection

This is half of a four-page letter on foolscap. It has not, so far as I know, been published previously. The text is as follows :

(c) Waterhouse to an unknown correspondent (W.H.M.M. (95443)) :

" . . . I have just finished reading the different state papers relative to the armed neutrality. Partial as I am to Old England, I must confess that I think these northern nations have truth, and reason on their side. I do not see at present what arguments Great Britain can bring to bear against them, unless it be the *ultima ratio regum*, and that may not be a conclusive one, while this confederacy is so strong, aided as it is, by so potent a monarch as that of Prussia. France will doubtless try to bring us into this combination, and probably will expect to accomplish her views under *Jefferson*, which she would have despaired of under *Adams*. She will nevertheless fail in her expectations. The merchantile interest has great weight in these States, and our Executive cannot bend it to its wishes.

"Jefferson is a prudent man. He sets out with conciliating parties. He says 'we are all federalists, all republicans', and has delivered *sentiments* universally approved & admired. His speech is doubtless in London before this time. As a fine composition the man of taste will read it with pleasure. Jefferson is besides a man of mild & pleasing manners, naturally disposed to complaisancy, whereas Adams was a perfect *John Bull*, and accompanied his honesty with a roughness that in some cases narrowed his way to usefulness. You will find President Jefferson's speech in one of the papers in the box containing the cheese.

"I have just written to our Medical Society to ask their advice respecting the best method of diffusing the vaccine matter through our Land. I have also proposed to them a plan for a *Vaccine Institution* for inoculating the poor gratis. I wish I could obtain a copy of the rules, directions &c &c of the Vaccine Institution in London. Had I thought of it earlier, I would have requested a copy of it from Dr. Pearson.

"I am sorry, very sorry to hear that Jenner & Woodville even glance in their respective works at anything like personalities. We have honored & esteemed these celebrated men for their beneficent productions, and shall lament if in place of affording us more good & wholesome fruit, they should produce thorns. For more than a year I have held up these two eminent physicians to the *American public*, as men who could scarcely err. On that account I feel doubly mortified, that two, out of the three oracles which I have constantly appealed to, should clash in opinion. We feel interested in those we admire.

"I think I have already said that the matter which was on thread between two plates of glass, enveloped in a note to you signed 'Jno. Cn. Wachsel', produced the disease to *perfection* in every patient I inoculated with it.

"I propose to write again in about a month by a Mr. Nancrede, one of our first booksellers. Till then adieu ! and remember that I am your affectionate friend

B. Waterhouse"

April 14th, 1801

In this letter the direct comparison of Jefferson with Adams is interesting. Waterhouse had had contacts with both these presidents of the United States. When he was at Leyden, John Adams was sent by Congress to Holland to court an alliance, but he was forced to remain a year before he was publicly recognized as the American minister. During this time Adams, his two sons, his secretary, and Waterhouse formed one family[9]. Twenty years later he sent Jefferson a copy of his pamphlet on cow-pox—that is, the first part of his "Prospect"—and on December 25, 1800, the President sent him a very cordial letter of thanks, which Waterhouse published in his second part[11]. Six months later Waterhouse wrote a long letter to Jefferson, giving instructions how to perform vaccination, enclosing infected thread and books and drawings. In this letter he also suggested that the President should arrange for an experiment to be made by "some cautious discerning person, perhaps his own family physician. A series of experiments may be directly instituted by him." Three unsuccessful attempts were made to vaccinate the President's family with three separate batches of "virus". A fourth attempt was successful. The President was attentive to all applications made to him for cowpox matter, and he it was who was thus responsible for introducing vaccination into the District of Columbia, Pennsylvania, Maryland and Virginia.

The reference to Woodville recalls the fact that he was one of the first in London—after Cline—to practise vaccination. But he performed the operation in the Smallpox Hospital, and three days after vaccinating he inoculated the patients with smallpox matter. The result was that the "cowpox matter" from the pustule was really a combination of cowpox matter and smallpox matter. This material, distributed far and wide, caused many smallpox rashes. Jenner had considerable difficulty in saving the situation.

The great esteem in which Waterhouse held Jenner is seen in this letter, and is even more fully expressed in the second part of his "Prospect"[19].

Back to Jenner

If much of this article has been devoted to persons other than Jenner he would not have minded—even on his birthday. In the mass of correspondence which has been preserved, dating from the time of publication of the "Inquiry", we get a very good picture of the man. During the early stages of the movement to promote vaccination he was the oracle to whom everyone turned for guidance, and loaded with honours as he was, he never lost his head. Even his erroneous views—and that there must have been erroneous views at that period when immunology was still unborn is obvious—were often blessings which kept some semblance of correctness when some men tended to stray into dangerous by-ways.

Jenner became almost at once a national hero, and his name was nearly as well known abroad as it was in his own country. His vast correspondence led him to term himself "the vaccine clerk of the whole world". His private practice certainly suffered, and in 1802 Parliament made him a grant of £10,000. In 1806 he was voted a further £20,000. To the end he worked unceasingly for the cause of vaccination. On January 26, 1823, he passed peacefully to his rest.

Jenner never cared very much for the high honours which he received; but he did care a great deal for the practice which he had discovered and helped to foster. That is why he would have perhaps preferred an article on the movement to a eulogy of the man.

[1] Baron, J., "Life of Edward Jenner", 1, 33 (1838).
[2] Jenner, E., Phil. Trans., 78, Pt. ii, 219–237 (1788).
[3] Baron, op. cit., (1), 1, 121.
[4] Underwood, E. A., presidential address to the Hist. Sect., Roy. Soc. Med. (1949).
[5] Baron, op. cit. (1), 1, 334–39.
[6] idem., ibid., 392.
[7] idem., ibid., 359.
[8] idem., ibid., 155.
[9] Welch, W. H., "The Jenner of America", Proc. Philadelph. Co. Med. Soc. (1885).
[10] Waterhouse, B., "A Prospect of Exterminating the Small-Pox" (Boston, 1800).
[11] idem., ibid., Part ii (Cambridge, Mass., 1802).
[12] Baron, op. cit., (1), 1, 386, and Waterhouse, op. cit. (10).
[13] idem., ibid., 439–43.
[14] Spalding, J. A., "Dr. Lyman Spalding" (Boston, 1916).
[15] Leikind, M. C., Bull. Hist. Med., 7, 671–86 (1939).
[16] Appleton's "Cyclopædia of American Biography", 5 (1888–89).
[17] Kelly, H. A., and Burrage, W. L., "Dict. of Amer. Med. Biography" (1928).
[18] See sonnet by Basil Lanneau Gildersleeve in H. Cushing's "Life of Osler", 1, 671.
[19] For other Waterhouse letters, see especially :
Halsey, R. H., "How the President, Thomas Jefferson, and Doctor Benjamin Waterhouse established vaccination as a public health procedure" (New York, 1936).
Fitz, R., Bull. Hist. Med., 11, 239–264 (1942).
Spalding, R. W., Bull. Hist. Med., 20, 69–75 (1946).
Trent, J. C., J. Hist. Med., 1, 25–40 (1946); and ibid., 1, 357–364 (1946).

BENJAMIN WATERHOUSE
AND
THE INTRODUCTION OF VACCINATION

John B. Blake

Benjamin Waterhouse
and the
Introduction of Vaccination

A Reappraisal

by

JOHN B. BLAKE

PHILADELPHIA

UNIVERSITY OF PENNSYLVANIA PRESS

Acknowledgments

ONE OF THE HISTORIAN'S MOST PLEASANT DUTIES IS AC-knowledging the help he has received from others. Particularly does this apply to the libraries and their staffs who have made his research possible. The Massachusetts Historical Society, the Harvard Medical School Library, the Boston Public Library, the Boston Medical Library, the Library of the New York Academy of Medicine, and the Rhode Island Historical Society have all generously allowed me to use manuscripts in their possession. To the Sterling Memorial Library at Yale I am indebted particularly for the use of the newspaper collection, and especially must I thank Miss Madeline E. Stanton and Mrs. Henrietta T. Perkins of the Yale Medical Library, and Miss Elizabeth H. Thomson of the Department of the History of Medicine at Yale, for their unfailing courtesy and attention to many requests. Throughout this project, Dr. John F. Fulton has given me his enthusiastic encouragement and steady support.

While working on this study, I have been aided by a James Hudson Brown Memorial Research Fellowship from the Yale University School of Medicine, and by a fellowship from the Commonwealth Fund.

Plates

Benjamin Waterhouse
and the
Introduction of Vaccination

I

In July, 1800, Dr. Benjamin Waterhouse, Harvard's first Professor of the Theory and Practice of Physic, introduced the practice of vaccination against smallpox into the United States. Innumerable articles, pamphlets, and books have recorded this fact, and few events in American medical history are more commonly known.[1] As early as 1817 T. J. Pettigrew noted in his memoir of John C. Lettsom that the vaccine lymph spread from Waterhouse "through the United States."[2] Waterhouse received full credit in John Baron's life of Edward Jenner,[3] and more recent British writers have afforded him similar recognition.[4]

For many years, however, American authors granted Waterhouse little more than passing notice. Although Josiah Bartlett of Charlestown, Massachusetts, mentioned him generously in 1810,[5] and James Thacher named him as the nation's first vaccinator,[6] the *Boston Medical and Surgical Journal*, while recalling his "early and decided" advocacy of vaccination and his designation as the "American Jenner," gave him only a brief obituary.[7] Oliver Wendell Holmes in 1869 at least referred to Waterhouse's achievement,[8] but he received remarkably scant and slighting treatment in Edward Warren's biographies of his distinguished father and brother.[9] Samuel D. Gross omitted Waterhouse from his selection of outstanding medical figures,[10] and the centennial history of American medicine mentioned him but once.[11]

Not until 1881 did Henry A. Martin present the first

11

extended notice of Waterhouse's work. After castigating the hereditary "Boston Clique" for its treatment of his hero, Martin recounted the vaccinator's struggles primarily in his own words, and reproduced several letters from Thomas Jefferson to document the story of their cooperation.[12] The same year, however, in an address to the Massachusetts Medical Society, Samuel Abbott Green also recognized Waterhouse's contribution and cited his books on vaccination.[13] Three years later Joseph Jones reprinted part of Martin's article and added new material on other early vaccinators.[14] Following their lead, William M. Welch published in 1885 a more complete account of Waterhouse's achievement and firmly entrenched his name in the annals of American medical history.[15] Since then innumerable authors have swelled the volume of praise, so that today Waterhouse is one of our leading medical heroes: a recent list of the twenty-five outstanding pioneers of public health in America, the consensus of a number of experts in the field, accords sixteenth place to the man who introduced vaccination.[16]

With few exceptions historians have portrayed Waterhouse as struggling against public and professional prejudice and hostility in Boston, in marked contrast to the friendship and support of Jefferson and Jenner. To account for this opposition writers have mentioned Waterhouse's adherence to the Society of Friends, his political support of the Jeffersonian Republicans, and petty personal jealousy aroused by his superior scientific qualifications, his skill in controversy, his appointment as a young Rhode Islander to the first Professorship of Physic at Harvard, and his recognition as "The American Jenner." Almost nowhere has it been intimated that any of his actions in connection with the introduction of vaccination offered the Bostonians any legitimate reasons, other than personal ones, for disliking or distrusting him.[17]

Accounts of Waterhouse's work, however, when not derived from purely secondary material, nearly always depend directly and almost exclusively on his own forceful version, on letters published by Baron and Pettigrew, and in a few instances on some of the manuscripts preserved by his family. Some years ago James A. Spalding [18] and Morris C. Leikind [19] published certain correspondence that calls for a reappraisal of the relations between Waterhouse and his professional brethren. This material, and much more in the files of Boston newspapers, has never been adequately analyzed.[20]

II

Early in 1799 Benjamin Waterhouse received a copy of Edward Jenner's *Inquiry into the Causes and Effects of the Variolæ Vaccinæ* from his London friend and correspondent, Dr. John C. Lettsom, and soon thereafter drew up a brief account of the new discovery, which the *Columbian Centinel*, a Boston newspaper, published on March 16, 1799.[21] Other reports soon followed, and by 1800 several American physicians were attempting to import cowpox virus. On July 8, 1800, Waterhouse achieved the first significant result when he vaccinated his son Daniel.[22] On August 2, after treating six more members of his household, he requested Dr. William Aspinwall, who maintained a hospital for this purpose in Brookline, to inoculate one of them with smallpox. The test was an unqualified success.[23]

As the news spread, practitioners soon deluged Waterhouse with requests for information and vaccine, but he was as yet unwilling to comply. Since, he explained, he had

taken much pains in this business, run no small risk of reputation, as well as of personal feelings, there are few he trusts that will wonder he is anxious to have the matter under his own eye until the practice is more firmly established by the public opinion. A few unsuccessful cases at the beginning, deprived *Scotland* of the blessings of inoculation for the small-pox for more than 20 years.[24]

Many physicians nevertheless continued to apply. Among them was Lyman Spalding of Portsmouth, New

14

Hampshire, who first wrote Waterhouse on August 25 of his plan to operate a smallpox inoculation hospital in conjunction with a Dr. Cutter, and of his interest in vaccination. Soon after, he sent another letter asking for cowpox "matter," and on September 6 Waterhouse replied:

I have only time to say that I have received your second letter, and that I will accomodate you with the matter &c at the same lay which has been offered to me but I declined, namely for one quarter of the profits arising from the inoculation & the contract to remain for 14 months from this time. Abandon the idea of inoculating for small-pox & throw all your attention to the Kine-pox.[25] If this idea suits you & Dr Cutter you shall be accomodated at once, for half a dozen practitioners stand ready to jump at that offer and two of them are not at very great distance from you.

I haste I am yours &c

Benjn. Waterhouse [26]

Four days later, dropping the idea of a partnership with Cutter, Spalding accepted these terms, but added, "on your part it is expected, that the like priviledge will not be granted to others in my vicinity." [27] This did not satisfy Waterhouse. He wanted young Spalding to join forces with an older and better established practitioner, who would bring in more business and therefore increase his share. After several more letters had passed between them, however, Waterhouse acceded to Spalding's insistence on a local monopoly and on September 25 sent him the virus in return for his written bond to pay one quarter of the profits.[28]

Meanwhile, Waterhouse allotted the rest of Strafford, Grafton, and Rockingham counties in New Hampshire, except for Hanover and its vicinity, to three brothers, Drs. Levi, Josiah, and Ezra Bartlett, and in exchange for similar bonds provided them with vaccine. Later, it appears, Dr.

Thomas Banning joined them. Other favored physicians included a Dr. Rowe in Vermont; and in Massachusetts, Stowe Ranney of Brentwood, Benjamin Billings of Mansfield, Ebenezer Perry of New Bedford, James Mann of Wrentham, and Zacheus Bartlett of Plymouth. Similar arrangements were presumably concluded with Dr. David King of Newport, Rhode Island, and a Dr. Dyer of Providence, while at least one small-town practitioner, less likely to attain an extensive practice, received the lymph for a flat fee of one hundred and fifty dollars. Nor were these cases exceptional. To Zacheus Bartlett, Waterhouse outlined his "custom of supplying practitioners" on October 1:

I would just observe to you that I have made a contract with several practitioners in different states & counties, and most of them have agreed to give me one quarter of the neat profits, others have given me a specific sum. In none have I less than a quarter of the profits.[29]

While thus distributing vaccine to selected country physicians who were unable to compete with him, Waterhouse denied it to those in the capital. In these circumstances his Harvard colleague John Warren on August 20 wrote to his son, a medical student in London:

The Cow or Kine pox is making some noise here. I wish you had thought of procuring and sending me some matter, as Dr Waterhouse is the only Physician who has received it from London and has begun to practice, and the other Physicians cannot readily obtain it. I should like to know from you what its present character is and if you can easily obtain it and send it in a closely sealed Phial. I may possibly have it in that way sooner than any other.[30]

At the same time another Boston physician, Samuel Brown, to whom the Humane Society of Massachusetts

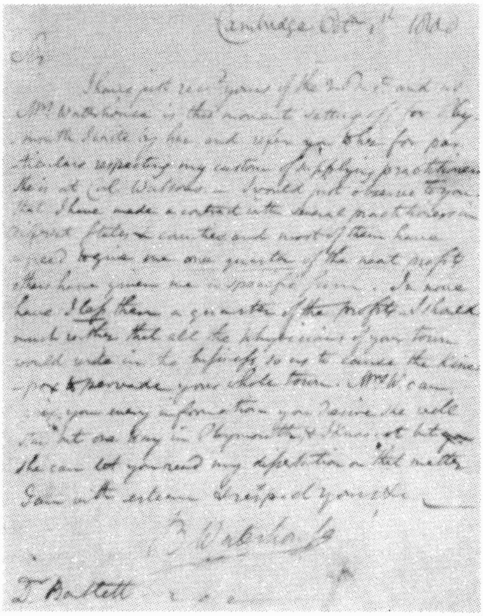

Plate I. Letter from Benjamin Waterhouse to Zacheus Bartlett, October 1, 1800. *(Courtesy of New York Academy of Medicine.)*

This certifies that I have given to Dr Zacheus Bartlett the matter of the kine-pox for the purpose of inoculation in Plymouth, but not to supply any other practitioner

B Waterhouse

Octr 1800
Cambridge

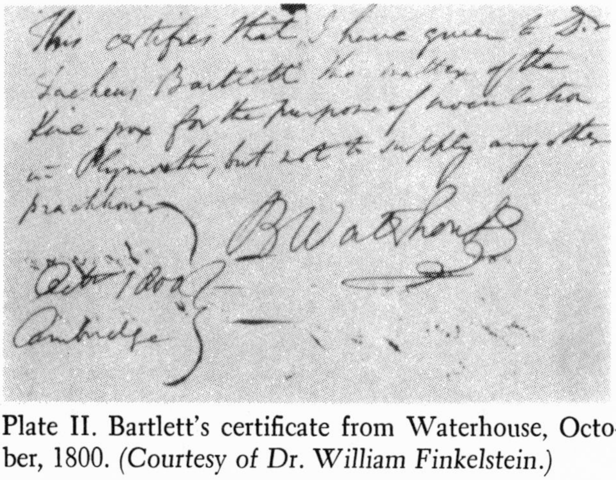

Plate II. Bartlett's certificate from Waterhouse, October, 1800. *(Courtesy of Dr. William Finkelstein.)*

had just awarded a prize for his treatise on yellow fever,[31] foiled in his attempt to obtain vaccine directly from the arms of some of Waterhouse's patients, advertised that if anyone having cowpox, "and not restricted to the contrary by oath, or solemn promise," would supply him with the "specific matter," he would "inoculate therewith *gratis*." Other physicians, he added, "without exception," might freely share in the vaccine thus produced.[32]

For this attempt to diffuse more widely the benefits of vaccination, an anonymous "Pedro" accused Brown of insolence, hypocrisy, arrogance, and quackery.

The public too well know [the writer continued], to require further proof, with what industry and fortitude Dr. WATER-HOUSE, in opposition to the most powerful prejudice, has reduced to a certainty the efficacious qualities of the matter produced from the *Kine Pox*. . . . And what animal could have been supposed sufficiently base, to wish to deprive the discoverer, or maturer of the discovery of a competent reward! . . . With the learned and captivating motto "PRO BONO PUBLICO," a stripling in his profession . . . offers, in terms of salvation, to heal the sick, assist the poor and needy, and even instruct his fathers and brethren of the lance, all *for nothing*, provided he can steal . . . something, that he never saw and knows nothing about! [33]

Apparently expecting this denunciation to have a salutary effect, Waterhouse noted in a letter to Lyman Spalding written the day it appeared that "Sam B.—— is in a fair way of being hooted out of Boston." But it did not entirely remove his apprehension. On September 12, insisting that Spalding's agreement to hand over the required percentage only until vaccination became public was "too vague," Waterhouse added, "Sam Brown may steal it before a month expires, and then in six months it may be diffused over Boston, or it may not." [34]

Soon it became evident, moreover, that others also endangered the monopoly. Having inaugurated the practice in Ipswich with vaccine direct from London, Dr. Thomas Manning advertised this fact in the *Columbian Centinel* on September 24. Still Waterhouse was not disheartened, since, as he wrote Spalding the next day, "Young Doctor Manning has the matter and will be as close with it as any of you, by what he says to me by letter." [35]

Hardly had Waterhouse penned this hopeful statement, when James Jackson returned from London. While there he had studied the new inoculation with Dr. William Woodville, one of its earliest and most important promoters, and, as he later wrote, "learned all then known about that business." Unfortunately Jackson's friends in Boston, though anxiously awaiting his return with vaccine, did not advise him of the local situation, and he brought only "a small piece of thread and four lancets charged with the matter." Arriving home on September 30, he discovered that "vaccination had just been introduced here, and Boston was full of it—so far as talking went." The next day he commenced practice.[36]

On October 7 Jackson hastily called upon his friend John Pickering in London to send more vaccine as soon as possible. "Everybody here," he wrote, "is in a rage to have the cow-pox. I brought matter here which has nearly failed and I fear will quite. If so, I may not be able to get a supply till this reaches me from London." [37] Learning the next day that his lymph had indeed failed, Jackson asked Waterhouse for a supply. The Cambridge professor apparently put him off with a promise, but his real attitude may be inferred from the triumphant note in his letter to Spalding of October 12: "Dr. Jackson *has not the matter*. He applied to me for it last week. He brought some, but it failed." [38]

Waterhouse was in part mistaken. As Jackson described it a month later,

Dr. Waterhouse had promised a supply, but I could not depend upon having it in season. I knew that Dr. Manning of Ipswich had received matter from his brother whom we saw in London; but it was said that he kept it to himself. Driven by despair, I went secretly to Ipswich determined to pay any price for a supply. My success was here as complete as unexpected. The Doctor gave all I asked and refused all compensation.[39]

Following this coup, Jackson on October 11 informed the public that he was prepared to inoculate for the cowpox.[40]

On the same day Warren informed his son that Jackson had begun to vaccinate. "Doctor Waterhouse," he wrote, "has made something handsome by it, (which he much needed) and it will probably be soon generally adopted here. He Dr Jackson . . . brought the matter with him—this has been hitherto monopolized but it will soon cease to be the case and there will be enough to be had by all the Physicians." [41] Warren's prediction proved true. Within a week other practitioners advertised their readiness to vaccinate, and by the middle of November Jackson noted that "the matter is now in the hands of all the physicians here." [42]

Throughout New England the monopoly was breaking down. From Stratham, New Hampshire, Josiah Bartlett in evident distress wrote to Spalding on November 3 that in his neighborhood many physicians were inoculating cowpox. They had, he thought, procured the virus in a "clandestine manner," and he added, "I believe that Doctor Manning has spread the Matter in this State, by way of Newbury. If he received the Matter from Dr. Waterhouse, as I heard that he did, and has spread it (as is reported of him) openly, Dr. Waterhouse ought to be informed of it."

Sorrowfully, Spalding replied that he too faced competition, "but in what manner Cutter or Dwight procured their infection, I cannot discover . . ." In these circumstances Josiah Bartlett concluded that it would be advisable to obtain Waterhouse's permission to sell the vaccine to other physicians. His brother Levi, believing this the only profitable recourse, concurred. Even then, he remarked, it soon would "not be so lucrative as other practice." According to the newspapers, he explained, "matter is dayly carried from Boston & disbursed to anyone who chuses. Dr. Hunt has been inoculating for the Kine Pox in Boston about three weeks without discrimination, Bond or any other security & anyone can I believe take matter from him. . . ."[43]

Though slow to accede to the Bartletts' request for permission to sell vaccine,[44] Waterhouse was apparently willing to have Spalding distribute it provided the recipients agreed to the usual terms. On October 25 one of Spalding's former students, Abraham Hedge of Chester, Vermont, had written to inquire how he could obtain the virus, "as it might now be of great service to me, and could not injure him [Waterhouse] or you, being at such a distance. It will soon doubtless become general," he pointed out, "when it can be no object."[45] On November 10 Spalding dispatched some virus to Hedge, and on the eighteenth the latter replied. He thanked Spalding for his description of cowpox and reported that he was seeking the town's permission to test some of his patients by variolation to convince the local people of the efficacy of vaccination. But he added, "The price you or your friends set on the infection sent me would have been gladly paid, had not I already received a supply which, that you may not think I act the rogue, I will inform you where I got it." His sources were Dr. Nathan Smith of Hanover (who ob-

to be supported — and in the present instance,
it may not only be excusable but absolutely
necessary —. You will not be hurt I am
well persuaded at any indiscretion that I may
be guilty of, in the Publication. I have nearly
compleated it, and shall submit it to your inspection before publication. —

I am Dear Sir
Yours respectfully
Chas. F. Bartlett

P.S. I send you copy of a note in answer to one I
wrote Dr King [illegible] regarding Cowpox Infection that
you may see how far liberality in some of our
Profession extends. —

Dr. Bartlett

Sir, I am very sorry 'tis not in my power
to comply with your request,
The Physician of [illegible] Inoculated the Kine Pox Matter
restricts me from supplying other Physicians, I
wrote him a second time representing the impropriety
of monopolizing — but he has again refused —
Your Humble Serv.
Monday morning
Novr 10th 1800 —
David King

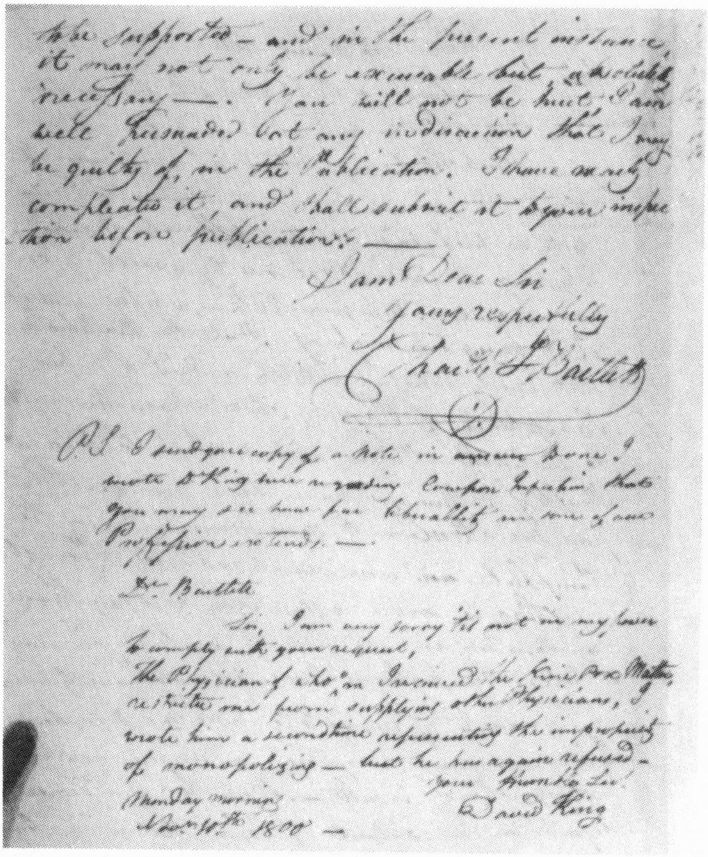

Plate III. Letter from Charles F. Bartlett to Moses Brown, November 11, 1800, quoting letter from David King. (*Courtesy of Rhode Island Historical Society.*)

tained it from "a Doctor More, from Dummerstown"), and an additional amount "left with Mr. Hubbard by my friend, Captain —— of Windsor." [46]

Nor was Hedge the only physician who sought vaccine from Spalding. From Sanborntown, New Hampshire, Samuel Gerrish wrote on November 12 that the new inoculation was "the topic and rage" in his vicinity.

I think it probable [he continued] that I may inoculate a larger number, and make more, even under Doctor Waterhouse's restrictions, than to omit till Spring. That only, induces me to submit to his restrictions. I think that his method of restricting New Hampshire will answer his expectations but a short time. . . . If you cannot supply me in 12 to 15 days, be so good as to write, that I may procure it from some other quarter. Pudding Time I fear will be short.[47]

Down in Dedham, meanwhile, Dr. Nathaniel Ames, as we learn from his diary, had also obtained vaccine:

[October] 16 [1800]. . . . Took kine pox matter from P. Gay to innoculate.

19. Innoculated L. Parsons & Sam Gay Kine pox, which in six days works like small pox, headache, soreness of axilla, inflamed arm, &c: & prevents taking small pox. I have full faith. . . .

26. Sam Gay's cow pox works right, arm inflamed, soreness of axilla, &c.

31. Dr. Tudor of Orford, N.H. bro't Letter for B. Bissel, got kine pox matter. The people are yet infidels in the Blessing of Cow pox, or kine pox they cannot yet realize the security against Small pox.[48]

Further south, in Rhode Island, David King was unable to accommodate Dr. Charles F. Bartlett of Newport: "Sir," he wrote, "I am very sorry 'tis not in my power to comply with your request, The Physician of whom I received the Kine Pox Matter, restricted me from supplying

other Physicians, I wrote him a second time representing
the impropriety of monopolizing—but he has again refused." But a Dr. Wheaton of Providence "found means
to procure the matter without Docr Waterhouse," and
through the good offices of the Quaker philanthropist
Moses Brown supplied the importunate Bartlett.[49]

III

THOUGH WATERHOUSE HAD RESTRICTED THE DISTRIBUTION
of cowpox virus to profit from a monopoly, he also seems
to have been genuinely worried that incompetent practitioners would obtain vaccine, or pseudo-vaccine, and give
the new preventive a bad name. He set forth this reason in
the *Centinel* on August 20 for not acceding to requests
for the lymph, and he reprinted the statement in an appendix to his first pamphlet on vaccination, *A Prospect of
Exterminating the Small-Pox*, which appeared about September 5.[50] In the latter he also pointed out that "there
are some circumstances, which if not attended to critically,
may bring the inoculation of this recently imported distemper into a temporary disrepute." The sources of spurious cowpox enumerated by Jenner, Waterhouse continued, were:

1st—That arising from pustules on the nipples, or udder of
the cow, which pustules contain no specific virus.
2dly—From matter, (although originally possessing the specific virus,) which has suffered a decomposition, either from
putrefaction, or from any other cause less obvious to the senses.
3dly—From matter taken from an ulcer in *an advanced stage,*
which ulcer arose from a true cow-pox. . . . He [Jenner] . . .
shews, that when the inoculated part has degenerated into an
ulcer, the matter, although it may possess the power of inflaming the patient's arm, is nevertheless, void of that specific virus
requisite to produce the genuine disease; and of course, incapable of securing the human system against the small-pox. . . .
Another circumstance, tending to discredit the idea of dis-

carding the small-pox and substituting the kine-pox, is mixing
the two diseases together, and perhaps giving one for the other,
as we presume was done in some of the hospitals in London.[51]

After the monopoly had been breached, Waterhouse re-
newed and intensified his attack on spurious cowpox. In a
letter to a country physician published in the *Massachusetts Mercury* of October 21 Waterhouse described "a vile
traffic" in purported vaccine carried on from Boston to
other towns. "What the matter is," he wrote, "I cannot
tell, but of this I am certain, more has been sent into the
country the last fortnight, than I have been able to collect
from all my patients for a month, and I have innoculated
[sic] twenty times as many as any man in the country." He
feared that this "abominable practice" would bring the
new discovery into disrepute:

As this is *spurious* matter it never produces the requisite symptoms, and of course will not preserve a person from the small-
pox, and one unfortunate instance would destroy all our exertions to extend far and wide one of the most important discoveries of modern times.[52]

At the end of the month an anonymous author came to
Waterhouse's support. Everyone, he wrote, should uniformly "discountenance every attempt to propagate the
disease, directed by avarice or assumed by ignorance, and
unsupported by reason or propriety." Dr. Waterhouse's
"unwearied exertions" to collect correct information, he
continued, "are perfectly known in this neighborhood,"
while his testing his own children by variolation evinced
his sincerity. Though the confusion of cowpox with small-
pox in England had brought the new procedure into disrepute, "the united efforts of a respectable body of Physicians" had overcome this setback, and in Europe vaccination was "triumphing over every objection. . . ."

A subject of such importance [the author concluded], it behoves the public to watch with scrutinizing vigilance. For as in eight instances out of ten, the whole visible effect of the inoculated Kine-Pox is confined to the neighborhood of the incision, it is easy for any person, by any extraneous body inserted into the arm, to produce a sufficient inflamation [sic], to impose on those not acquainted with the appearances in the true disease. Thus while the deluded patient vainly supposes himself secured from the attacks of the Small-Pox, his imaginary safety leads him into situations where his life is endangered, and the properties of a disease, interesting to the world, are inveloped [sic] in doubt or brought into contempt by the crimes of avarice or the mistakes of ignorance.

'The mischief arising from ignorance or artfulness in the management of this disease in Europe, have been sufficiently demonstrated by Dr. Waterhouse's publication on the subject; it therefore remains for Americans to encourage those gentlemen only, whose respectability of character places them beyond the charge of ignorance or suspicion.[53]

Unfortunately, however, Waterhouse's method of parceling out vaccine had rendered his motives suspect. Some practitioners believed that he warned against spurious cowpox in order to retain his monopolistic control. In the *Independent Chronicle* of November 3, a Bostonian, probably a physician, with biting sarcasm answered Waterhouse's letter to the country doctor. Since the new inoculation had become "considerably fashionable," he wrote, more cowpox matter had been "*sold* into the country, than could be made use of without involving the practitioner in inevitable disgrace and reproach. . . ." Yet "this 'abominable practice,' this 'vile traffic' " was among "the earliest exertions 'to extend far and wide one of the most important discoveries of modern times'!" Waterhouse, he implied, had failed to give those who purchased vaccine the instruction in its proper use which he should have

provided. But "the vender," he supposed, might consider
this of little consequence, provided he could "get rid of
his commodity" at his own price.

Had Waterhouse not appealed, the letter writer continued, to

the feelings of humanity, the pure principles of religion and the
dearest interests of our country, . . . he would not have so justly
incurred the imputation of insincerity and hypocrisy. Humanity, the principles of religion and the interests of our country
have a powerful claim upon our best exertions; but it is an insult
upon religion to attempt to enlist it in the cause of self-interest
and sordid gain:—the Doctor had forgotten the scripture declaration—"Ye cannot serve God and Mammon."

Whether there had been enormous exports of spurious
cowpox virus from Boston, the writer professed not to
know. Perhaps if Waterhouse would define the word
"traffic," it could then be determined whether he was not
himself the only one who had dealt in the "vile traffic" he
so violently denounced. "We hope," the writer continued,
"he has not combined deception in the quality of the
Kine-Pox matter with extravagance of demand for it." And
in a footnote he charged,

It is a fact, and Dr. Waterhouse will not deny it, that the
right of inoculating for the Kine-Pox disease has been actually
districted upon shares, to certain physicians in the country, and
for a series of years to come; this right has been purchased for
one half or one third of the gain. Other physicians, I am told
have paid, or conditioned to pay, the round sum of 150 dollars
for the vaccine matter. These demands flow from the purest
principles of philanthropy, and are authorised by the Doctor's
unparalelled [sic] exertions to fix and establish the credit of the
new discovery!!

Moreover, Waterhouse had declared spurious vaccine
whose effect he knew nothing about—"a perfectability in

the science which, it is presumed, no one had contemplated, and but few will aspire to." If Waterhouse really possessed

a test by which he can infallibly determine the genuineness of the cow-pox matter, whether he has seen it or not, or knows at what time of the disease it was procured, he ought, for the instruction of his brethren of the faculty, and the good of the community, to let it be known:—humanity, religion, and our country, require it, and certainly the Doctor will not turn a deaf ear to these urgent calls.

Partly because Waterhouse's motives were questionable, and partly because of ignorance or, in some cases, knavery, large amounts of spurious cowpox were despite additional warnings [54] distributed through New England during the fall of 1800 and the following winter. Though Waterhouse's colorful account of this business [55] has often been repeated, it may not be amiss to mention some additional evidence. A Dr. Babbit of Sturbridge, for example, inoculated Cyrus Fay in December, 1800, with supposed vaccine obtained from a Connecticut physician.

The matter [Fay later wrote] had a purulent cast, and was part of a shirt-sleeve worn during the plentiful discharge from the ulcerous state of the pustule. The inoculated arm appeared inflamed by the fourth day, and went on inflaming till about the 8th, when it became a running sore. . . . I concluded I had passed through the true disease, but as neither Dr. BABBIT nor myself had ever seen the disease, we were at a loss to determine respecting the appearance of the arm. . . . I had thoughts of trying the experiment of the Small-Pox; had I unluckily done it, I should have added another spurious case, to perplex, confound and discourage the unexperienced Practitioner.[56]

Nor were some of the country folk above treating themselves. On December 8 James Parker of Shirley, Massa-

chusetts, recorded in his diary, "David and Moody weare
enocklated for the kin pox by Eastman . . ." Eight days
later he noted, "I & Jam at evening put matter on our
Arms in the Thine line [sic] or Cowpox." [57]

The most lamentable result of this malpractice occurred
in Marblehead. Using virus that his seafaring son had
taken from the arm of a sailor inoculated in London, Dr.
Elisha Story on October 2 inoculated his daughter. Twelve
days later, no symptoms having appeared, he concluded
that the virus was bad and sent another son to Waterhouse
to obtain a supply. On October 17, however, the girl broke
out with cowpox, as Story supposed, so he did not use
what Waterhouse had sent.[58] Actually she had smallpox,
but Story, not realizing this, inoculated others, and before
long the disease was rapidly spreading. Unable to control
it, the town of Marblehead on November 10 decided on a
general smallpox inoculation. In two days Story alone variolated more than a thousand persons. When the epidemic
was over, sixty-eight persons had died. Meanwhile, about
the time that Story's daughter first became ill, Waterhouse
had vaccinated the son of Dr. John Drury, another Marblehead physician, to provide the latter with vaccine. Drury in
turn treated some forty patients, all but one of whom later
contracted smallpox. "However," the newspapers added, "it
is only justice due to Dr. WATERHOUSE to acknowledge,
that the two patients whom he inoculated with the Kine-
Pox, were exempted from the general contagion. . . ." [59]

In his notice in the Centinel of August 20, 1800, Waterhouse had written that the preferred season for vaccination
was from August to November. "Very cold weather," he
asserted, "is unfavorable to the Kine-pox." But on September 25 he wrote Lyman Spalding, "I have no doubt but the
inoculation will do very well all through the winter. I
mean, at least, to try it." Toward the end of October, how-

ever, Waterhouse, like some other physicians, was running into difficulties. "By a late letter from him [Waterhouse]," wrote Josiah Bartlett to Spalding on October 30, "I find that the failure within his practice is equal to ours." [60] He was, as he later admitted, seriously perplexed, and to controvert the opinion of those who thought that in Marblehead cowpox had changed into smallpox, he wrote to the *Centinel* on November 14 that "If we are to judge of the force of the disease by the number of pustules, it certainly becomes milder as it recedes from the cow." It was well known, he added, that "cold diminishes the activity of febrile poisons," and it was obvious that the "vaccine poison" was less active now than it had been during the summer.[61]

On December 20 Waterhouse in another public letter stated that "For about two or three weeks in the month of November the matter seemed to have undergone a *deterioration* in my hands." He had had to inoculate several persons four or five times before the virus would take; with three or four he never could achieve success, and with some he was "still uncertain whether they have passed *fairly* through the disease or not." He was of the opinion, he continued, that *"the kine pox matter becomes milder as it recedes from the Cow, and that in process of time it gets worn out, and . . . needs renewal."* The fact that all the vaccine so far used in America "(some received at Ipswich excepted)" came from his stock lent support to the idea. He had therefore written to Jenner, Pearson, Woodville, and several other English physicians to suggest an arrangement whereby he might receive a monthly supply of vaccine "as *direct from the Cow* as possible" until cowpox was "naturalized" in America.[62] "Previously to which," he concluded, "I shall venture another communication entitled 'practical observations on the local appearance, symptoms,

and mode of treating the kine-pox,' which I hope to make
through the medium of the public papers." [63] After this
statement Waterhouse, who had already stopped vaccinating, retired from the field until March, when he received
a new supply of good lymph from England.[64]

IV

THOUGH MANY PHYSICIANS WERE INOCULATING SPURIOUS cowpox during the fall of 1800, some were at least as competent as Waterhouse. Dr. Thomas Manning of Ipswich, who had imported his own lymph and soon supplied several other physicians, wrote a friend in Edinburgh on October 3 that cowpox was "rapidly becoming very general." There could be "no doubt of its universal diffusion," as fast as practitioners could obtain the virus. "Professor Waterhouse's occasional publications have done much in preparing the way for this comparatively benign substitute for the terror of the fair," he added, "and his practice has done still more in introducing it. I have inoculated many, all of whom either have done, or are doing extremely well." Moreover, at Manning's request the town of Ipswich on October 16 granted him permission to variolate ten persons who had had cowpox. The test was a complete success.[65] Josiah Bartlett of Charlestown, Massachusetts, vaccinated his son George on November 11, and "the appearance of his arm, and the symptoms, so fully corresponded with the plates and publications I had then seen, as to convince me, and others of my medical friends, that he had the *disease*." Their judgment was apparently correct, for two years later George was exposed to smallpox with impunity.[66] As late as January 20, 1801, James Jackson was still vaccinating, and with success, in the opinion of Drs. John Jeffries, John Warren, Thomas Welsh, and Aaron Dexter.[67]

Another known vaccinator was James Mann of Wren-

31

tham, several of whose patients were tested by variolation in 1800.[68] After signing a bond,[69] Mann received some thread from Waterhouse which he tried on twelve persons. This failing, he applied for more, and acquired enough to treat four patients. From their arms he supplied himself with additional lymph; "but uninformed with respect to the state of the pox, when the matter might be taken to communicate the disease, and having not read Dr. Jenner's Treatise at that time," he had to depend upon his own judgment, took the virus too late, and obtained only spurious cases. After many perplexing difficulties, Mann in time learned how to distinguish genuine cowpox from false, and when to take lymph from the vesicles of his patients. To a Boston physician—not Waterhouse—he wrote on November 8:

I am happy that I have it in my power to correct my errors, and I am willing to acknowledge that I have been extremely ignorant respecting the progress and appearance of the specific disease of the Kine-Pox; and that I acquired the only accurate state of the genuine disease by an inspection of your patients, although I had had several, who I am well satisfied had passed regularly through it. And I moreover confess that I had not a divided idea, at what state of the disease, the virus should be taken for use, until I received information from you. I am now in the faith, that in no instance, we may have a spurious case, and since obtaining the matter in its limpid and transparent state; early inflammation, and superficial scabby arms have entirely disappeared.[70]

Though Waterhouse had provided Mann with vaccine, he had to learn from another physician how to use it properly.

Other incidents also show that Waterhouse was not the only, and perhaps not even the most careful, student of vaccination in Boston during this first year. The man who castigated his methods of distributing vaccine in the *Inde-*

pendent Chronicle of November 3 had remarked that the local physicians relied on Jenner's descriptions, believing that he "had almost as much knowledge of the nature and practice of the disease as any physician in the country." After the publication of Waterhouse's letter of December 20, another Boston physician also attacked Waterhouse's self-appointment as teacher of vaccination to America.[71] If cowpox inoculation, he wrote, required much nicer discernment than variolation, if no distinguishing criteria could with certainty be affixed to it, and "if in order to prevent spurious cases, a monthly importation of the vaccine-matter is necessary; then all our fair prospects . . . vanish at once. . . ." The idea of "some physicians," he continued, "that 'the Kine-Pox matter becomes milder as it recedes from the cow, and that in process of time it gets worn out, . . .' cannot be admitted as a satisfactory solution of the difficulty. . . ." It was "in direct contrariety" to all that was known concerning the nature of contagion, and it could not be sustained "upon any established principles of analogy. . . ." Moreover, he wrote, "The idea is opposed to all the experience of European Physicians:—they positively assert, that the vaccine matter is equally specific and efficacious after having passed through an indefinite number of patients as when taken immediately from the cow."

After presenting his own (incorrect) theory on the cause of the current difficulties, the writer suggested that "A collection of facts from the different Physicians in this town" on this subject was "a very desirable object, as promotive of public good;" but he would pause for now "and wait until favored with the promised publication of 'Practical Observations, &c.,' " in which he hoped to find all doubtful points and difficulties fully and fairly considered, and the true criteria of cowpox ascertained. But he also hoped that the Marblehead practitioners would communicate their observations. "Facts from this quarter," he wrote, "must have more weight in fixing the public sentiment than any thing that has yet appeared in this country." Finally, this Boston physician enclosed a letter "replete with real facts and judicious remarks" for publication in the newspaper—the letter from James Mann quoted earlier.

Obviously the author did not feel that Waterhouse, for all his talk, had as yet contributed significantly to the discussion of the new technique. It seems possible that Waterhouse sent an extract of a letter that he had received from Mann to the Centinel a few days later partly to show that he too was still the valued friend, correspondent, and confidant of the Wrentham physician.[72]

Then, a month later, in a communication to the Centinel, James Jackson reported on his experiences. Although thousands of English cases attested to the preventive power of cowpox, any apparent deviation from the general principle, he noted, should be fully and publicly recorded. "It is also proper for me to declare to those whom I have inoculated for the cow-pox," he added, "that my confidence in it is not so perfect as it once was." He then reported in detail upon the case of a man named Wheelock whom he had vaccinated in October, who had been inoculated with smallpox in January, and who had developed symptoms that led Jackson to believe that he might have contracted the disease. Those who knew him, Jackson continued, would readily conceive "that I have not witnessed these circumstances without mortification. But it will not save my feelings to conceal the facts. It is more pleasing to me to give my evidence in favor of the truth even against an opinion of which I have been an advocate." The case, he urged, should be independently examined by other gentlemen of the faculty. Should they find him in error, he re-

marked, "no person will be more gratified than myself."
He would not say for sure, he concluded, that Wheelock
had had smallpox. But his case had "excited in my mind
doubts, which I thought I should never find there." At the
most it could only prove "that the cow-pox does not always
preserve the subject of it from the small-pox; but this is an
inconsistency in the operations of nature to which we
should not give full credit without the clearest evidence." [73]

An honor to Jackson's candor and modesty, this statement also gave at least two other doctors an opportunity to
differ publicly with his diagnosis and to express their confidence in vaccination. The experiment, wrote one, "does
not by any means demonstrate, even in that case, that the
small-pox did actually supervene." Similar cases had occurred, he continued, without leading the attending physician to believe that the effect was more than a local inflammation. Though willing to admit his error should "uncon-
trovertible evidence" stare him in the face, Jackson's communication gave him "no reason to change an opinion
which has been established upon actual experiment made
by himself that the Cow pox renders the human system
unsusceptible to the small-pox." [74]

With this view another practitioner agreed:

Dr. J's personal opportunity in *England* to gain a full knowledge of the true characteristics of Cow-pox, no medical gentlemen would be so uncandid as to suppose he could have left on
his mind a single doubt whether his patient had the disease.
While we render the Dr. the just praise due for the accuracy of
his statement, his liberality, and love of truth, we trust he will
not take offence, should we differ from him in opinion that
doubts which previous to this case never have existed, ought to
be entertained of the efficacy of cow-pox, and that the doubts
as to small pox, in which the case is enveloped, are *alone* sufficient to confirm, rather than weaken his original opinion, and

ought not to excite in the public mind, prejudices, already too indiscriminate, against what we have the fullest ground of belief, will be found most essential to the happiness of the world at large.[75]

The incident also brought a tactful letter from Manning, which Jackson transmitted to the newspaper:

Of those, who have been inoculated in this vicinity with vaccine matter from the same source as your's, ten have since been inoculated with variolous matter, and exposed to its infection. None of them had the least degree of symptomatic fever; several had their arms more or less inflamed, and one of them had two or three pustules.

Upon the whole the balance of experimental evidence appears at present in favor of the vaccine disease, and while this is the case I think it entitled to our undiminished confidence.[76]

V

While awaiting new vaccine from England during
the winter of 1801, Waterhouse seems to have concluded
that his original method of distribution had been a serious
mistake. After his supply had been reestablished in March,
1801, he acted upon different principles. Receiving requests for lymph from unknown correspondents in the
South, he sent it instead to Thomas Jefferson, who had
already expressed an interest in the new preventive. The
President in turn supplied many physicians throughout the
South and as far north as Philadelphia with their first genuine cowpox virus. No hint of monopoly or recompense in-
truded upon these negotiations. They were highly credita-
ble to Waterhouse's character and professional skill, as well
as to Jefferson's humanity and ingenuity.[77]

In Boston, the first result of this new attitude appeared
in the *Centinel* on April 1, 1801. After announcing the receipt of good vaccine from England, Waterhouse wrote
that when he had commenced the new inoculation in
America, he had had "special reasons for wishing to confine the trials, for awhile, to three or four practitioners."
Accordingly he had given the virus to three physicians
"long experienced in the inoculated small-pox, even before
the disease had gone through my own family." But since
these considerations no longer existed in their full force,
he would "adopt a different conduct" and "try to avoid
the blunder of dispersing it to so many inexperienced persons at a distance."

Recent information from England, Waterhouse continued, confirmed his assertion that a person who had undergone cowpox was secure from smallpox. Yet, since the accidents at Marblehead and the Wheelock case had created doubts, vaccination should be tested by variolation, as it had been in England and on the Continent. He wished now, he wrote, principally

to suggest the idea of a VACCINE INSTITUTION in *Boston*, or its neighborhood for the inoculation of the poor *gratis*, and so arranged as to admit of the trial of the small-pox *after* the kinepox, and that this institution should be *immediately* under the direction of AGED and EXPERIENCED practitioners, and *remotely* under the controul of the *Board of Health*.

Pointing out in support of this proposal that a general smallpox inoculation caused many deaths and universal business distress, a Bostonian called upon the wealthy to found such an institution and pay the cost of testing vaccinated persons. "Interest should induce our merchants to take this measure," he concluded, "and every other, which may introduce a general inoculation for the vaccine disease; as otherwise the town must ere long be shut up for a general variolous inoculation." By the end of May subscription papers were available in State Street insurance offices for those who wished to contribute.[78] But the only public response of the "aged and experienced practitioners," who had heard of the bonds and knew that Waterhouse had monopolized the practice in Boston as long as he could, was that implied in a letter from Jackson published on April 8, in which he announced the receipt of some "cow pox matter" from London. He and some other Boston physicians were vaccinating all poor applicants gratis, he noted, and no doubt all those interested in the introduction of the new preventive would do the same. "While the poor are benefitted by this arrangement," he explained, "the physician will find a compensation in the constant supply of fluid matter, on which depends very much the certainty of success in inoculating for this disease." [79]

Four days earlier, Waterhouse had met Isaac Rand, the president of the Massachusetts Medical Society, on a street in Boston. He told Waterhouse that the Society had just received some vaccine which had been ordered from London in January, that it had been distributed among a few of the members but had failed in their hands, and that he feared it would fail in his own.[80] On the following day, April 5, Waterhouse sent to Rand what he later described as an official letter, enclosing some lymph. Since he had made arrangements for a monthly supply from England, he wrote, he hoped to be able to afford the Society a never failing source.

Having imported a new disease, or to speak more properly, a new remedy [Waterhouse continued], I am, as may be supposed, ambitious to diffuse its benefits through our land, but am entirely at a loss for the just and proper method; on which account I feel disposed to submit the matter to the advice and direction of the Massachusetts Medical Society. I acceeded [sic] to the written proposals of a number of practitioners, at a distance, the past season; but that mode was never wholly to my satisfaction. In order then to give satisfaction to the faculty, to the public and to myself, I wish now to place myself under the direction and advice of the Society.

Waterhouse then suggested that since neither he nor the Society had been able to obtain an accurate account of the Marblehead epidemic, it might be advisable to appoint a committee to make the necessary investigation on the spot.[81] It is unfortunate that Waterhouse, whose proposal was sincere,[82] sent the letter to Rand rather than to the Corresponding Secretary, to whom, as an official letter, it should have been addressed. For Rand considered it personal, and never brought it to the Society's attention.[83]

When the Council met on April 29, Waterhouse came
to Boston and personally urged various members to appoint
a committee of inquiry.[84] The Council, acceding, picked
Waterhouse, President Rand, and Vice-President Warren.
When the day planned for the trip arrived, however, Warren and Rand, being both unable to go, dispatched
a servant to tell Waterhouse (they subsequently averred),
but Waterhouse apparently never received the message and as a result found himself alone in Marblehead.
Warren informed his colleague a few days later that he had
been called to an urgent case, and Rand immediately wrote
to the Society explaining why he had been detained; yet
Waterhouse conceived that he had been intentionally left
in the lurch. Though the committee never officially reported, the Council decided on June 3 that the receipt of
four letters on the epidemic "prevented the necessity of
any further attention to that subject." [85]

Thus in the spring of 1801 the Boston profession had
ignored Waterhouse's suggestion for a vaccine institution.
The Massachusetts Medical Society, never having received
his letter to Rand, had failed to act upon it. And the President and Vice-President of the Society, Waterhouse believed, had purposely left him to face the angry citizens of
Marblehead alone. A contentious person by nature, Waterhouse understandably felt bitter.

After waiting in vain for an answer to his request for advice and direction, Waterhouse late in June reverted to the
newspapers. Since people were less willing to believe events
occurring at a distant time or place, he argued, it was essential to publicize all American cases that demonstrated the
efficacy of vaccination. It had been hoped, he went on,
that "some *Medical* or *Philosophical Society*" would act
as a center for collecting and disseminating such information. "But as a propitious season is fast passing away, with-

out any prospect of such an advantage, Dr. WATERHOUSE is constrained to adopt a more diminutive plan, and to go on in this business as he began it—*alone*." Calling for case reports from practitioners who had successfully "put the kine pox to the *test* of the small pox," he concluded by requesting printers throughout the nation to republish his letter, "and *Patriotism* will carry it to their credit." [86]

During the rest of 1801 and throughout 1802 Waterhouse performed yeoman service. He distributed both lymph and instructions gratuitously not only to Jefferson, but also to Valentine Seaman in New York,[87] to the United States Army, and to many other practitioners. So extensive did his correspondence become, that in April, 1802, to save the labor of handwriting, he reprinted some concise directions which Jenner had recently sent him.[88] Waterhouse also kept up his propaganda barrage in the *Centinel* and other Boston newspapers. He sent information on proper techniques; warned against spurious cases and inexperienced or lay practitioners; investigated reports of smallpox following cowpox; transmitted accounts of the tested success of the new inoculation; relayed information from New York, Philadelphia, and England on the progress of vaccination; and drew up a long list of cases in an attempt to prove that the protective power of cowpox lasted for life.[89]

At the same time, Waterhouse was not the only medical man promoting vaccination in the Boston newspapers. In the *Palladium*, for example, "A Physician" sharply answered "A Tradesman" who hoped the town would allow a general smallpox inoculation in Boston during the summer of 1801.[90] One Cyrus Fay supported Waterhouse's contention that many had used spurious matter.[91] From Hallowell, Maine, came the report of a previously vaccinated man who had been variolated four times without effect,[92] and from Portsmouth, New Hampshire, an account of a successful public experiment by Lyman Spalding.[93] In October, 1801, both the *Palladium* and the *Chronicle* reprinted a certificate by Asaph Coleman, a Connecticut inoculator, that he had been unable to give smallpox to several persons vaccinated by Dr. Samuel Cooley of Bolton.[94] The following month the *Chronicle* carried the news that cowpox had been found in American cattle by three country physicians in southern New England,[95] and the *Palladium* printed reports in February and June, 1802, of the successful experiments of Nathaniel Miller of Franklin, Massachusetts.[96] In August, 1802, the *Centinel* published a letter from Dr. John G. Coffin of Boston describing the resistance of several persons in Maine to smallpox infection following vaccination. "This statement," he wrote, ". . . may be esteemed an addition of some importance to that weight of other evidence which has produced a conviction in my mind, that . . . vaccination . . . destroys the susceptibility [to smallpox] . . . for the remainder of life." [97]

The newspapers also informed their readers of Jefferson's progress with the lymph that Waterhouse had sent, of his endorsement of the procedure, and of his donation of the blessing to Little Turtle and other visiting Indians.[98] They extracted accounts from books and other journals of the advance of vaccination in England, France, Sweden, and Russia, as well as in New York, Baltimore, and Charleston.[99] From local citizens, too, came occasional messages. One urged doubters to read C. R. Aikin's *Concise View* on cowpox, which was reprinted in Charlestown in 1801; another warned against apparent failures due to spurious cases; and a third sent a statistical table of seven eighteenth-century smallpox epidemics in Boston to emphasize the benefits of the new preventive.[100]

Nevertheless, many citizens remained skeptical. Some were no doubt innately suspicious of anything new. Others probably considered the whole business a scheme pushed by the doctors for their own profit. Rumors persisted that persons who had been vaccinated had subsequently been infected with smallpox, and if these were exposed as cases of spurious cowpox, they nevertheless lent credence to a belief that the new inoculation was so difficult and uncertain in practice that variolation remained the only sure way to acquire immunity. And the old procedure was further reinforced by the assertion that the protective power of even a properly performed vaccination would last but a few years.[101]

Though rarely expressed in public print, the rationale of the opposition was in part exposed by Dr. William Aspinwall. After Waterhouse had first successfully tested his family in that physician's hospital in August, 1800, the inoculator reportedly exclaimed, "this new Inoculation of yours, is no sham. As a man of humanity, I rejoice in it; although it will take from me a handsome annual income." [102] Describing these events in September, 1800, Waterhouse generously acknowledged that he could not have completed his tests without Aspinwall's assistance. The latter, he wrote, "met these experiments, which apparently militate at present, with his interest, with a candor, and ingenuousness much to his praise." His conduct had done "honor to his liberality as a practitioner, and to his patriotism as a citizen." [103]

On October 1, 1801, however, to an advertisement of his hospital in the Chronicle, Aspinwall appended a notice that "Six persons who were inoculated with the KINE-Pox last year, and supposed to have had that disease, have been inoculated at the above said Hospital, the present year,

and five of the six have had the Small-Pox perfectly." [104]
The first reaction, which appeared in the next issue of the
same paper, was an observation by "A correspondent" that
the "five persons who had been supposed to have gone
through the Kine-Pox" were not, as some had inferred,
Waterhouse's patients: "The fact is six of Dr. Waterhouse's family, and another person he sent in this summer, and which Dr. Aspinwall inoculated, all withstood
the small-pox." [105]

Soon after, Waterhouse published a letter in the Palladium reiterating this point. Furthermore, he wrote, he
had supplied the vaccine for only one of the five, an em-
ployee whom Aspinwall had himself vaccinated.[106] When
Aspinwall's advertisement next appeared in the Chronicle,
it was immediately succeeded by another statement from
the Cambridge professor. He had applied to Aspinwall
for an explanation, he declared, "and having waited ten
days for an answer, have concluded that he does not mean
to give one." Had Aspinwall added a note that none of the
reported failures were Waterhouse's patients, he continued, it would have "obviated the uneasiness of some
parents, and added one more to the obligations I felt myself under to Dr. Aspinwall." And, he remarked, "I still
hope the Dr. will give to the public all the circumstances
of the inoculations mentioned in his too concise advertisement." [107] Privately, Waterhouse's reaction was considerably more acrid. On October 20 he wrote to Matthias
Spalding, a former student then in London, that Aspinwall, whose "candor and liberality was all affectation," had
"shown his teeth" by inoculating those "whom he knew
had never gone fairly through the disease," and then advertising the result. "It was just his harvest time," Waterhouse asserted, "it staggered several who were balancing
between the S. pox and kine pox, and occasioned perhaps

20 or 30 to go into his hospital. He gives out that the K. pox will preserve from infection for a few months *but no longer*." [108]

Soon after this outburst, Aspinwall named the six persons and presented some of the details relating to their vaccination. As to Isaac Sawyer, the one whom he had himself treated the previous November, he claimed that "Whether he had the *genuine* Kine-pox, or *spurious*, the matter with which he was inoculated, was received by me directly from Dr. WATERHOUSE, and immediately used." Waterhouse, he continued, had supplied him with vaccine four times, with which he had inoculated thirteen persons, "and on some of them it had no effect—on some it produced very sore arms, and one only, the *Kine-pox*, less equivical [sic] than that of Sawyer." [109] Less directly, through the remarks of "A Friend," Aspinwall had already offered the reason for his original publication: while professing entire confidence in the protective powers of cowpox, he contended that there was "*less certainty in its taking*, than in the SMALL-POX;" he was not convinced that there would be a gain in "discarding one to adopt the other." He did wish for "a fair trial and candid experiment." [110]

Apparently mollified, Waterhouse thanked Aspinwall for his explanatory statement. "It is by such open and candid discussions," he continued, "that we may expect to come at the truth. . . ." After giving further details and some notes on the sources of spurious vaccination, he disavowed any intention to reflect on Aspinwall. He was, Waterhouse wrote, more attached to the old inoculation, with which he had been so successful, than to the new. This was natural, Waterhouse explained: "He is like other men attached to his interest, but I believe he is attached to the great cause of humanity more." His only sentiments towards Aspinwall, Waterhouse concluded, were "those of respect and esteem." [111] Nor were these remarks intended solely for public consumption. The following spring Waterhouse wrote to Matthias Spalding that he hoped John Ring would "not name Aspinwall in terms that may hurt his feelings. I have many apologies to make for him," he added. "There are hundreds worse than he is in the opposition. His hospital is his own property and he will lose 1500 guineas a year by it." [112]

Meanwhile, during the year ending April 1, 1801, the Boston Board of Health had removed some sixty sailors suffering with smallpox from vessels arriving at the port. Though several persons had broken out with the disease in the town itself during the fall of 1800, the Board had controlled the incipient epidemic by taking most of the sick to the quarantine hospital on Rainsford Island and confining the rest in their homes.[113] When another case appeared in Boston in May, 1802, many neighbors, terrified despite the health officials' prompt isolation of the patient, hastened to Aspinwall's hospital.[114] Though the Board of Health had in June, 1801, rejected James Jackson's request for permission to test some of the people he had vaccinated, alleging that "the avocations of the Board would not permit that attention which the plan proposed by Dr. JACKSON required," [115] Waterhouse forcefully memorialized the Board on May 31, 1802, to undertake a convincing public experiment. Accepting his proposal, the Board, after consulting James Lloyd, Isaac Rand, Samuel Danforth, John Warren, Charles Jarvis, and John Jeffries, as well as Waterhouse, obtained the town's permission to perform the smallpox inoculations at some spot outside the peninsula. On August 16 nineteen young volunteers were vaccinated at the health office and a week later the examining physicians pronounced them "fit subjects for the Experiment contemplated." After erecting a temporary hospital on Noddle's Island, the Board secured fresh small-pox virus in November from a Falmouth inoculator and subjected the nineteen, along with another lad vaccinated two years previously, both to variolation and to contact with two unprotected controls who were inoculated to prove that the smallpox matter was active. The test was a complete success. Finally, the Board published a detailed report in mid-December with a supporting statement signed by eleven physicians and urged the public to use the new preventive.[116] "This decisive experiment," Water-house wrote soon after, ". . . has fixed forever the practice of the new inoculation in Massachusetts." [117]

VI

WHILE BENJAMIN WATERHOUSE'S EFFORTS DURING AND after 1801 to diffuse the benefits of vaccination were presumably sincere, he was not wholly candid about his operations during the summer and fall of 1800. Recognizing, perhaps, that his own approach had in fact fostered vaccination quackery and a speculative, mercenary attitude, and that his efforts to build a monopoly ill accorded with his pretensions to philanthropy; knowing that he could no longer in any event retain exclusive control over the supply of vaccine; and probably realizing that his actions, if widely known, would not only reflect upon his own character but also tend to discredit vaccination itself, Waterhouse sought to explain away or conceal his own culpability.

To Lettsom, for example, he wrote on April 6, 1801, that he had asked the Massachusetts Medical Society for their opinion as to the best way to distribute the cowpox virus, "for last year it got into the hands of speculators and quacks, notwithstanding every effort of mine to prevent it, which one of my friends at Bath [John Haygarth?] seems to have misunderstood." [118]

Writing to President Timothy Dwight of Yale on March 23, 1801, Waterhouse was more emphatic. So insistent was the demand for vaccine, he explained, that he had found it necessary to give up his original plan for "a rigid set of experiments," and he went, he feared, "into the opposite extreme." The clamor, he continued, "had a doubly bad effect, which I did not at first foresee, but which I was sensible of when they began to apply for it from Connecticut, which accounts for my refusal of them. But the motive of my refusal was misconstrued and they obtained some sort of matter elsewhere." When failures resulted, those who had formed "extravagant expectations" were the first to denounce vaccination as a "delusion" and "mere money speculation!" No wonder accidents occurred when a practitioner would even encourage children to treat each other, just to destroy a rival's business. "Contrast this abominable conduct," he wrote, "with the extreme care and caution exercised in *England* and lately at *Paris* in this new innoculation." [119]

Even more illuminating is a letter to Jefferson which Waterhouse sent on October 1, 1801, just after hearing that the President had successfully established vaccination in Washington and parts of Virginia. "Avarice, rivalship, and mistrust," he remarked, had attended the introduction of the practice in New England. Some physicians had ridden night and day to reach Cambridge ahead of their professional brethren, and others claiming to be his agents had endangered the lives of the people by hawking spurious matter. Six New Hampshire practitioners, he asserted, "absolutely new districted the State, and then applied to me for the matter, and offering me their conjoint bonds to give me a fourth part of all that were inoculated by them & their subordinates! so that before I well knew the spirit & extent of the plan, I found myself the centre of a vile speculation." But by sending the virus to Jefferson, Waterhouse wrote, he had forestalled similar events in the South.[120]

At a later date, April 2, 1803, Waterhouse explained in a letter to Major Daniel Jackson his refusal to accept any pay for sending vaccine and instructions for treating soldiers. In promoting this procedure, he wrote, he had had "*more powerful motives than private emolument.*" But since the work was inevitably attended with considerable expense, he decided, after consulting "leading medical and clerical characters," to impose a "small assessment" on those practitioners who sought instruction and vaccine solely for their own profit. Gladly would he have avoided this "tax," but "not being a man of property, *it was impossible.*" To medical societies, vaccine institutions, and "*influential characters,*" however, he had "*unremittingly and gratuitously*" distributed both the lymph and written instructions. "Supplying the means for inoculating the Battalion under your command," Waterhouse concluded, "I can consider in no other light than that of a PUBLIC BENEFIT, and when considered in this view I have invariably refused any pecuniary consideration whatever." [121] Most of this appears to be true. But it is hard to think of "$150 for a district not containing more inhabitants than Kittery," [122] or one quarter of the profits of a year's practice, as a "small assessment."

Despite these disclaimers, the story of the bonds refused to die. On July 21, 1802, Waterhouse wrote a letter to the *Centinel* contradicting the assertion that vaccination conferred only temporary protection:

After the absurd doctrine respecting the *short duration* of the efficacy of the kine-pock, is no longer urged [he concluded], there is but one other scheme to which the enemies of the new inoculation can have recourse for effecting its disgrace, and that is throwing it into the hands of improper persons. . . . I should not have glanced at this subject at this time, were not the same practices now going forward in a town close by *Boston*, where from the delusive offers of inoculating *gratis*, or for a very small fee, people have been induced to receive the disease from persons not qualified to judge between the *true* and the *spurious* pustule; the consequence has already been that children have followed the example and inoculated one another. The result will be, some of these imprudent people will go into the neighbouring hospital, take the small-pox, and then the odium will as usual revert to me, because the matter used was taken from my patients. I therefore feel it no more than justice to myself, (considering the pains I have taken to mature this business) and a duty I owe to the public, to notice this conduct of ignorance and presumption.[123]

Two men thought this letter aimed specifically at them. One obtained a private explanation with which he was satisfied.[124] The other, who had something of a temper, demanded a public disavowal, and in the next issue of the *Centinel* appeared a notice signed by Waterhouse denying any allusion to John C. Howard: ". . . from my knowledge of Mr. HOWARD's classical and medical education," he added, "it cannot be supposed that I meant to rank him with the ignorant and presumptuous." [125]

Had Waterhouse refrained from further personal observations, this would undoubtedly have ended the matter. But on August 2 he embroidered his first brief acknowledgment with another newspaper statement. In the earlier note, he addressed the editor, he "neglected to mention" an important point:

Some time last May I inoculated Mr. John Howard's child at Dorchester, WITH A VIEW to shew him the disease and FOR THE EXPRESS PURPOSE of giving him the genuine vaccine virus to make experiments with, agreeably to a promise I had long made him.—This forgotten fact speaks for itself.—In further justice to myself I feel now free to declare that it was only since that publication, that I was acquainted with the extent of the inoculations performed by a Merchant and a Lawyer in Dorchester and Roxbury. Had I have known it, I should hardly have been so forgetful of propriety as to have advertised the gentlemen, but seeing I was the originator of the experiments in Dorchester as well as in Roxbury, I should probably have taken the liberty to interpose my friendly advice, and that for the following rea-

sons, which I deem sufficiently important to VACCINATION, at *this period*, to merit a place in your paper.

First, all *gratuitous* inoculations on an extensive scale should be commenced and conducted by a PUBLIC VACCINE INSTITU-TION. . . .

Second, young physicians, (not to mention those who are not physicians) have universally conceived more lightly of this new inoculation than is consistent with the nature of things. . . . I fear lest this new inoculation should not be commenced and *tested* by persons sufficiently experienced in the kine-pock and in the SMALL-POX. Have not occurrences in own [*sic*] country justified this fear? How has it happened that of between 20 and 30 young Doctors to whom I have given the vaccine virus, have almost all of them within a few months got a ground and given up the business? They found as they went on, that this *very simple business*, required more attention than they at first imagined. . . .

As to gentlemen acting out of the line of their profession, . . . Has not a disregard to these lines of "*demarkation*" given origin, in the case before us, to a practice among mechanics and day labourers . . . ? [126]

It is hardly surprising that Howard, who, although not then in general practice, was a regularly educated physician,[127] felt called upon to reply. He had been willing, he wrote, "tacitly to acquiesce" in Waterhouse's first acknowledgment, but his new communication required some further observations. "Dr. WATERHOUSE insinuates," he noted, "that I had requested him to inoculate my child with the Vaccine virus with a view to show me the disease." To be sure, he had asked Waterhouse for some lymph, "but a long time having elapsed, without obtaining it," he had resorted to another physician, "who had more than once furnished Dr. W. and who promised to supply me at any time." Since he had frequently loaned Waterhouse publications on vaccination, Howard continued, he had considered himself authorized to make such an application "without incurring the hazard of a tax on my gratitude, which I might hereafter be unwilling or unable to pay. Although a merchant, I was not then aware that this virus had been, and still was a subject for traffick and barter." Some time later Waterhouse called and without Howard's knowledge or consent insisted upon vaccinating his child.

Furthermore, Howard rejoined, he had "positive and respectable evidences" to prove that Waterhouse was before his first "exceptionable publication" fully aware of the extent of Howard's practice in Dorchester. Indeed, Waterhouse had "expressed much surprize and dissatisfaction at my procedure; and more than insinuated that I was not competent to the business I had undertaken." Had it not been for this fact, Howard wrote, he would not have bothered to demand an explanation. But he conceived it due to those whom he had treated to remove all doubts "which any malevolent insinuations of my incapacity" might have aroused. He continued:

It was my good fortune to have been in England when the happy discovery of Vaccine Inoculation was first announced by Doct. JENNER. At once impressed with the importance of the subject I soon felt an interest in its success. From this early date my confidence in the efficacy of the Vaccine Inoculation has not been impaired; and I have been sedulous to inform myself of its progress by the regular importation of most of the publications on the subject. Deriving my information then from such sources, it can hardly be supposed that I sought any instructions from Dr. W. although he seemed to pretend to a superior knowledge of the disease, and wished to secure an exclusive practice in it. Time will discover if this were the best mode for making this invaluable discovery the most generally useful; and whether its blessings were best to be diffused by imparting the matter for inoculation generally to those only, who would give bonds for a proportion of the pecuniary profits resulting from its use, or by selling it like the *nostrums* of quackery and empiricism.

Until public skepticism had been overcome, Howard believed, gratuitous vaccination was the most likely means of extending the practice. It hardly seemed probable that this would endanger the "regular and honest profits" of the medical profession.[128] To this letter Waterhouse at that time made no public reply.[129]

Once again, in the fall of 1802, the bonds were mentioned. During the course of the experiment conducted by the Board of Health, Isaac Rand alluded to them in a private conversation with Waterhouse, "and pointed out to him what I [Rand] thought if the report was true might extricate him from the injurious consequences of it to his character." Waterhouse, however, denied the whole charge, and the matter rested.[130] In December the health officials presented their report, and shortly thereafter Waterhouse published his second volume on vaccination, *A Prospect of Exterminating the Small Pox Part II*.[131] During the next few years occasional references to the man and his work, none derogatory, appeared in the *Centinel*, but Waterhouse himself retired from his public literary labors in this cause.[132]

VII

PRAISED BY JENNER AND RING, HONORED BY PHYSICIANS AND laymen in other American cities, acclaimed in the news-papers of his own locality, Waterhouse might well have felt content in contemplating the contribution he had made to the welfare of the nation. But such was not the nature of the man. The real and fancied slights that he had received from the profession in Boston continued to ran-kle, and in 1806 he sent to the *Centinel* a slashing attack upon the Massachusetts Medical Society and a spirited de-fense against the imputation of personal profit-seeking.

After presenting in familiar phraseology his own version of the introduction of vaccination, his warnings against spurious cases, and the reaction which followed the Marble-head epidemic, he recounted his troubles with the Society. Understanding that the vaccine which it had received from London had failed, he wrote, he sent some of his own and at the same time requested the appointment of a commit-tee to investigate the Marblehead affair. But the other members of the committee, after making every arrangement, "left me alone to encounter, for aught they knew, the re-sentment of an enraged populace." The public should know, he thought, how he had been treated by those who should have offered him every encouragement.

So much was I engaged in pushing vaccination as a *public bene-fit*, and so little avaricious of personal profit or reputation, that in 1801, when I had obtained a new recruit of matter from *England*, and when my practice was free from spurious cases, I offered to put myself under the advice and controul [sic] of the

55

Massachusetts Medical Society. I wished to make them the central point to which every thing relating to this new inoculation might be reflected, and every where extend its power of illumination. But an illiberal construction was put on my application, and I was compelled to go on in this business, as I began it, ALONE.

Soon after, he reported, he again felt it his duty to warn the public against ignorant pretenders and spurious cases. But "the most illiberal part of the profession" attributed this "disinterested advice" to a desire to "create doubts and fears, and to raise difficulties and perplexities, in order to confine the business to my own hands." Despite a resulting abusive publication and anonymous threats, he continued to devote all his time and attention to the promulgation of the truth. Knowing the physicians of Boston would not follow his lead, he had memorialized the Board of Health to make a convincing experiment, which this *"standing committee of humanity"* had carried through to a triumphant conclusion.[133]

When the Massachusetts Medical Society convened for its annual meeting in June, this attack not unnaturally occasioned some remarks. Directed to inquire into the matter, the Counsellors appointed a committee of investigation headed by Dr. William Eustis (who was, incidentally, by far the most prominent Jeffersonian-Republican politician among the members of the profession in Boston [134]). Seeking explanations, Eustis called upon Waterhouse, who replied with a "letter of defiance": [135]

Sir, I have been too sick ever since the day you called on me, to attend to any business whatever; even this is written by repeated efforts, and is merely to thank you for your kindness; and I think I reciprocate it, when I say that I trust the gentlemen of the Medical Society will play their game with caution, when I assure them that *I have some trump cards in my hand.*[136]

Thereupon the committee and the Counsellors, after searching the Society's files, drew up their report.[137]

They could find no evidence, they wrote, that Waterhouse had sent vaccine to the Society or had offered to put himself under its control. Probably Waterhouse had, "after a certain period," given the virus to individual members; that they had also supplied him was "unquestionably true." If Waterhouse did propose to any members of the Society to place himself under its direction, the Society had taken no order upon the subject, and therefore could not be charged with want of liberality. Getting to the heart of the matter, they declared:

The assertion of Dr. W. that he was pursuing vaccination as a public benefit, and not for personal profit, does not accord with a notorious fact, viz. that until the virus had been received from Europe through other channels, he kept the matter in his own hands, excepting that it was imparted to those, who were ready to give him bonds for a pecuniary remuneration, proportionable to the profits of the business. When Dr. W. intimates that other physicians doubted the success of the inoculation, ought he not in candor to state, at the same time, his own embarrassments, arising from many spurious cases among his own patients?

The fact that the Society had sent to England for lymph in January, 1801, the committee reported, proved that it was not indifferent to the diffusion of vaccination; moreover, this importation did not fail, as Waterhouse himself well knew. "Nor is there better foundation for his attempt to propagate the opinion," they added, "that physicians here were averse to the introduction of the vaccine disease; for no where has it been better received by medical men." Since Waterhouse had been informed as soon as practicable of the reasons why the other members of the Marblehead committee had been unable to go, they were, they concluded, "at a loss to conceive, what motives could suggest, and what excuse can palliate the intimation of insincerity on the part of the committee." [138]

Obviously awaiting this opening, Waterhouse then produced his "*trump cards*," the letter he had written to Rand in April, 1801. What shall we think of a Society, he demanded, "who shall so conduct, as to allow a simple individual to meet them publicly with such a flat contradiction as is this *official* letter?" Though Rand would no doubt claim it was private, the attention given to the request for a Marblehead committee proved that the Society had seen the letter and treated the rest of it with "silent neglect." [139]

Taking up the cudgels for the Society, an anonymous Fellow (probably John Collins Warren and James Jackson [140]) returned blow for blow.

It is with reluctance [he began] I call the attention of the public to Dr. WATERHOUSE. They I know are fatigued and disgusted with the frequent displays of himself which he has made. Few persons need be informed of his impotence in every thing but vain-boasting of himself, and dark and artful insinuations respecting others. But continual misrepresentations must be exposed.[141]

Backed by statements from Rand and others, the Fellow pointed out in this and subsequent letters that Rand had indeed considered the letter private and that the Society, never having seen it, could not be charged with illiberality. That the Counsellors had appointed the Marblehead committee was irrelevant, for Waterhouse had personally urged many of them to take this step.

As the battle continued, Waterhouse maintained that he had never denied the existence of the bonds, and that he had never received a farthing from them. With supporting evidence the Fellow retorted that Waterhouse most certainly had given the impression of denying taking bonds, that only now when proof was available did he for the first time admit it. Charge was met with countercharge, invective with invective, until in his final letter the Fellow mercilessly pilloried his adversary:

He talks of the dignity of moderation, who has exhausted our language of abusive terms; he talks of personality, who has loaded with opprobrious epithets a most respectable physician [Rand]; he declaims on the nicety of moral character, who has publicly violated the ninth commandment; he pretends to value himself for his "cardinal point of veracity," who before the world, has been proved guilty of repeated falshoods. . . . This gentleman has long been desirous of persuading the literati of Europe, that his transcendent talents have made him the object of envy and persecution in America. Regarded only with derision, even by the youngest Physicians in Boston, he was willing to relinquish his small claims to the friendship of his brethren, and invite the persecution, which was to lay the foundation for his greatness. . . . When W. accidentally was the first to receive vaccine matter from Europe, he thought it ought to be retained in his own possession; and this, not from any interested nature. . . . The vaccine fluid was, however, soon imported from Europe by others, and it was then rapidly diffused; . . . and other Physicians, as well as he, took the liberty to vaccinate. Then did he begin to hate his brethren of the faculty, and to store up instruments of vengeance. . . . The public was not long in discerning that W. knew no more of vaccination than others; and conceiving that, for what pains he had taken, he paid himself by praising his deeds in the newspapers, became averse from him, and the business of vaccinating was gradually transferred to the hands of more respectable Physicians, so that by the spring of 1806, his practice in Boston was nearly or quite annihilated. Then the direful passions, long pent up, began to rage with unconquerable fury; then the treasured weapons were drawn out, and some new forged; . . . disappointment and revenge were the causes which excited him to action. Let him now fly to the shades of retirement, that he may revolve in his mind new plots, and enjoy *those reflections* and *that reputation* to which the execution of former ones entitle him.[142]

To enhance his fame as "The Jenner of America," Waterhouse had started this fight. In the event he lost.[143]

VIII

BETWEEN 1799 AND 1802 WATERHOUSE UNQUESTIONABLY
contributed significantly to the diffusion of vaccination.
While his friendship with Lettsom and Haygarth gave him
an initial advantage, he worked hard to convince skeptics
and to teach erring practitioners the importance of careful
attention to the subject. He furnished active vaccine to
Virginia and other Southern states through Thomas Jefferson, to New York through Valentine Seaman, and to many
other communities. For nearly all this work he neither
asked nor received any pay. From March, 1801, on, he
maintained a continuity of cases and resupplied many who
failed. He made himself through devotion to this cause one
of the leading American vaccinators during the years when
the practice was first becoming established.

At the same time, the basic discovery and the most important early works on vaccination were English. Waterhouse was not an originator, but a promoter. Nor was he
the only American physician who imported the lymph. Dr.
John Chichester successfully vaccinated one person in
Charleston, South Carolina, in the winter of 1799 and subsequently tested him by variolation.[144] Dr. George Pearson
sent a thread to David Hosack in New York late in 1798,
but this and a second thread failed.[145] Dr. Edward Miller
of New York received threads from Pearson in March,
1800, and in the following summer, also without success.[146]
About the same time John Ring sent some virus to Dr.
John Crawford of Baltimore, but he too was probably unable to propagate it.[147] Though these events played no part

61

in actually establishing vaccination in the United States, they illustrate the obvious fact that Waterhouse was not the only physician sufficiently interested in the new procedure to try it out.

Moreover, several practitioners did successfully import vaccine. Thomas Manning of Ipswich received his shortly after Waterhouse, and the Massachusetts Medical Society obtained good virus in April, 1801. James Smith of Baltimore first vaccinated in that city on May 1, 1801, using lymph which had come from London. After testing his patient by variolation, he published the result and offered to dispense free vaccine to members of the profession. The following March he established the first vaccine institution in the United States.[148] Dr. John Redman Coxe introduced vaccination in Philadelphia on November 9, 1801, with virus received from Jefferson, but four or five days later equally good virus arrived from London.[149] Furthermore, even in Boston the newspapers printed a wealth of material promoting the practice which had not come from Waterhouse, and the nation's only professional journal, the *Medical Repository*, was fully alive to the importance of the new preventive.

Vaccination spread across the nation with remarkable rapidity. By the spring of 1802 it had reached all the major seaports and many smaller communities in the East, and as far west as Mississippi, Kentucky, and Ohio.[150] Though Waterhouse emphasized the difficulties he encountered and the people's reluctance to accept it, less ardent and contentious men viewed its rate of advance with equanimity. The editors of the *Medical Repository* believed by the summer of 1802 that "none of our readers at the present day can doubt that body of testimony on this subject which has been long since and repeatedly laid before the public." [151] Despite the opposition and prejudice which the discovery had encountered, they later observed, "We believe no improvement in the practice of physic, of any great importance, was ever adopted by the community with so much readiness as the vaccine inoculation." [152] Benjamin Russell, editor of the *Columbian Centinel* and a staunch advocate of the new practice, commented in December, 1802, that its progress had been "rapid and permanent." [153] For his part in this work, Waterhouse deserves much credit. Yet it is only reasonable to conclude that vaccination would have spread throughout the United States almost as quickly as it did had Waterhouse never lived.

In Boston, the physicians were evidently not as zealous or as vocal as Waterhouse in promoting this innovation. They probably did fail to continue vaccinating through the summer and fall of 1801.[154] Some may have at first questioned the value of the practice. Jackson in February, 1801, admitted to some loss of confidence in vaccination as a perfect security against smallpox. Yet it is certainly a travesty to declare or insinuate, as many writers beginning with Waterhouse have, that the profession as a whole hindered or opposed the introduction of vaccination. Aspinwall was the only doctor who publicly dissented, and his attitude was based at least in part on apparently honest doubts as to the ability of practitioners to be sure that they had communicated genuine cowpox to their patients.

The early interest, advocacy, and success of some physicians of Boston and nearby towns have already been described. To this may be added a statement made in 1808 by John Warren, Aaron Dexter, James Jackson, and John C. Warren:

The high interest which this discovery excited in this country at the time of its annunciation, and the evidence, which was immediately offered by Dr. Jenner and his coadjutors, did, at a very early period, engage the attention of almost every individual among us in the medical profession; and that evidence was so perfectly satisfactory to the public, that a formal investigation of the subject by this [Massachusetts Medical] society, at that period, was altogether unnecessary.[155]

Though this statement, being late, has by itself little evidential value, Waterhouse himself wrote to Jefferson in June, 1801, that although the new practice had some adversaries even among the faculty, "The most eminent physicians in this region, as well as the most distinguished characters, in the two other learned professions, are advocates for this inoculation." In January, 1802, he wrote Valentine Seaman of New York that "all the old Physicians in Boston are advocates of the practice, & have introduced it into their own families;" the opposition came from "those who are candidates for fame, & business." Popular opinion, he continued, was also favorable.

While the common people see that characters the most distinguished for knowledge and rank in Society, as well as the most respectfull Physicians have their own children Inoculated & perceive that its opponents are the ignorant & the interested, they will duly appreciate the idle stories, here & there floating in the breath of rumour.[156]

In September, 1802, a group of twelve young physicians applied to the Board of Health for permission to use its office for a vaccine institution. Although they waited to announce the plan (which was fully approved by the "elders of the faculty") until after the health officials completed their experiment, this was certainly not because they needed to be themselves convinced.[157] Nor is it without significance that the American Academy of Arts and Sciences was the first organization in this country to honor Jenner formally, and that Harvard was the first university anywhere to confer upon him an honorary degree.[158]

If the physicians of Boston did not oppose vaccination, the possibility remains that they exhibited hostility toward Waterhouse personally. One of the Cambridge professor's principal targets in 1806 was Isaac Rand, but the latter produced several certificates testifying to his benevolent attitude during the critical period. Though this may not prove much, Waterhouse's own statement that he consulted Rand before publishing his attack on lay vaccinators in August, 1802, indicates that the two were not then inveterate enemies. And in 1807, apparently relieved by the previous year's act of catharsis, Waterhouse conceded that Rand was at an early period one of the most decided supporters of vaccination.[159] Waterhouse, it would seem, feeling that those who did not actively and vocally support him opposed him,[160] greatly magnified in his own mind the extent of his colleagues' aversion. He attributed to Rand and Warren, in connection with the Marblehead episode, a malicious attitude which there is no real evidence to believe they had. It is probable, moreover, that historians have tended to transfer back to an earlier period animosities engendered by Waterhouse's later difficulties with Harvard [161] and other subsequent controversies.

The existence of hostility toward Waterhouse is nevertheless evident. Samuel Brown, John C. Howard, and one or two other physicians attacked him in the newspapers. "Clericus" declared in the Centinel in 1803 that Waterhouse had "encountered prejudice and opposition at almost every step, and not the least from the faculty," while another writer noted that some people had termed his publications private advertisements.[162] An undercurrent of enmity is also apparent from the lack of articles by Boston physicians sympathetic to Waterhouse and from their failure to adopt his term, "kine pock."

Many writers have attributed this attitude in part to

political differences.[163] Waterhouse was not, like John Warren, a high Federalist. He did not look upon the election of Jefferson in 1800 as a national calamity: he reacted favorably to the conciliatory phrase, "We are all Republicans, we are all Federalists," in the President's Inaugural Address.[164] On the other hand he was not at this time an ardent Republican. Indeed, as late as the spring of 1806 a Boston magazine declared that Waterhouse paid "no regard to party politicks." [165] In the published correspondence between Waterhouse and John Adams, the first suggestion of political animus toward the Essex Junto—the extreme Federalist leaders of Massachusetts—does not occur until August, 1805. As late as December, 1809, two years after his son's break with the Federalists, Adams was apparently surprised to find that his friend had Republican leanings. "I did not before know," he wrote, "but you was one of those respectable People who do not read the *Patriot*." It is from this letter that we learn of Waterhouse's "concern of Mind to write upon Politicks." [166] Writing to Lettsom on July 15, 1810, Waterhouse was even more explicit: "I was of this Fœderal party until within this year or two, as far as it regarded my voting; but I never was active or zealous; I, however, have abjured them since I find they prefer the honour of a foreign country to our own." [167]

Mild as these views were, Waterhouse's emphasis on Jefferson's support of vaccination and his failure to join the jihad against the President may not have endeared him to his Federalist colleagues.[168] It is clear, however, that politics had no significant connection with the introduction of vaccination. Waterhouse sent his first and most of his subsequent communications to the *Centinel*, one of the nation's most outspoken Federalist journals, and he transmitted his views to Connecticut in a letter to the high priest of Federalism, "Pope" Dwight of Yale. Samuel Brown's attempt to secure the virus in 1800 was denounced as an example of "*Jacobin benevolence*," and as another of the current weapons aimed "not only at law and property, but at civility, and the absolute rights of individuals!" [169] When the Republican *Independent Chronicle* in 1802 tried to make political capital out of Jefferson's support of vaccination and John Ring's opinion of "our illustrious President," Benjamin Russell, the editor of the *Centinel*, quickly replied that he considered Jefferson's patronage of the new preventive, long since acknowledged in his newspaper, "as amongst his most praise-worthy actions." And he added Ring's equally complimentary remarks about Adams.[170] Evidently Russell was unwilling to have anyone believe that Federalists supported vaccination less ardently than Republicans, and his own continued and vigorous promotion of the practice indicates that they were not.[171] Nor would the Massachusetts Medical Society, if actuated by political motives, have appointed William Eustis in 1806 to head a committee to investigate Waterhouse's charges. That Waterhouse was later an outspoken Republican is completely beside the point.

While it is difficult to perceive any correlation between political beliefs and attitudes toward vaccination, it is of course possible that Waterhouse's religious opinions [172] may have prejudiced others against him. It is equally true that petty jealousy evoked by his original appointment as Professor of Physic and by the recognition which he received from Jenner and others may have colored the views of some Bostonians. Nevertheless, Waterhouse's own actions and words solely in connection with the introduction of vaccination amply justified any existing hostility or distrust. He did not incur others' enmity because he inaugurated the practice, but because of the way he did it.

Throughout his newspaper articles and books Waterhouse exhibited a distinct tendency to self-glorification. He pointedly and unnecessarily emphasized his personal correspondence with Jenner and other British physicians.[173] He made great use of the first person singular pronoun. Repeatedly he pointed out that "I" first pronounced that cowpox would ever after secure a person from smallpox, that "I" warned against the dangers of spurious cases, that no patient "I" vaccinated had subsequently contracted smallpox, that "I" could not vouch for the practice of others.

Furthermore, Waterhouse studiously neglected the achievements of other physicians in this country. He disregarded almost completely American publications on vaccination, except for his own. Although the *Medical Repository* had previously printed an account of Jenner's work, cowpox, according to Waterhouse, was before his first article "a disease totally unknown, and till then unheard of in this quarter of the world." [174] The extensive literature submitted by others to the Boston newspapers and to the *Repository* received no credit in Waterhouse's *Prospect of Exterminating the Small Pox Part II, . . . a Narrative of Facts Concerning the Progress of the New Inoculation in America.*

Throughout this history Waterhouse conveyed the impression that he encountered little but opposition and stupidity. Almost invariably, he alluded to those who were vaccinating as early as 1800 only to discuss their failures or their requests to him for vaccine and instruction. It was remarkable, he wrote, that in neither New York, Philadelphia, Charleston, nor Savannah, did any of the vaccine repeatedly imported from England ever communicate the disease—despite Coxe's plain statement that he had successfully vaccinated with virus obtained from London.[175] Waterhouse noted in passing the failure of Baltimore doctors who used imported threads and declared that the physicians of Maryland, among others, were supplied from his stock through Jefferson.[176] He never mentioned James Smith. He referred to Manning's importation only once— in a newspaper article in December, 1800.[177] In his narrative Waterhouse described his June, 1801, request for reports of other practitioners' successfully tested cases of vaccination, but he failed to note the returns he received or any of the other public demonstrations of the efficacy of vaccination concluded in New England prior to the experiment supervised by the Boston Board of Health late in 1802.[178]

Waterhouse was equally reluctant to admit that the physicians of Boston had played a role in the introduction of vaccination. For example, he declared that in the summer of 1802 "The faculty in that town, with but one exception, had not given it their decided approbation and countenance." While it is not clear to which of the many supporters of vaccination Waterhouse referred, perhaps he had James Jackson in mind, for three pages later he mentioned Jackson's request to the Board of Health in 1801 for permission to test some of his patients by variolation. But Waterhouse immediately deflated whatever credit might have accrued to the young physician for this effort by calling him "my ingenious and esteemed pupil." One might suppose from this passage that Waterhouse had taught Jackson how to vaccinate.[179]

Waterhouse's account was not only incomplete, but in some cases lacking in candor. Particularly instructive is a careful examination of his treatment of the failures in November, 1800. At the time he attributed his own difficulties to a degeneration of the vaccine caused either by repeated human transfer or by cold weather. In April, 1801, however, after a letter from Jenner taught him the importance of taking the vaccine on the eighth or at the very latest the ninth day, Waterhouse acknowledged his error to Lettsom and Jenner and blamed his spurious cases on taking the lymph from the arms of his patients at too late a stage of the eruption.[180] In *Prospect Part II*, moreover, he in effect admitted that during the fall of 1800 he did not know when the vaccine should be taken.[181]

Yet earlier in this same volume, after referring to the warning against spurious cowpox in *Prospect* (Part I), Waterhouse wrote:

I felt it my duty in November of the same year [1800] to acquaint the public, through the medium of the newspaper, that the kine-pock had, in many places, degenerated from its original mild character, and that this deviation appeared to have arisen from the inoculator taking his matter from the pustule at *too late a period*.[182]

Actually, the only suggestion in the newspaper publication to which Waterhouse was here referring (which first appeared not in November but on December 27) that taking the vaccine at too late a period caused spurious cases was a repetition of Jenner's warning, already printed in *Prospect* (Part I), against "matter taken from an ulcer in an *advanced stage*. . . ." [183] This caution, thrice given, was Waterhouse's only published statement prior to June, 1801, of the importance of taking the lymph at the proper time.[184] As his own experience proves, it was too indefinite to be of critical value.[185] No one, surely, would consider "an ulcer in an *advanced stage*" an accurate description of the vaccination pustule on, for example, the thirteenth day.

Waterhouse continued his narrative by relating that before Story's unfortunate mistake spread smallpox in Marblehead, Drury, who "took matter for his inoculations on the thirteenth day," [186]

had inoculated about forty persons, from the arm of his son whom I had vaccinated, but did not adhere to my directions respecting the time of taking the matter. ALL that he inoculated took the small-pox, either casually, or by inoculation, one excepted. . . . Although I saw clearly the cause of this disaster, (for I repaired immediately to Marblehead, and saw the chain of their calamity, and examined every link of it in conjunction with Dr. S. and Dr. D.) I found it vain to attempt to explain or palliate, but left its development to time, that infallible test of truth.[187]

Since Waterhouse himself was at this time taking vaccine too late, it seems more likely that.Drury erred not so much because he failed to follow Waterhouse's directions —if Waterhouse gave him any—as because the directions were inadequate. A comparison of this account with Waterhouse's newspaper statements of November and December, 1800, moreover, reveals additional discrepancies. From these it appears that Waterhouse did go to Marblehead on November 12 or 13, when he obtained from Story a candid history of the introduction of the smallpox infection.[188] On December 20, however, Waterhouse wrote:

Having heard that several persons, who had been inoculated for the Kine-Pox at Marblehead, have since taken the small-pox, I wrote to the inoculator [Drury] in that town, requesting an acurate [sic] history of the business, and having waited a due time for an answer without receiving any, I can no longer defer giving you a few important facts respecting it. . . .

I inoculated . . . the son of a practitioner [Drury], a boy of about eight or nine years of age. His father brought him to my house in Cambridge. I put the thread in his arm, and gave his father a small portion of the same, but never saw nor heard any more of the boy afterwards, and of course I never knew whether

he ever had the genuine *local affection,* and *specific fever,*
which constitute that peculiar distemper, which I have said and
still believe secures the human system from the small-pox. Yet
from this boy's arm was taken, as I am informed, all the matter,
with which all the others in Marblehead were inoculated. If the
matter therefore, which I used, did not give the genuine disease
in the *first* instance, which happens very frequently, then all the
cases that followed it must of course be *spurious,* and absolutely
incapable of securing the system from an attack of the small-
pox. . . . The wide avenue which these facts open to uncertainty
must be apparent to every discerning individual.[189]

In fact, as late as April, 1801, Waterhouse complained that
he had been unable to obtain an accurate account of the
accidents at Marblehead.[190] So much for his later claim
that he immediately explored the circumstances with Drury
and saw clearly the cause of his failure.

Were such inaccuracies Waterhouse's only sins, they
might be overlooked, in view of his services, as the foibles
of an egotistical and contentious character. But it is no
longer possible to ignore his efforts to restrict the diffusion
of vaccine in the late summer and early fall of 1800 in order to profit from a monopoly, or the bonds which he secured from other practitioners requiring them to remit one
quarter of their profits in return for a supply of the virus.
The existence of the bonds was known, or at least reported,
as early as November, 1800. Publicly Waterhouse simply
ignored that charge and John C. Howard's similar accusa-
tion in August, 1802. In letters to John C. Lettsom, Timothy Dwight, and Thomas Jefferson, however, he implied
that the imputation was false, and Isaac Rand, John Warren, and Thomas Welsh all stated that in the fall of 1802
he had in effect denied taking such bonds.[191] Indeed, according to one member of the Massachusetts Medical Society, "Almost every physician in *Boston* is of opinion that

Dr. W. has on this subject used such expressions as to make them suppose he *did not take,* or meant to *deny taking* those bonds." [192]

In 1806, when Waterhouse could no longer evade the issue, he declared that the matter had been misrepresented, that he had never concealed the existence of the bonds, and that he had never intended to make any money from them. The following year he presented his full explanation. After the result of the test on his children in Aspinwall's hospital spread the fame of the new preventive, he wrote, he was deluged with "innumerable and embarrassing" requests for the virus.

By far the greatest number who applied for matter, and for instructions how to use it, were utter strangers to me. I discovered afterwards, that some of them were not even practitioners of physic, but *speculators in kine pock matter.* I saw what would be the consequence of this junction of avarice, ignorance and presumption, and warned the public in the *Centinel* against spurious matter.[193] The evil I predicted was spreading through the country, when I had a number of applicants of a different class from the first, namely, practitioners of known repute. After much consultation respecting the best mode of diffusing *genuine* vaccination, and repressing speculation in spurious matter, a plan of this sort was concluded on, and offered to me for consideration, viz. that I should supply these reputable physicians with matter continually, and with every instruction and assistance, even to visiting their district, if required; that they should notify to the public that I was at the head of their inoculation; and that they would in return give me a fourth part of the profits.[194] The gentlemen I refer to will doubtless do me the justice to declare that I objected to the last part of this agreement, remarking, that it was my duty as a professor, as well as my inclination, to diffuse all I know in medicine for the public good; but they absolutely refused to take matter from me on any other condition. They did not stop here;—they proposed that this scheme should be ratified by an exchange of bonds, while I thought a few lines expressive of each other's meaning would be sufficient;—they, however, urged that with bonds they could better regulate their own business with other practitioners; who were to be, as I found afterwards, subsidiary to them. I consented, but never relished the idea; so that this business of the bonds was a thing that did not originate with me; nor did I ever consider them of so much consequence as ever to ask any of these gentlemen to fulfil their conditions. . . . I never proposed to enrich myself by vaccination, and accordingly I never have. . . . [195]

It is entirely possible that Waterhouse's bonds failed to return much money. When he applied to the Massachusetts General Court in 1810 for some remuneration for his labors, a sympathetic committee reported that "although it is not pretended that he is poorer for what he has done in this new line of practice, yet your Committee are far from supposing that by means of it he has made himself rich." [196] No one, however, can carefully read the Waterhouse–Spalding–Bartlett letters without concluding that Waterhouse intended to profit from his original monopoly of the cowpox virus,[197] and that his later explanation of the bonds, so palpably improbable, was a complete fabrication. Though Waterhouse might well have charged a fee to cover his expenses and provide a reasonable income, his actions in the summer and early fall of 1800 were morally indefensible. They contradicted his own pretentions to philanthropy; they rendered his motives for warning against spurious cases suspect; and they fostered the spirit of commercialism which at first damaged the cause of vaccination. Furthermore, his later attempts to explain the bonds only served to convict him of lying. Knowing the basic facts, the physicians of Boston were fully justified in regarding Waterhouse with suspicion and hostility.

NOTES

I

1. See such standard works as J. H. Baas, *Outlines of the History of Medicine and the Medical Profession* (H. E. Handerson, trans., New York, 1889), 711; F. H. Garrison, *An Introduction to the History of Medicine* (4th ed., Philadelphia, 1929), 375; Arturo Castiglioni, *A History of Medicine* (E. B. Krumbhaar, trans., 2d ed., New York, 1947), 643; *Dictionary of American Biography* (Allen Johnson and Dumas Malone, eds., New York, 1928-36), XIX, 529-532; *Dictionary of American Medical Biography* (Howard A. Kelly and Walter L. Burrage, eds., New York, 1928), 1266-1269.

2. Thomas J. Pettigrew, *Memoirs of the Life and Writings of the Late John Coakley Lettsom* . . . (London, 1817), I, 121-122.

3. John Baron, *The Life of Edward Jenner, M.D., LL.D., F.R.S.* . . . (London, 1838), I, 385-389.

4. Edgar M. Crookshank, *History and Pathology of Vaccination* (Philadelphia, 1889), I, 425-429; "The Diffusion of Vaccination: History of Its Introduction into Various Countries," *British Medical Journal*, 1896, I, 1269; F. Dawtrey Drewitt, *The Life of Edward Jenner, M.D., F.R.S., Naturalist, and Discoverer of Vaccination* (London, 1931), 59; R. Hingston Fox, *Dr. John Fothergill and His Friends: Chapters in Eighteenth Century Life* (London, 1919), 375-376; James J. Abraham, *Lettsom: His Life, Times, Friends and Descendants* (London, 1933), 333-335, 363-364.

5. Josiah Bartlett, *A Dissertation on the Progress of Medical Science, in the Commonwealth of Massachusetts* (Boston, 1810), 28-29.

6. James Thacher, *American Medical Biography* . . . (Boston, 1828), I, 29.

7. "Death of Benjamin Waterhouse, M.D.," *Boston Medical and Surgical Journal*, XXXV (1846–47), 206. See also J. F. W. Lane, "Some Statistics of Small-Pox and Vaccination," *American Journal of the Medical Sciences*, n.s. XII (1846), 128.

8. O. W. Holmes, "The Medical Profession in Massachusetts," *Medical Essays 1842–1882* (The Writings of Oliver Wendell Holmes, Riverside Edition, IX, Boston, 1891), 349.

9. E. Warren, *The Life of John Warren, M.D.* . . . (Boston, 1874), 403-406; *The Life of John Collins Warren, M.D.* . . . (Boston, 1860), I, 77-78. See also E. Warren's intimation that Waterhouse was not "an authority that could be relied upon." *Ibid.*, I, 85.

10. S. D. Gross, *Lives of Eminent American Physicians and Surgeons of the Nineteenth Century* (Philadelphia, 1861). Gross credited David Hosack with being among the first, if not the very first, supporters of vaccination. *Ibid.*, 317.

11. E. H. Clarke and others, *A Century of American Medicine 1776–1876* (Philadelphia, 1876), 15.

12. H. A. Martin, "Jefferson as a Vaccinator," *North Carolina Medical*

Journal, VII (1881), 1-34. A Boston physician specializing in vaccination, Martin felt that the treatment he received from the ruling powers of the Massachusetts Medical Society was surpassed in scurrility only by that meted out to Waterhouse and Zabdiel Boylston.

13. S. A. Green, *History of Medicine in Massachusetts* . . . (Boston, 1881), 106-110.

14. Joseph Jones, *Contagious and Infectious Diseases, Measures for Their Prevention and Arrest* (Baton Rouge, 1884), 178-212; also in Jones, *Medical and Surgical Memoirs* . . . , III, part I (New Orleans, 1890), 310-344.

15. W. M. Welch, "The Jenner of America," Philadelphia County Medical Society, *Proceedings*, VII (1884–85), 172-201.

16. Wilson G. Smillie and others, "The Great Pioneers of Public Health in America 1610–1925," *American Journal of Public Health*, XLIII (1953), 1077-1084. The most important recent works on Waterhouse and vaccination are Robert H. Halsey, *How the President, Thomas Jefferson, and Doctor Benjamin Waterhouse Established Vaccination as a Public Health Procedure* (New York Academy of Medicine, History of Medicine Series, No. 5, New York, 1936); Reginald Fitz, " 'Something Curious in the Medical Line,' " *Bulletin of the History of Medicine*, XI (1942), 239-264; Josiah C. Trent, "Benjamin Waterhouse (1754-1846)," *Journal of the History of Medicine and Allied Sciences*, I (1946), 357-364. Other accounts include: J. H. Hunt, "Dr. Benjamin Waterhouse and the Introduction of Vaccination into the United States," *Brooklyn Medical Journal*, X (1896), 391-395; Francis R. Packard, *The History of Medicine in the United States* (Philadelphia, 1901), 91-92; *ibid.* (New York, 1931), I, 89-90; James G. Mumford, *A Narrative of Medicine in America* (Philadelphia, 1903), 276-277; Thomas F. Harrington, *The Harvard Medical School, a History, Narrative and Documentary 1782–1905* (New York, 1905), I, 91-93, 315-330; A. K. Stone, "Benjamin Waterhouse," *Boston Medical and Surgical Journal*, CLXXIV (1916), 285-286; George C. Whipple, *State Sanitation: a Review of the Work of the Massachusetts State Board of Health* (Cambridge, 1917), I, 10-14; J. W. Courtney, *Benjamin Waterhouse, M.D.: American Pioneer* (Communication faite au Vme Congrès International d'Histoire de la Médecine, Geneva, 1926), 3-7; Louis H. Roddis, *Edward Jenner and the Discovery of Smallpox Vaccination* (Menasha, 1930), 99-102; Henry R. Viets, *A Brief History of Medicine in Massachusetts* (Boston, 1930), 119-125; S. B. Woodward, "The Story of Smallpox in Massachusetts," *New England Journal of Medicine*, CCVI (1932), 1188-1190; C. J. Brim, "Benjamin Waterhouse (1754-1846): An Underestimated American Medical Pioneer," *Medical Life*, XLI (1934), 283-285; H. G. Partridge, "Benjamin Waterhouse," *Rhode Island Medical Journal*, XXIV (1941), 125-127; M. C. Leikind, "The Introduction of Vaccination into the United States," *Ciba Symposia*, III (1941–42), 1114-1124; Archibald Malloch, *Medical Interchange between the British Isles and America before 1801* (London, 1946), 43-44; Maurice B. Gordon, *Æsculapius Comes to the Colonies* . . . (Ventnor, N. J., 1949), 277-279; E. Ashworth Underwood, "Edward Jenner, Benjamin Waterhouse, and the Introduction of Vaccination into the United

States," *Nature*, CLXIII (1949), 823-828; I. B. Cohen, "Edward Jenner and Harvard University," *Harvard Library Bulletin*, III (1949), 352-357.

17. Edward Warren was obviously biased. Otherwise, Roddis (*op. cit.*, 102) remarked without amplification that Waterhouse was remembered for attempting to monopolize and commercialize vaccination. Courtney (*op. cit.*, 7) noted that Waterhouse was charged with commercializing the practice.

18. J. A. Spalding, *Dr. Lyman Spalding: the Originator of the United States Pharmacopœia* . . . (Boston, 1916), 52-109, *passim*.

19. M. C. Leikind, "An Episode in the History of Smallpox Vaccination in New Hampshire," *Bulletin of the History of Medicine*, VII (1939), 671-686.

20. Neither Halsey, Fitz, nor Trent appears to have used either Spalding's book or Leikind's article. Even Underwood, who did, declared (*loc. cit.*, 824, 825) that we must go to Waterhouse's own publications for a "true appreciation" of his difficulties, and that the letters published by Spalding and Leikind illustrated "an amusing incident, which was perhaps unavoidable in the social atmosphere of that time," but which was not representative of Waterhouse's character and work.

II

21. This was not the first publication on vaccination in the United States: see, "The Following Important Account of a New Publication in Great-Britain, by Dr. Jenner, Entitled *An Inquiry into the Causes and Effects of the Variolæ Vaccinæ, or Cow Pox*, Is Extracted from the *Analytical Review* for July, 1798," *Medical Repository*, II (1798-99), 255-258. This number appeared in December, 1798 (*ibid.*, 146). Despite Waterhouse's oft-quoted comment ("This publication shared the fate of most others on new discoveries. . . .") in *A Prospect of Exterminating the Small-Pox; Being the History of the Variolæ Vaccinæ, or Kine-Pox, Commonly Called the Cow-Pox; as It Has Appeared in England: with an Account of a Series of Inoculations Performed for the Kine-Pox, in Massachusetts* (Cambridge, 1800), 8 [hereafter cited as *Prospect* (Part I)], he wrote Lettsom on Apr. 10, 1799, that the news "excites the public curiosity as much as any thing that has occurred in the medical line since my remembrance." Thomas J. Pettigrew, "On the Priority of the Transmission of Cow-Pock Matter to America," *Philosophical Magazine and Journal* (London), XLIX (1817), 278. The *Centinel* article was also reprinted in *J. Russell's Gazette. Commercial and Political* (Boston), Mar. 21, 1799. When Waterhouse reprinted this account in *Prospect* (Part I), 4-8, he gave the date of its original publication as Mar. 12, an error which has frequently been repeated.

22. For the details of Waterhouse's work to this point, see Fitz, *loc. cit.*, 239-247.

23. Waterhouse, *Prospect* (Part I), 18-25; *Columbian Centinel*, July 19, Aug. 16, 1800; *Russell's Gazette*, Aug. 7, 1800. Waterhouse offered Aspinwall his choice of three patients for the first test, and he picked a

twelve-year-old servant boy, not one of Waterhouse's own children. The latter were tested shortly thereafter. Waterhouse, *Prospect* (Part I), 25; *Columbian Centinel*, Sept. 20, 1800.

24. *Ibid.*, Aug. 20, 1800.

25. Another term for cowpox, coined by Waterhouse.

26. Spalding, *op. cit.*, following p. 54.

27. The transcription published by Underwood, *loc. cit.*, 826, is somewhat more accurate than that in Spalding, *op. cit.*, 54.

28. *Ibid.*, 55-58.

29. *Ibid.*, 57-58; Leikind, *loc. cit.*, 682-683; *Columbian Centinel*, July 12, 16, Aug. 6, 1806; *The Repertory* (Boston), July 15, 1806. Waterhouse to Z. Bartlett, Oct. 1, 1800, MS. in New York Academy of Medicine. See Plate I. Waterhouse indicated in this letter that "I should much rather that all the physicians of your town would unite in the business, so as to cause the kine-pox to pervade your whole town," but sometime in October he also signed a note, "This certifies that I have given to Dr. Zacheus Bartlett the matter of the Kine-pox for the purpose of inoculation in Plymouth, but not to supply any other practitioner." See Plate II. Courtesy of Dr. William Finkelstein, of Waterbury, Connecticut. For David King, see C. F. Bartlett to Moses Brown, Newport, Nov. 11, 1800; for Dyer, see Brown to Bartlett, Providence, Oct. 17, 1800, Moses Brown Papers, Rhode Island Historical Society. With regard to King and Dyer, the direct evidence indicates only that they were restricted from giving the vaccine to anyone else. The presumption is that they paid, or promised to pay, a substantial fee to Waterhouse. I am indebted to Mr. Mack Thompson of the University of California at Riverside for calling the material in the Moses Brown Papers to my attention.

30. John Warren to John Collins Warren, Boston, Aug. 30, 1800, Warren Papers, IV, Massachusetts Historical Society. Halsey (*op. cit.* [note 16], 16) quoted this letter to illustrate his opinion that the profession in Boston so bitterly opposed anything emanating from Waterhouse that they would not even accept vaccine from him. No doubt Warren was slower than Waterhouse to see the prospective benefits of widespread vaccination: on July 8, 1800, he wrote his son that "The small pox will probably before long, go through this place. . . ." Warren Papers, IV.

31. Samuel Brown, *A Treatise on the Nature, Origin and Progress of the Yellow Fever* . . . (Boston, 1800), iii.

32. *Columbian Centinel*, Aug. 30, 1800.

33. *Ibid.*, Sept. 6, 1800. Halsey (*op. cit.*, 16) quoted the final portion of this letter (omitted here) as an example of the calumnious opposition endured by Waterhouse!

34. Spalding, *op. cit.*, 54-55. Note Waterhouse's implied assumption that Brown's motives were as selfish as his own. For Brown's temperate reply to Pedro, see *Columbian Centinel*, Sept. 10, 1800. The New Hampshire group, like Waterhouse, made their patients promise or even bond themselves not to allow anyone else to take lymph from their arms. The problem of preserving the monopoly against this threat is mentioned at some length in the letters printed by J. Spalding and Leikind. See especially, Leikind, *loc. cit.*, 684-685.

35. Spalding, op. cit., 58. Spalding's identification of "Young Doctor Manning" as Samuel Manning of Cambridge is no doubt mistaken. It is not clear exactly when Manning first vaccinated. In 1829 he wrote, "by 2 spring ships from London in 1800 I rec'd from a brother Dr. I. C. Manning then in London persuing medical research vaccine virus direct from Dr. Woodvilles small pox vaccine institution . . . I communicated the disease . . . in the summer & autumn of 1800." Henry B. Shafer, *The American Medical Profession, 1783–1850* (Faculty of Political Science of Columbia University, ed., Studies in History, Economics and Public Law, No. 417, New York, 1936), 110. This claim being twenty-nine years late, it is possible to say only that Manning began vaccinating sometime before Sept. 24. By Oct. 3 he had already "inoculated many." *Annals of Medicine, for the Year 1800* (Edinburgh), V (1801), 479 (I have assumed that the letter here quoted, which is described only as dated from Ipswich, Massachusetts, was written by Manning).

36. James J. Putnam, *A Memoir of Dr. James Jackson . . .* (Boston, 1905), 218-222. Since Jackson has been derided as a follower of Woodville (in contrast to Waterhouse, the disciple of the unerring Jenner), it is worth pointing out that although Woodville blundered at first, he was well aware of it by the time Jackson studied with him. John C. McVail, "Cow-Pox and Small-Pox: Jenner, Woodville, and Pearson," *British Medical Journal*, 1896, I, 1271-1276. Moreover, Waterhouse himself frequently cited Woodville approvingly in his publications, and in April, 1801, he wrote to an English correspondent, "For more than a year I have held up these two eminent physicians [Jenner and Woodville] to the American public, as men who could scarcely err." Underwood, loc. cit. (note 16), 827.

37. Putnam, op. cit., 221. Jackson admittedly hoped to "make a mint of money in a bit of time." But unlike Waterhouse, he made no great professions of philanthropy, nor did he attempt to keep others from the practice.

38. Spalding, op. cit., 59.

39. Putnam, op. cit., 222.

40. *Columbian Centinel*, Oct. 11, 1800.

41. John Warren to John Collins Warren, Boston, Oct. 11, 1800, Warren Papers, IV, Mass. Hist. Soc. Apparently Warren did not know of Jackson's ride to Ipswich.

42. John G. Coffin in *Columbian Centinel*, Oct. 15, 1800; Samuel Hunt, Jr., in *Boston Gazette. Commercial and Political*, Oct. 16, 1800. Jackson to Pickering, Nov. 13, 1800, Putnam, op. cit., 223.

43. Spalding, op. cit., 61-62; Leikind, loc. cit., 680-681.

44. Levi to Josiah, Nov. 28, 1800, ibid., 681.

45. Spalding, op. cit., 64. Spalding had taught chemistry to medical students at Dartmouth.

46. *Ibid.*, 65. Emily A. Smith incorrectly credited Nathan Smith with practicing vaccination as early as August, 1800, on the basis of a letter to L. Spalding dated Aug. 25, 1800. *The Life and Letters of Nathan Smith, M.B., M.D.* (New Haven, 1914), 25. The full letter, dated (probably correctly) Aug. 25, 1801, is in Spalding, op. cit., 89-90.

47. *Ibid.*, 66-67. See also, S. H. Rose to L. Spalding, Bridgehampton, N. Y., Nov. 17, 1800, *ibid.*, 67; N. Noyes to Spalding [Newburyport?], postmarked Oct. 14, 1800, *ibid.*, 73-74.

48. Edna F. Calder, ed., "Extracts from the Ames Diary," *Dedham Historical Register*, X (1899), 121. See also, the advertisements of Dr. Pickman in *The Salem Gazette*, Oct. 14, 1800, and of Dr. Torrey of Danvers, *ibid.*, Oct. 31, 1800.

49. C. F. Bartlett to Moses Brown, Sept. 5, Oct. 23, 28, 29, Nov. 11, Dec. 13, 22, 1800; Moses Brown to C. F. Bartlett, Oct. 17, 1800. Moses Brown Papers, R. I. Hist. Soc. See Plate III.

III

50. *Prospect* (Part I), 38-39. Waterhouse added a footnote, probably aimed at Samuel Brown: "Dr. W. is happy to find that every GENTLEMAN of the faculty in Boston and its vicinity, has understood this, and conducted accordingly." The pamphlet was advertised as "*This day published,*" in the *Massachusetts Mercury* (Boston), Sept. 5, 1800.

51. Waterhouse, *Prospect* (Part I), 25-27. See Edward Jenner, *Further Observations on the Variolæ Vaccinæ, or Cow Pox* (London, 1799), 4.

52. Note that in form this was not a letter from Waterhouse to the paper.

53. *The Independent Chronicle: and the Universal Advertiser* (Boston), Oct. 30, 1800.

54. *Columbian Centinel*, Nov. 19, 1800 (reprinted in *Mass. Mercury*, Nov. 21, 1800); *Columbian Centinel*, Dec. 27, 1800 (reprinted in *Independent Chronicle*, Jan. 5, 1801).

55. For Waterhouse's descriptions, see, in addition to the newspapers cited above, *Independent Chronicle*, May 11, 1801; *Columbian Centinel*, Aug. 12, 1801; June 19, 1802; "Narrative of Facts Concerning the Inoculation of the Kine-Pock," *Medical Repository*, V (1801–02), 373-381; *A Prospect of Exterminating the Small Pox Part II, Being a Continuation of a Narrative of Facts Concerning the Progress of the New Inoculation in America; Together with Practical Observations on the Local Appearance, Symptoms, and Mode of Treating the Variola Vaccina, or Kine Pock* . . . (Cambridge, 1802), 8-9 (hereafter cited as *Prospect Part II*); Waterhouse to Valentine Seaman, Cambridge, Jan. 12, 1802, in Seaman, *An Account of the Introduction of Vaccination or Kine-Pock Inoculation in N-York* [New York, 1802?], 55-57, MS., New York Academy of Medicine.

56. *Independent Chronicle*, Nov. 16, 1801. See also, H. C. Bolton, "Memoir of Dr. Elisha North," *Connecticut Medical Society, Proceedings*, n.s. III, no. 4 (1887), 138-139; L. Bartlett to J. Bartlett, Kingston, Nov. 28, 1800, Leikind, *loc. cit.* (note 19), 681-682; *The Connecticut Courant* (Hartford), Jan. 25, 1802.

57. E. S. Bolton, ed., "Extracts from the Diary of James Parker of Shirley, Mass.," *New England Historical and Genealogical Register*, LXX (1916), 142. The persons mentioned in addition to the diarist were

apparently all his children except Eastman, who may have been a school teacher.

58. It is at least possible that Waterhouse demanded the usual quid pro quo, and that Story decided to use his own importation so that he would not feel obliged to send Waterhouse his cut.

59. The Mercury and New-England Palladium (Boston), Jan. 16, 1801 (hereafter cited as New-England Palladium). See also, Columbian Centinel, Nov. 19, Dec. 27, 1800; Mass. Mercury, Nov. 11, 1800; Waterhouse, Prospect Part II, 9-14; Mass. Hist. Soc., Proceedings, LII (1918–19), 322; Benjamin Lynde Oliver and William Currie, Letters on the Kine Pox, and a Variety of Other Medical Subjects (Philadelphia, 1802), 7. Additional interesting details may be found in The Diary of William Bentley, D.D. (Salem, 1905–14), II, 355-357.

60. Spalding, op. cit. (note 18), 58, 61. Waterhouse wrote Lettsom on Nov. 13, 1800, that the vaccine "fails in more than half I inoculate for several weeks past." Pettigrew, loc. cit. (note 21), 279.

61. Columbian Centinel, Nov. 19, 1800.

62. Waterhouse planned to inoculate a cow as soon as he received fresh vaccine from England (letter to Lettsom, Nov. 13, 1800, Pettigrew, loc. cit., 279), and did in fact do so. He "obtained from her a crop of matter on the ninth day, which produced the disease in the human subject to perfection." Waterhouse to Jenner, Apr. 24, 1801, Baron, op. cit. (note 3), I, 441-442. No longer believing that repeated human transfer weakened the lymph, Waterhouse apparently did not repeat this experiment.

63. Independent Chronicle, Jan. 5, 1801 (reprinted from Columbian Centinel, Dec. 27, 1800). The promised communication never appeared. On Apr. 24, 1801, Waterhouse wrote to Jenner, "I here inclose a newspaper containing a communication written in the clouds last December. . . . When I had lost my way, and wandered into the wilds of conjecture, I stood still. I gave out that the winter was an unfavourable season for this new inoculation, and by that means I suspended the practice throughout the country from that period until the arrival of fresh matter and your letter." Baron, op. cit., I, 440. In 1802 Waterhouse wrote of this period, "I perceived that the vaccine disease had deviated from its original character. . . . I endeavoured to account for this change . . . by persuading myself that the virus became milder as it receded from the cow; and that it would at length become effete by passing through a given number of human subjects." But the experience of Marblehead and the writings of certain English physicians had led some to believe that cowpox increased in virulence with time. Waterhouse continued: "I silently entertained another whim, that the cold weather aggravated this disease. . . . I wrote to . . . England for a fresh supply of the vaccine virus, and gave out that the present season was less favourable to the inoculation than the spring." Prospect Part II, 14-15. See also, Fitz, loc. cit. (note 16), 251. The reiterated statement that he "gave out" that the winter was unfavorable may have been a reference to the letters published in the Columbian Centinel on Aug. 20 and Nov. 19 (the Dec. 20 letter did not mention weather), but more probably referred to personal communications with those who requested vaccine or vaccination. On Nov. 22, 1800, for example,

Waterhouse wrote Moses Brown, "Respecting the supplying Dr. Bartlett with the matter of the kine-pox, I shall return him the same answer I have uniformly given to all applicants for a week or two past, namely that I decline diffusing any more matter untill the opening of the Spring, being firmly persuaded that the winter season is not the most favourable for conveying the infection and conducting the disease to the greatest advantage." Waterhouse also pointed out that "Without the greatest care & attention the matter depreciates & becomes spurious. It has done so with every practitioner [torn] and has I fear degenerated in the hands of many of those whom I have supplied." He did not mention his own difficulties. Moses Brown Papers, R. I. Hist. Soc. The phrase "gave out," and this letter, suggest that Waterhouse used the cold-weather theory chiefly as an excuse; his public letters stressed the idea that repeated human transfer caused the vaccine to deteriorate. Apparently Waterhouse actually believed that both theories offered possible explanations for his failures. Letters to Lettsom, Nov. 13, 1800, and Dec. 13, 1800, Pettigrew, loc. cit., 279-280. Waterhouse did not until some time later explicitly and publicly admit his failure to keep the virus going: one might assume from the Dec. 20 letter that despite his difficulties he was still attempting to vaccinate.

64. Waterhouse to Spalding, Dec. 18, 1800, Spalding, op. cit., 60. Waterhouse did publish a letter from James Mann reporting his successful vaccinations (Columbian Centinel, Jan. 14, 1801); and an answer (Independent Chronicle, Mar. 16, 1801) to an advertisement (ibid., Jan. 26, 1801) of an alleged case of the failure of cowpox to protect against smallpox.

IV

65. Annals of Medicine, for the Year 1800 (Edinburgh), V (1801), 479; Joseph B. Felt, History of Ipswich, Essex, and Hamilton (Cambridge, 1834), 197; Shafer, op. cit. (note 35), 110; letter from an Essex County physician (undoubtedly Manning) to Jackson, Columbian Centinel, Apr. 8, 1801. Manning also made a similar test in May, 1801. Massachusetts law prohibited variolation in any town without the voters' permission in town meeting.

66. Boston Board of Health, "Report [on Vaccination Experiment]" (Broadside, Boston, Dec. 16, 1802), reproduced in New England Journal of Medicine, CCXVII (1937), 534.

67. Columbian Centinel, Feb. 14, 1801. In a temperate and reasoned letter supporting vaccination an anonymous writer pointed out in The Salem Gazette, Dec. 30, 1800, that although some trials had failed, "nine Physicians out of ten in this country, and probably a much larger proportion in Europe, who have subjected their patients to the test, have been successful."

68. Columbian Centinel, Jan. 14, 1801.

69. Ibid., July 16, 1806.

70. Independent Chronicle, Jan. 5, 1801. For another successful test, probably in Rhode Island, of a girl vaccinated in December, 1800, see

Dorcas Earl to Moses Brown, Apr. 30, 1801, Moses Brown Papers, R. I. Hist. Soc.

71. *Independent Chronicle*, Jan. 5, 1801. The author was identified as "B****," which suggests that he may have been Samuel Brown.

72. *Columbian Centinel*, Jan. 14, 1801. For contemporary strictures on Waterhouse's first pamphlet by a competent and sympathetic critic who was not involved in the local situation, see John Ring, *A Treatise on the Cow-Pox* . . . (London, 1801–03), I, 443-459.

73. *Columbian Centinel*, Feb. 14, 1801. Wheelock had a fairly severe local reaction at the site of inoculation and some constitutional symptoms. While he may possibly have been infected with the smallpox virus, he had only one real pock and his affliction was much milder than usual for inoculated smallpox. Almost certainly his vaccination had afforded him a large degree of, if not perfect, protection. It is of course true that vaccination is not a perfect preventive of smallpox.

74. *Columbian Centinel*, Feb. 25, 1801.

75. *Ibid.*, Mar. 14, 1801.

76. *Ibid.*, Apr. 8, 1801. The author (identified only as a physician of Essex County, but undoubtedly Manning) also pointed out that occasionally individuals had smallpox more than once, and suggested that this might happen with cowpox. Jackson still believed that Wheelock's case represented a deviation from the rule, but he also wrote, "No man is less ready than I am to deny the power attributed to cow pox, as generally existing." Waterhouse also refused to admit that Wheelock had smallpox. *Ibid.*, Apr. 1, 1801. Jackson's second letter and a portion of the first were reprinted in Putnam, *op. cit.* (note 36), 230-233.

V

77. Their cooperation has been amply described by Halsey, *op. cit.* (note 16).

78. *New-England Palladium*, May 1, 26, 1801.

79. *Columbian Centinel*, Apr. 8, 1801.

80. Actually one case was successful. *Ibid.*, June 18, 1806.

81. Waterhouse to Rand, Apr. 5, 1801, *ibid.*, July 2, 1806. The emphatic type of the printed letter, which was not all in the original, has been omitted.

82. See Waterhouse to Lettsom, Apr. 6, 1801, Pettigrew, *op. cit.* (note 2), III, 212; to an unknown English correspondent, Apr. 14, 1801, Underwood, *loc. cit.* (note 16), 827.

83. *Columbian Centinel*, June 18, July 12, 16, 1806.

84. It is significant that Waterhouse pressed this request much more assiduously than his offer to place himself under the "advice and direction" of the Society.

85. The pertinent extracts from the records of the Society are in Walter L. Burrage, *A History of the Massachusetts Medical Society* . . . *1781–1922* (Norwood, Mass., 1923), 58-59. The letters were from Elisha Story,

Thomas Manning, John D. Treadwell of Salem, and Waterhouse. See also, *Columbian Centinel*, July 16, 23, 30, Aug. 2, 1806.

86. *Ibid.*, June 27, 1801. The notice was reprinted in *Independent Chronicle*, July 2, 1801; *Conn. Courant*, July 13, 1801; *The Spectator* (New York), July 4, 1801 (Halsey, *op. cit.*, 29-30); and no doubt in other newspapers. It is worth noting that this inquiry was far from scientific: Waterhouse asked for favorable reports only.

87. Valentine Seaman, "A Report on the Vaccine or Kine-Pox Inoculation in New-York," *Medical Repository*, V (1801–02), 236-238. Jackson had sent virus to New York in the fall of 1800, but it had proved spurious on trial. David Hosack to John Redman Coxe, Jan. 15, 1802, Coxe, *Practical Observations on Vaccination: or Inoculation for the Cow-Pock* (Philadelphia, 1802), 128-129. Seaman claimed to have received on May 22, 1801, the first genuine vaccine to reach New York, but some from Elisha North of Goshen, Conn., may have preceded it. Seaman, *op. cit.* (note 55), 8; Bolton, *loc. cit.* (note 56), 140-142.

88. Waterhouse to Jenner, Apr. 8, 1802, Baron, *op. cit.* (note 3), I, 593-594; W. R. LeFanu, *A Bio-Bibliography of Edward Jenner 1749–1823* (Philadelphia, [1951]), 60-62. The instructions are reproduced in *ibid.*, plate XVIII.

89. *Columbian Centinel*, July 15, Aug. 5, 12, Oct. 7, Nov. 7, Dec. 16, 1801; June 19, July 17, 28, Nov. 13, 1802; *Independent Chronicle*, June 18, 1801; June 28, July 15, Aug. 5, 1802; *New-England Palladium*, July 21, 1801; Jan. 19, Mar. 2, Apr. 16, May 21, 1802.

90. *Ibid.*, May 29, June 2, 1801. It is, however, quite possible that the anonymous physician was in this case Waterhouse; the argumentative style and some of the phrases suggest as much. If so, it is particularly significant that the writer suggested that "A Tradesman" could obtain from the eldest physician in the North End "a chain of information" which would convince him of the value of vaccination.

91. *Independent Chronicle*, Nov. 16, 1801.

92. *New-England Palladium*, July 17, 1801. The vaccinator was Dr. Benjamin Page, Jr.

93. *Ibid.*, Aug. 14, 21, 1801. For further details, see Spalding, *op. cit.* (note 18), 88. L. Spalding made a second public test in July, 1802. *Ibid.*, 104-105; *Columbian Centinel*, July 17, 1802.

94. *New-England Palladium*, Oct. 23, 1801; *Independent Chronicle*, Oct. 29, 1801. By March, 1802, Cooley claimed to have vaccinated more than 600 persons, a large number of whom had been tested both by inoculation and exposure to patients. *Conn. Courant*, Mar. 1, 1802. He was evidently much interested in the subject: one of the curiosa of vaccination is an edition of Jenner's *Inquiry* reprinted from the second London edition for Cooley in Springfield, Mass., in 1802. See also, *Conn. Courant*, Oct. 19, 1801.

95. *Independent Chronicle*, Nov. 9, 1801.

96. *New-England Palladium*, Feb. 23, June 1, 1802.

97. *Columbian Centinel*, Aug. 7, 1802.

98. *Ibid.*, July 11, Sept. 26, 1801; *New-England Palladium*, July 7, 1801; Feb. 26, 1802; *Independent Chronicle*, May 20, 1802.

99. *Columbian Centinel*, May 19, June 12, Sept. 18, 1802; *New-England Palladium*, July 31, 1801; Mar. 12, May 18, 21, July 16, 1802; *Independent Chronicle*, Aug. 24, 1801; Mar. 11, June 7, July 19, 1802.

100. *New-England Palladium*, June 30, July 24, 1801; *Columbian Centinel*, July 24, 1802.

101. The continued skepticism of some Bostonians may be documented by the continued existence of Aspinwall's inoculation hospital. See especially his advertisement, *Independent Chronicle*, June 21, 1802. Since the newspapers rarely published anything derogatory to vaccination, the arguments of the opposition must in general be inferred from those used by Waterhouse and others to combat it.

102. Benjamin Waterhouse, "Small Pox and Kine Pock," *Boston Medical Intelligencer*, IV (1826–27), 33.

103. *Columbian Centinel*, Sept. 20, 1800.

104. *Independent Chronicle*, Oct. 1, 1801. The advertisement was repeated in *ibid.*, Oct. 8, 15, 22, 29, 1801.

105. *Ibid.*, Oct. 5, 1801.

106. *New-England Palladium*, Oct. 13, 1801.

107. *Independent Chronicle*, Oct. 15, 1801.

108. Walter C. Alvarez, "Some Correspondence Relating to the Introduction of Vaccination into America," *California and Western Medicine*, XXIII (1925), 584. Aspinwall, so far as I know, wrote nothing publicly about any time limitation on the efficacy of cowpox, but he may have made such statements orally or in private letters.

109. *Independent Chronicle*, Nov. 2, 1801.

110. *Ibid.*, Oct. 29, 1801. For a similar argument elsewhere, see *Conn. Courant*, Mar. 1, 1802. In December, 1801, Dr. B. L. Oliver wrote that although the physicians of Salem had confidence in cowpox, it was "generally thought" that they did not yet possess "all the diagnostic signs, necessary for ascertaining when the system is secured from the small-pox by the vaccine disease." He expected that time would soon remove the obscurity. Oliver and Currie, *op. cit.* (note 59), 8-9.

111. *Independent Chronicle*, Nov. 9, 1801.

112. Alvarez, *loc. cit.*, 584.

113. *Columbian Centinel*, Apr. 1, 1801; Boston Board of Health, Records (1799–1806), 132, 154-157, 159-160, 164, 167, MS. in Boston Public Library.

114. *Columbian Centinel*, May 19, 22, 1802; Aspinwall's advertisement, *Independent Chronicle*, June 21, 1802; Waterhouse, *Prospect Part II*, 49. Not having been through a general smallpox inoculation since 1792, Boston undoubtedly contained thousands of susceptible inhabitants.

115. Boston Board of Health, "Report," *New England Journal of Medicine*, CCXVII (1937), 534; Waterhouse, *Prospect Part II*, 51.

116. Boston Board of Health, *loc. cit.*; idem, Records (1799–1806), 215-222, 225-229; Boston Registry Department, *Records Relating to the Early History of Boston* (Boston, 1900–09), XXXV, 133-134; *Columbian Centinel*, July 3, 24, Aug. 18, 25, Dec. 18, 1802; *New-England Palladium*, June 25, July 2, Aug. 20, 27, Dec. 21, 1802; *Independent Chronicle*, July 1, Dec. 20, 1802; Spalding, *op. cit.*, 107-109. The test was delayed

until November because of difficulties in securing the smallpox virus. Even Aspinwall had none that was good at this time. Though the experiment has often been described, no one, I believe, has noted that two members of the Board of Health, Ozias Goodwin and Daniel Scott, offered their own sons for the test.

117. *Prospect Part II,* 64.

VI

118. Pettigrew, op. cit. (note 2), III, 212. This suggests that rumors about Waterhouse's effort to monopolize the practice had reached England.

119. *Independent Chronicle,* May 11, 1801, reprinted from *Connecticut Journal* (New Haven), Apr. 29, 1801. The letter has been reprinted in Halsey, op. cit. (note 16), 24-27.

120. *Ibid.,* 42-43. Waterhouse did not explicitly deny in this letter that he accepted and approved (if he did not initiate) the offer of one quarter of the profits, but he certainly gave that impression. Ironically, Halsey pointed out (p. 3) Jefferson's antipathy to making money from a monopoly. Thoroughly imbued with Waterhouse's side of the story, but apparently knowing nothing about the bonds or the Waterhouse–Spalding letters, Halsey concluded (p. 57) that Waterhouse had no desire to restrict the use of vaccination and made every effort to spread the knowledge of its value. "Though offered large financial inducements for exclusive rights he refused them as a 'vile conspiracy' and took every adequate means to prevent the organization of monopolies in various states and towns." See also, Fitz, *loc. cit.* (note 16), 248. More recently, Laurence Farmer has noted that this letter reflected sadly on the other physicians' (but not Waterhouse's) ethical standards. *Doctors' Legacy: a Selection of Physicians' Letters 1721–1954* (New York, 1955), 78.

121. *Columbian Centinel,* Aug. 13, 1806. A MS. copy of the letter in the Harvard Medical School Library varies from the printed version in minor ways.

122. Waterhouse to L. Spalding, Sept. 25, 1800, Spalding, op. cit., 58.

123. *Columbian Centinel,* July 28, 1802. Also printed in *Independent Chronicle,* Aug. 5, 1802 (without the final section beginning, "I should not have glanced . . ."); and in Waterhouse, *Prospect Part II,* 40-48.

124. *Ibid.,* 48.

125. *Columbian Centinel,* July 31, 1802. After Waterhouse's letter appeared on July 28, Howard first wrote for an explanation or apology. Receiving no answer, he then requested a friend, William Sullivan, to call upon the Cambridge physician. Taking his brother as a witness, Sullivan went to Waterhouse, who, after some discussion, reluctantly drew up this notice, which the Sullivans deemed acceptable. They handed it to Howard, who, presumably, inserted it in the newspaper. *Ibid.,* Dec. 30, 1807.

126. *Ibid.,* Aug. 11, 1802.

127. Howard later signed the physicians' statement for the December, 1802, report on vaccination by the Board of Health, and he was one of the young physicians who established a vaccine institution in Boston immediately following the publication of this report. *Independent Chronicle,*

Dec. 23, 1802. Shortly thereafter, he resumed general practice. *Columbian Centinel*, Mar. 9, 1803. He was admitted to the Massachusetts Medical Society in 1803. Walter L. Burrage, *The Massachusetts Medical Society: a Catalogue of the Honorary and Past and Present Fellows 1781–1931* (Boston, 1931), 124.

128. *Columbian Centinel*, Aug. 14, 1802.

129. In *Prospect Part II*, 48-49, Waterhouse said that he deemed it his duty to attack the practice of vaccination by mechanics and day laborers but that before sending the letter published on Aug. 11, he read it to the president of the Massachusetts Medical Society (Isaac Rand), "determining to suppress it, should the principles and design of it, meet his disapprobation. Its publication, notwithstanding, let loose all 'the angry passions.'" As an example he cited, but did not quote, Howard's reply.

130. *Columbian Centinel*, July 12, 1806. This is Rand's version of the conversation. Waterhouse declared that Rand was perverting the facts (*ibid.*, July 16, 1806), but John Warren, Thomas Welsh, and others supported Rand in substance (*ibid.*, July 19, Aug. 6, 1806).

131. Though dated 1802 on the title page, it actually appeared about Feb. 1, 1803. See William Hilliard's advertisement, *Columbian Centinel*, Feb. 5, 1803.

132. *Ibid.*, Mar. 30, Apr. 9, May 21, June 15, 25, July 16, Nov. 26, 1803; Apr. 11, May 26, Nov. 7, 28, Dec. 1, 1804; May 4, 1805.

VII

133. *Columbian Centinel*, Apr. 19, 23, 1806. A third letter (*ibid.*, May 31, 1806) was devoted to technical matters that had nothing to do with Waterhouse's controversy with the Society.

134. *Dict. Amer. Biog.*, VI, 193-194.

135. This description of the letter was by the Society's chief defender. *Columbian Centinel*, July 12, 1806.

136. *Ibid.*, Aug. 2, 1806. Quoting the letter from memory, Waterhouse wrote that it was "meant to convey nothing disrespectful."

137. *Ibid.*, June 18, July 9, 12, 16, 19, 1806.

138. *Ibid.*, June 18, 1806.

139. *Ibid.*, July 2, 1806.

140. Warren Papers, VI, Mass. Hist. Soc.

141. *Columbian Centinel*, July 9, 1806.

142. *Ibid.*, July 30, 1806.

143. For the full record of this extended controversy, see *ibid.*, Apr. 19, 23, June 18, 21, July 2-Aug. 13, Aug. 23, 1806. *Repertory*, July 15, 1806. Two or three years prior to this controversy, Waterhouse had gone to the Society seeking the letter to Rand. Unable to find it in the files, Waterhouse turned to Rand himself. The latter still had it and gave it back to Waterhouse at his request. In September, 1806, after the newspaper battle was over, Waterhouse "returned" the letter to the Massachusetts Medical Society to be placed on its files where it belonged, remarking that "had it not been over looked & forgotten, . . . it would have been returned as

it indeed ought, directly on my taking a copy of it." Copies of letters to John Warren and to the President and Council of the Massachusetts Medical Society, both dated Cambridge, Sept. 28, 1806, in Harvard Medical School Library. The effrontery of this man was monumental. Two or three years prior to this episode, Jackson, J. C. Warren, and a few other young physicians organized a private medical improvement society which met weekly. In 1806 they published a series of unsigned articles on vaccination in the *Repertory*, several of which contained allusions obviously directed against Waterhouse. The most pointed was one by Warren ridiculing the term "kine pox" in the issue of Sept. 2. For the whole series, see *ibid.*, June 3, 24, July 11, 22, Aug. 5, 22, Sept. 2, 26, 30, Oct. 14, 28, Nov. 11, Dec. 9, 1806. See also, E. Warren, *Life of J. C. Warren*, I, 77-78; Putnam, *op. cit.* (note 36), 252-253.

VIII

144. Chichester received his vaccine from Pearson and tried it on several persons, but on only one did it take. His reason for going no further does not appear. Nathaniel H. Rhodes, "Evidence of the Precise Date of the Cow-Pock in America," *Philosophical Magazine* (London), XVI (1803), 252-253. Chichester's claim was noted by Fox, *op. cit.* (note 4), 376n.

145. Hosack to J. R. Coxe, New York, Jan. 15, 1802, Coxe, *op. cit.* (note 87), 128; Thacher, *op. cit.* (note 6), 28n. See also, Oliver and Currie, *op. cit.* (note 59), 11-12.

146. *Medical Repository*, III (1799–1800), 310; *ibid.*, IV (1800–01), 79; *Mass. Mercury*, Apr. 8, 1800.

147. Ring, *op. cit.* (note 72), I, 459. See also, J. R. Quinan, "The Introduction of Inoculation and Vaccination into Maryland, Historically Considered," *Maryland Medical Journal*, X (1883–84), 118; J. E. Wilson, "An Early Baltimore Physician and His Medical Library," *Annals of Medical History*, ser. 3, IV (1942), 66.

148. Quinan, *loc. cit.*, 118-119, 129-131; Whitfield J. Bell, Jr., "Dr. James Smith and the Public Encouragement for Vaccination for Smallpox," *Annals of Medical History*, ser. 3, II (1940), 502-504; H. C. Brooke, "A Proposal for a Free Vaccine Clinic in Baltimore in 1802," *Bulletin of the Institute of the History of Medicine*, III (1935), 83-91.

149. Coxe, *op. cit.*, 120-122. In the fall of 1801 Dr. Samuel Cooley of Bolton, Mass., noted that his vaccine "came to me with Dr. Jenner's treatise," which suggests that he too may have imported it directly from England. *Conn. Courant*, Oct. 19, 1801. See also, *ibid.*, Jan. 25, 1802.

150. Coxe, *op. cit.*, 130-134, 151-152; John Spence, "Observations on the Inoculation of the Kine-Pock," *Medical Repository*, V (1801–02), 381-387; *Columbian Centinel*, June 19, 1802; Madge E. Pickard and R. Carlyle Buley, *The Midwest Pioneer, His Ills, Cures, & Doctors* (Crawfordsville, Ind., 1945), 23.

151. Review of Coxe, *op. cit.*, in *Medical Repository*, VI (1802–03), 206.

152. Review of Waterhouse, *Prospect Part II*, in *Medical Repository*, VI (1802–03), 410.

153. *Columbian Centinel*, Dec. 18, 1802.

154. Waterhouse to Matthias Spalding, Oct. 20, 1801, Alvarez, *loc. cit.* (note 108), 584; *Columbian Centinel*, Dec. 16, 1801. An anonymous Boston physician, whose MS. "Kine pox inoculation records" are in the Boston Medical Library, vaccinated Oct.-Nov. 1800, Apr.-June 1801, and Mar.-June 1802.

155. "Report on Vaccination," Mass. Med. Soc., *Medical Communications*, vol. I, no. 2, part 2 (1808), 90.

156. *Prospect Part II*, 29; Waterhouse to Seaman, Cambridge, Jan. 12, 1802, in Seaman, *op. cit.* (note 55), 44-45.

157. Boston Board of Health, Records (1799–1806), 224, MS. in Boston Public Library; *Columbian Centinel*, Dec. 22, 1802; *Independent Chronicle*, Dec. 23, 1802; *New-England Palladium*, Dec. 24, 1802. The members of the institution were John Fleet, Jr., William Ingalls, Samuel Brown, Thomas Danforth, John G. Coffin, James Jackson, Benjamin Shurtleff, Jacob Gates, Isaac Rand, 3d, Samuel Hunt, Jr., John C. Warren, and John C. Howard. See also, the decisive statement published by the Boston Dispensary, *Columbian Centinel*, June 25, 1803.

158. Baron, *op. cit.* (note 3), II, 449-451; I. B. Cohen, "Edward Jenner and Harvard University," *Harvard Library Bulletin*, III (1949), 347-358. In Philadelphia, on the other hand, when Jenner was proposed as an associate of the College of Physicians, he failed of election. S. Weir Mitchell, *Celebration of the Centennial Anniversary of the Institution of the College of Physicians of Philadelphia* [Philadelphia, 1887], 32.

159. *Columbian Centinel*, July 19, 30, 1806; Dec. 12, 1807; *Prospect Part II*, 48-49.

160. Urging L. Spalding to take a partnership with Cutter, Waterhouse remarked in a letter dated Sept. 15, 1800, "Besides, 'he that is not with you' as the Bible says 'will be against you.'" Spalding, *op. cit.* (note 18), 56.

161. William Coolidge Lane, "Dr. Benjamin Waterhouse and Harvard University," Cambridge Historical Society, *Publications*, IV (1909), 5-22; I. B. Cohen, *Some Early Tools of American Science* (Cambridge, 1950), 103-106; Samuel Eliot Morison, *Three Centuries of Harvard 1636–1936* (Cambridge, 1936), 222-223.

162. *Columbian Centinel*, May 21, June 15, 1803. These writers may well have been influenced by Waterhouse's recently published *Prospect Part II*.

163. The most vigorous expression of this theory is in C. J. Brim, "Benjamin Waterhouse (1754–1846): An Underestimated American Medical Pioneer," *Medical Life*, XLI (1934), 277-301. Displaying a remarkable inattention to the significance of dates and changing opinions, Brim, who cited no sources, blundered badly. For example, he quoted (p. 284) as one letter from John Adams to Waterhouse dated Sept. 10, 1800, parts of two letters, one with the date given, the other actually dated Dec. 18, 1809. For the original letters, see John Adams, *Statesman and Friend: Correspondence of John Adams with Benjamin Waterhouse 1784–1822*

(Worthington C. Ford, ed., Boston, 1927), 10-11, 45-46. Brim's findings are obviously worthless.

164. For a contemporary expression of Waterhouse's political views, see his letter to an unknown English correspondent, dated Apr. 14, 1801, in Underwood, *loc. cit.* (note 16), 827. In a letter to M. Spalding dated Apr. 15, 1802, Waterhouse noted, "[Caleb Strong] has a majority of votes over [Elbridge] Gerry of *ten thousand.*" Alvarez, *loc. cit.*, 584. Unfortunately Waterhouse neglected to indicate whether this result pleased or dismayed him. Incomplete election returns in the *Columbian Centinel* of Apr. 14, 1802, showed Strong (transcribed "Geo. Stroud" by Alvarez), the Federalist candidate for governor, leading Gerry, the Republican, by a vote of 23,577 to 14,893.

165. "Sketch of the Life of Benjamin Waterhouse, M.D." *The Polyanthos*, II (1806), 85-86.

166. Adams, *op. cit.*, 28-29, 45. But see Adams to Waterhouse, Jan. 3, 1806, just after the election of Fisher Ames, a leading Essex-Junto Federalist, as president of Harvard (he declined): "I wish you may have all the Satisfaction in him [Ames] which you anticipate and I have no reason to doubt that you will." *Ibid.*, 33. Actually Adams was none too happy about the choice. The *Boston Patriot* was a leading Republican newspaper.

167. Pettigrew, *op. cit.* (note 2), II, 490.

168. Waterhouse later claimed that this was the case, in a letter to Dr. James Tilton dated Cambridge, Mar. 24, 1815, copy in Harvard Medical School Library. However, Waterhouse wrote this letter, which related his past and present political services and sufferings in the cause of Republicanism, in the hope of obtaining a government job and may well have dressed the story up.

169. *Columbian Centinel*, Sept. 6, 1800. "Jacobin" was of course a favorite Federalist epithet for Jeffersonians. Incidentally, William Aspinwall was active in Republican party politics.

170. *Independent Chronicle*, Nov. 11, 1802; *Columbian Centinel*, Nov. 20, 1802. The *New-England Palladium*, another Federalist paper, had earlier remarked (Feb. 26, 1802), "President JEFFERSON may be considered as the great patron of the Kine-Pock inoculation in America."

171. The selectmen of Milton, in a well-deserved tribute, addressed Russell in 1809 as "the Man whose exertions have been so ably engaged from the earliest period to make evident that great blessing, and who has uninteruptedly [*sic*] persevered in that benevolent pursuit." *Columbian Centinel*, Nov. 22, 1809. For a brief account of the circumstances, see Green, *op. cit.* (note 13), 110-111.

172. Raised a Friend, Waterhouse retained his sympathy for this sect, but apparently was not actually a member of the Society. His daughter married a Unitarian minister, son of Harvard's professor of divinity.

173. See, for example, J. B. Blake, "An Unrecorded Jenner Imprint," *Journal of the History of Medicine and Allied Sciences*, IX (1954), 233-234. S. E. Morison has remarked that after receiving the snuffbox from Jenner, Waterhouse became "insufferably vain." *New England Journal of Medicine*, CCXVI (1937), 82.

174. *Prospect Part II*, 77. See above, note 21. Seaman gave the Med-

ical Repository full credit for its early and continuing work in publicizing vaccination. Op. cit. (note 55), 3-6.

175. Prospect Part II, 35; Coxe, op. cit. (note 87), 120. Waterhouse had read Coxe's book: he quoted it in Prospect Part II, 32-34.

176. Ibid., 16-17, 37.

177. In his letter dated Dec. 20, 1800, Waterhouse mentioned "that all the vaccine matter hitherto used in America (some received at Ipswich excepted) came from less than two inches of infected thread which I received from Bath, in England last June. . . ." Independent Chronicle, Jan. 5, 1801. But Waterhouse wrote Lettsom on Dec. 13, 1800, "I am the only person who ever succeeded in obtaining efficient matter from England. . . ." Pettigrew, loc. cit. (note 21), 280. Possibly this was a slip of the pen.

178. Prospect Part II, 38-39. Waterhouse did, however, refer to some of the tests in his newspaper articles.

179. Prospect Part II, 48, 51. Jackson had been Waterhouse's pupil only insofar as he had attended the medical lectures at Harvard before he went abroad. His preceptor was Dr. Edward A. Holyoke of Salem. Waterhouse did not mention the fact, well known in Boston, that Jackson had studied under Woodville.

180. Pettigrew, op. cit. (note 2), III, 211-212; Baron, op. cit., I, 439-443. See also, Waterhouse to Ring, Aug. 6, 1801, abstracted in Ring, op. cit., II, 886-889. The letter from Jenner (dated Mar. 4, 1801) to which Waterhouse referred in the reply quoted by Baron, was published in Prospect Part II, 110-116. From this letter Waterhouse really first learned of the proper time, according to Jenner, for taking vaccine.

181. Prospect Part II, 14-16, 26-27, 109-116.

182. Ibid., 7.

183. Independent Chronicle, Jan. 5, 1801, reprinted from Columbian Centinel, Dec. 27, 1800. See Waterhouse, Prospect (Part I), 26-27. There was a similar warning in the extract of a letter from Waterhouse to a physician in the country, Mass. Mercury, Oct. 21, 1800, but Waterhouse did not refer to this publication in Prospect Part II. Waterhouse's only indication in Prospect (Part I) as to when he obtained the vaccine from his childrens' and servants' arms was a remark (p. 21) that he took it from "a full maturated pustule" on his three-year-old. With a typical take, this occurs about the twelfth day.

184. In the Columbian Centinel, June 27, 1801, Waterhouse stated that the previous year's spurious cases arose "from taking the matter at too late a period." See also, ibid., Aug. 12, 1801. Not until the issue of Oct. 7, 1801, did he give (in a quotation from a letter from Jenner) a specific statement of the "golden rule" of vaccination: never to take the virus after the formation of the efflorescence.

185. Waterhouse was still taking vaccine as late as the eleventh day early in April, 1801. Letter to Rand, Apr. 5, 1801, Columbian Centinel, July 2, 1806. Some practitioners, to be sure, did take matter from suppurating ulcers, but many did not.

186. Reverend Mr. Story (Dr. Story's brother) to Waterhouse, May 7, 1801, Waterhouse, Prospect Part II, 12.

187. *Ibid.*, 10.

188. *Columbian Centinel*, Nov. 19, 1800.

189. *Independent Chronicle*, Jan. 5, 1801.

190. *Columbian Centinel*, Apr. 1, 1801; letter to Rand, Apr. 5, 1801, in *ibid.*, July 2, 1806.

191. *Ibid.*, July 12, 19, Aug. 6, 1806.

192. *Ibid.*, July 19, 1806.

193. Waterhouse's first such warning in the *Columbian Centinel* was actually printed Nov. 19, 1800.

194. Note the false statement that this scheme was devised *after others* were disseminating spurious vaccine.

195. *Columbian Centinel*, Dec. 12, 1807. Waterhouse also reported in this letter that he had again variolated four of his children more than seven years after their original vaccination to demonstrate its lasting efficacy. He claimed that he had from the beginning given vaccine freely to the physicians of Boston—a demonstrable falsehood. And he added opprobrious personal references to John C. Howard, which led to another newspaper squabble, but a brief one, since the editor could not perceive "the smallest use in the prolongation of the controversy. Our readers are heartily tired of it." *Ibid.*, Dec. 16, 23, 30, 1807; Jan. 2, 1808.

196. *New-England Palladium & Commercial Advertiser*, Feb. 10, 1824. The committee favored granting Waterhouse a township in Maine, but the resolution was rejected. *Columbian Centinel*, Mar. 3, 1810. A MS. note (in Waterhouse's hand?) on page 39 of the Yale Medical Library's copy of his *Information Respecting the Origin, Progress, and Efficacy of the Kine Pock Inoculation* . . . (Cambridge, 1810) charges the Essex Junto with engineering this defeat.

197. It is interesting to note that on Dec. 13, 1800, Waterhouse wrote Lettsom, "You already know, perhaps, that I introduced that distemper [cowpox] here, and led the way in its inoculation, and that very much to my advantage. . . ." Pettigrew, *loc. cit.* (note 21), 279. According to W. B. McDaniel, 2d, Waterhouse's MS. notes on John Hunter's lectures indicate that he "had a just regard for his guineas and his opportunities. . . ." "Benjamin Waterhouse's Manuscript Notes on the Lectures of John Hunter, 1777–78," *Journal of the History of Medicine and Allied Sciences*, IX (1954), 108-110.

INDEX

Adams, John, 66–67
American Academy of Arts and Sciences, 64
Ames, Nathaniel, 21
Aspinwall, William, 14, 43–46

Babbit, Dr., 27
Baltimore, vaccination in, 61–62, 69
Banning, Thomas, 16
Baron, John, 11, 13
Bartlett, Charles F., 21–22
Bartlett, Ezra, 15
Bartlett, Josiah, of Charlestown, 11, 31
Bartlett, Josiah, of Stratham, 15, 19–20, 29
Bartlett, Levi, 15, 20
Bartlett, Zacheus, 16
Billings, Benjamin, 16
Board of Health, 56, 69; tests vaccination, 46–47; and vaccine institution, 64
Bolton, Mass., vaccination in, 42
Bonds, BW requires, 15; not taken by Samuel Hunt, Jr., 20; public discussion of, 54, 57–59, 72–74; BW denies taking, 54, 72–73; BW admits taking, 73–74
Boston, vaccination in, 17–18, 20, 32–33, 41, 63–64, 69; vaccine distributed from, 20, 24–26; vaccine institution in, 38, 64; smallpox in, 46
Boston Medical and Surgical Journal, 11
Brentwood, Mass., 16
Brookline, variolation in, 14, 43–46
Brown, Moses, 22
Brown, Samuel, 16–17, 65, 67

Charleston, S. C., vaccination in, 61, 68

Charlestown, Mass., vaccination in, 31
Chester, Vermont, vaccination in, 20
Chichester, John, 61
Coffin, John G., 42
Coleman, Asaph, 42
Cooley, Samuel, 42
Cowpox, found in American cattle, 42; see vaccination, vaccine
Coxe, John Redman, 62, 68
Crawford, John, 61
Cutter, Dr., 14–15

Danforth, Samuel, 46
Dedham, vaccination in, 21
Dexter, Aaron, 31, 63
Dorchester, vaccination in, 51, 53
Drury, John, 28, 71
Dwight, Timothy, 48, 67, 72
Dyer, Dr., 16

Eustis, William, 56, 67

Falmouth, variolation in, 47
Fay, Cyrus, 27, 41
Franklin, Mass., vaccination in, 42

Gerrish, Samuel, 21
Green, Samuel Abbott, 12
Gross, Samuel D., 11

Hallowell, Maine, vaccination in, 41
Hanover, 15, 20
Harvard, honors Jenner, 64; BW and, 67
Haygarth, John, 48, 61
Hedge, Abraham, 20
Holmes, Oliver Wendell, 11
Hosack, David, 61
Howard, John C., 51–54, 65, 72
Hunt, Samuel, Jr., 20

93

BENJAMIN WATERHOUSE,
HARVARD'S FIRST PROFESSOR OF PHYSIC

John B. Blake

Benjamin Waterhouse, Harvard's First Professor of Physic

JOHN B. BLAKE, PH.D.*

Division of Medical Sciences, U.S. National Museum, Smithsonian Institution, Washington, D.C.

Hailed abroad as the Jenner of America, but contemned at home for self-seeking and dishonesty; appointed at the age of 28 as Harvard's first Professor of Physic but fired some 30 years later; lauded by historians who considered him the victim of unjust political, professional, religious, and personal persecution, but ignored or scorned by others; Benjamin Waterhouse emerges as one of the most controversial figures in the early medical annals of America. But like most men he was, in fact, neither the thorough blackguard some of his colleagues thought him nor a martyred saint.

Born in Newport, Rhode Island, on March 5, 1754, Benjamin was the son of Timothy and Hannah (Proud) Waterhouse, the latter a Quaker born in England and first cousin of the noted London physician, Dr. John Fothergill. After a typical classical education and several years' apprenticeship under Dr. John Halliburton, Waterhouse sailed from Newport in March, 1775, just before the Revolution, "consigned by my family," as he later wrote, "to Doctor Fothergill, in London, for farther improvement."

Cordially received by his mother's cousin, Waterhouse at his advice went to Edinburgh in the fall to study under such noted teachers as William Cullen, Joseph Black, and Alexander Munro. Returning to London 9 months later, he "walked the wards" of London hospitals, like other students of physic, and attended lectures by John Hunter, George Fordyce, and other medical

greats. To very few, however, were given his opportunities, for he lived as a member of the family with Fothergill, whose home was "the resort of the most distinguished philosophers of the age." Inspired by his teacher and friend with "a taste for the works of nature," Waterhouse also attended

Photo by Henry A. Curtis
Courtesy of Redwood Library and Athenaeum, Newport, Rhode Island.

BENJAMIN WATERHOUSE AS A STUDENT
PAINTED BY GILBERT STUART

lectures on experimental philosophy, botany, and mineralogy.

Although the Westminster Monthly Meeting certified in October, 1778, that the young man was "of a Sober life and conversation,"[1]

* Associate Curator, Div. of Medical Sciences, United States National Museum.

[1] Ms. in Waterhouse Papers, Harvard Medical School Library.

771

not all his time was spent in study. With a friend of Newport days, the artist Gilbert Stuart, he explored the byways of London until warned of the hazards of footpads in the big city. Thinking perhaps of these escapades, Fothergill sent Waterhouse on to Leyden in the fall of 1778, "to acquire, as he smilingly said, a little of the Dutch phlegm."[2]

In Leyden, Waterhouse matriculated at the University as "Liberæ Reipublicæ Americanæ Fœderatæ Civis." This aroused some concern among the authorities, because Holland had not yet recognized the United States. Meanwhile our prospective minister, John Adams, was also staying at Leyden, and Waterhouse lived with him and his sons.[3] As Adams later wrote:

... finding him, though a sprightly genius, very studious and inquisitive, as well as sociable, I had no inquiries to make, but whether his moral character was good, and whether he was a loyal American. As to his morals, I could hear of no reproach or suspicion; as to his politics, though he came over from England, he came from the guardianship and pupilage of Dr. Fothergill, who was as good a friend to America, as any Englishman could be ... and his conversation was in the style of a good American. I did not, therefore, hesitate to consider him, in some respects, as one of my family.[4]

In April, 1780, Waterhouse presented his thesis, *De Sympathia Partium Corporis Humani*, and took his M.D. degree. After another year of travel and additional courses in history and the laws of nations, he sailed from Spain late in the summer of 1781 on a leisurely journey via the Canaries and West Indies, returning to Newport the following

June. He was, writes Dr. Henry Viets, "perhaps the best educated physician in America at that time." How he would use his training and talent remained to be seen.[5]

Waterhouse at first started to practice in Newport, but soon he was called to a higher post. In September, 1782, the Harvard Corporation established a medical school, primarily at the instigation of John Warren, who was chosen on November 22, at the age of 29, as Professor of Anatomy and Surgery. A month later, on December 24, 1782, Waterhouse was picked to be Professor of the Theory and Practice of Physic, and in May, 1783, the election of Aaron Dexter as Professor of Chemistry and Materia Medica completed the original faculty. The professors were inducted into office in October, although the first lectures did not begin until November 24, 1784.[6]

Many practitioners, however, seem to have considered the new Institution more of a threat than an asset, and they resented especially the strategic position it gave to John Warren. Jealous of its prerogatives, the Massachusetts Medical Society foresaw Harvard impinging on its right to grant licenses to practice. This conflict was soon resolved, and harmonious relations were restored; John Warren, in fact, was vice-president of the Society from 1800 to 1804 and then president until his death in 1815. More serious was the lack of clinical facilities. With no hospital available in Cambridge, the Corporation in 1784 urged Boston's overseers of the poor to appoint medical professors physicians to the almshouse, but the Boston Medical Society blocked this effort by insisting that the

---

[2] Benjamin Waterhouse, *An Essay on Junius and His Letters* (Boston, 1831), v–vi, xiii–xiv; Waterhouse, *The Botanist* (Boston, 1811), xiv; "Sketch of the Life of Benjamin Waterhouse, M.D.," *Polyanthos*, 2:76, 1806; William Dunlap, *A History of the Rise and Progress of the Arts of Design in the United States* (F. W. Bayley and C. E. Goodspeed, eds., Boston, 1918), 1:204–11; Josiah C. Trent, "The London Years of Benjamin Waterhouse," *J. Hist. Med.*, 1:25–40, 1946.

[3] Waterhouse, *Junius*, vi–vii.

[4] W. C. Ford, ed., *Statesman and Friend: Correspondence of John Adams with Benjamin Waterhouse 1784–1822* (Boston, 1927), 45n.

[5] *Polyanthos*, 2:77–79; Henry R. Viets, " 'A Journal, of a Young Man of Massachusetts, ... Written by Himself.' Boston: 1816, and a Note on the Author," *Yale J. Biol. Med.*, 12:613, 1939–40.

[6] Edward Warren, *The Life of John Warren, M.D.* (Boston, 1874), pp. 245–258, 284; Thomas F. Harrington, *The Harvard Medical School, a History, Narrative and Documentary* (New York, 1905), 1:80–87, 99–100; Samuel Eliot Morison, *Three Centuries of Harvard 1636–1936* (Cambridge, 1936), pp. 167–170; T. E. Moore, Jr., "The Early Years of the Harvard Medical School: Its Founding and Curriculum, 1782–1810," *Bull. Hist. Med.*, 27:543–44, 1953. The date of the first lectures, hitherto uncertain, is established by an advertisement in the *Massachusetts Centinel*, Nov. 20, 1784.

"public medical business" be distributed equally.[7]

Waterhouse, too, was the object of professional jealousies. At the time of his appointment, he was, as John Warren's son later wrote, "a townsman and friend of my mother, was considered a young man of talents and attainments, and had received ...a foreign education." His appointment nevertheless aroused resentment, in part at least among those who thought the post should have gone to a local son of Harvard.[8] Jealous rumor easily invented reasons for the choice other than the young man's merit. Waterhouse, wrote Ephraim Eliot,

...was a relation and pupil of the excellent Dr. Fothergill of London, who, it was said, had contemplated such an establishment at this university; and, although he had died, it was also reported that Dr. [John C.] Lettsom had succeeded to much of his business, and meant to fulfill his benevolent intentions. This was only a gossiping story, but was believed, or rather hoped for, by many persons. Dr. Waterhouse was therefore determined upon for the other professorship.[9]

Waterhouse, on the other hand, found that not all at Harvard was to his liking. The financial rewards, which for nearly 10 years depended solely on the students' fees, were small. The University failed to provide proper classroom accommodations until 1801, when, after a forceful complaint from Waterhouse, Holden Chapel was at last fitted up for the medical professors' use.[10] Moreover, his European experience as Fothergill's protégé had left Waterhouse ill prepared for the exigencies of a doctor's life in a small New England town. Feeling superior to other local physicians, Waterhouse assumed a pompous and pedantic air. Yet his practice was small. As Oliver Wen-

dell Holmes remarked, "the good people of Cambridge listened to his learned talk when they were well, and sent for one of the other two doctors when they were sick."[11] Waterhouse himself admitted in 1794:

The fact is, I have no taste for the practice of physic as it is conducted in this country. It is not worth a man's attention. I feel such a mighty difference between transcribing from the great volume of Nature, and practising among the very vulgar, that is, conforming to the whims and nonsense of old women and silly people, that I am sometimes almost determined to renounce it for ever. I know how a London physician gets his bread, but with us it is widely different: a man like me of a weakly frame, addicted to study, is liable to be called out five or six miles on horseback in a severe winter night, and to remain out all night, and to receive (in the course of the year) a guinea for it! We are obliged to be physician, surgeon, apothecary, and tooth-drawer, all under one; and if we are not attentive to small things, and if we do not give consequence to trifles, we are dropped for some one who does. You are spoiled (say some of my friends) for practice in this country, by living so long with Dr. Fothergill, which is in a great measure true.[12]

Although never one to lose sight of his interests, John Warren, in contrast to the Professor of Physic, was much less disturbed by conditions in Cambridge. Not having been "spoiled" by European patronage, he had a firmer grasp on the realities of life in America and one of the most successful practices in Boston. Moreover, he also received greater recognition for his professional attainments. To see Warren thus preferred must have sorely rankled the Rhode Islander's heart. One thing is certain: the two men came to detest each other.

One reason perhaps why Waterhouse did not have a larger practice was that he spent so much time on natural history, despite Fothergill's advice to regard it "only as an

[7] E. Warren, *op. cit.*, pp. 285–295; Harrington, *op. cit.*, 1:100–113, 274–78.

[8] E. Warren, *op. cit.*, p. 255; John Adams to Waterhouse, Sept. 8, 1784, in Ford, *op. cit.*, p. 3; *Polyanthos*, 2:79–80.

[9] Quoted in Harrington, *op. cit.*, 1:79.

[10] I. Bernard Cohen, *Some Early Tools of American Science* (Cambridge, 1950), pp. 73–74; Josiah Quincy, *The History of Harvard University* (Boston, 1860), 2:266–69.

[11] O. W. Holmes, "Medicine in Boston: Additional Memoranda," in Justin Winsor, ed., *The Memorial History of Boston* (Boston, 1880–81), 4:564.

[12] Quoted in Thomas J. Pettigrew, *Memoirs of the Life and Writings of the Late John Coakley Lettsom* (London, 1817), 2:464–65.

agreeable adjunct to the healing art."[13] In 1784 the College of Rhode Island (now Brown University) had elected him Professor of Natural History. His first set of lectures in Providence in 1786 was received, according to one newspaper, "with the greatest pleasure and satisfaction by large assemblies of the most respectable characters, both ladies and gentlemen." He repeated the series in 1787, and then in 1788 the Harvard Corporation authorized him to deliver a similar course in Cambridge, to students who had their parents' permission.[14]

Although the prescribed Harvard curriculum had included some biology since the seventeenth century, the College had heretofore done virtually nothing to advance teaching or study of natural history. Waterhouse, therefore, as he wrote in 1805, "had first to excite a curiosity and then to gratify it." Though the students at first were few, Waterhouse persevered, "animated with the ambitious sentiment of being considered hereafter the *Founder* of Natl. History in the first University in America." By 1795 he had nineteen pupils, and in 1796 the number doubled again.[15]

One reason, no doubt, for the increasing popularity of the course was the publicity Waterhouse gave it by repeatedly publishing a syllabus in newspapers, broadsides, pamphlets, and magazines, beginning as early as 1786.[16] Another and perhaps more significant reason was the development of the College collections. Prior to 1790 Harvard's "museum" had consisted of a miscellaneous assortment of curiosities such as two Egyptian mummies and an inkstand "wrought of the Lava of Vesuvius." But a personal gift of about 50 fossils from Lettsom inspired Waterhouse to build a "cabinet" of minerals. In answer to a request from Cambridge,

Lettsom sent Harvard a series of rich donations between 1793 and 1796 which were supplemented by gifts from James Bowdoin and the Republic of France. Totaling about a thousand, the collection was "by far the richest and most extensive" in the country at the time. Under Waterhouse's care the specimens were numbered, described, and catalogued "in a very ingenious and elegant manner," and arranged in a mahogany cabinet 18 feet long and 10–12 high, "for the inspection of the curious." Until he began collecting, Waterhouse knew less of mineralogy than any other branch of natural history. But he immersed himself in the available books and, "Plunging into fire and phlogiston," began lecturing to an increasing circle of students.[17]

Arousing interest in natural history and developing the mineralogical cabinet was one of Waterhouse's most significant contributions as a member of the Harvard community. The other, for which he is best known, was his role in the introduction of vaccination, a story that needs only brief retelling here.[18] Early in 1799 Waterhouse received from Lettsom a copy of Edward Jenner's historic *Inquiry into the Causes and Effects of the Variolæ Vaccinæ* (London, 1798) describing for the first time the practice of vaccination, or inoculation with cowpox. As Waterhouse saw, this offered several advantages over the existing practice of variolation, or inoculation with smallpox, which had become since its introduction in 1721 a commonplace medical procedure.[19] According to early reports (which have proved essentially true), vaccination, in contradistinction to variolation, was never fatal to the patient, and it eliminated the possibility, inherent in variolation, of spreading a virulent disease by natural infection.

[13] Waterhouse, *Botanist*, xiv.

[14] J. Walter Wilson, "The First Natural History Lectures at Brown University, 1786, by Dr. Benjamin Waterhouse," *Ann. Med. Hist.*, Ser. 3, 4:390–98, 1942; *Massachusetts Centinel*, Sept. 20, 1786; Cohen, *op. cit.*, p. 100.

[15] *Ibid.*, pp. 96–100; William C. Lane, "Dr. Benjamin Waterhouse and Harvard University," Cambridge Historical Society, *Publications*, 4:11–12, 1909.

[16] *Massachusetts Centinel*, Sept. 20, 1786; Cohen, *op. cit.*, pp. xix, 101–102, plates 10, 11.

[17] *Ibid.*, pp. 97–99, 115–122; Pettigrew, *op. cit.*, 1: 192–93; 2:465–71.

[18] John B. Blake, *Benjamin Waterhouse and the Introduction of Vaccination: a Reappraisal* (Philadelphia, 1957), and works cited there, especially in note 16.

[19] The literature on the history of variolation is extensive. See especially Genevieve Miller, *Adoption of Inoculation for Smallpox in England and France* (Philadephia, 1957).

Soon after receiving Jenner's volume, Waterhouse published an abstract in a Boston newspaper. Then, after several fruitless attempts, he obtained vaccine from England and in July, 1800, first used it on his own family. After testing them by variolation, Waterhouse began vaccinating others. Subsequently he published numerous newspaper articles and a book in two parts publicizing the practice, and himself in the process. During the late summer and fall of 1800 he distributed vaccine to selected physicians in New England, and beginning in 1801 he sent it to numerous other more distant localities. For some 5 years he devoted much of his time to promoting the new preventive.

Unfortunately, however, Waterhouse assumed an attitude of insufferable superiority and arrogantly denigrated the contemporaneous efforts of other Boston physicians to advance the practice. Even more important, during the fall of 1800, until others imported the virus from England, he refused to let a single nearby physician have any vaccine, and he sent it to those at a distance only on their written promise to pay him a quarter of their profits and to keep the supply from anyone else. Whatever Waterhouse may later have claimed, the evidence of contemporary documents affords incontrovertible proof that all the while he professed philanthropic motives, he actually sought excessive personal pecuniary profit from monopolistic control of the vaccine. These efforts, which became well known to other physicians in and about Boston, would certainly be considered unethical now, and they were so then. Together with his egotism and the self-adulation of many of his newspaper publications, they explain in large measure the personal hostility that Waterhouse encountered, and they continued to plague him for the rest of his professional career.

From this time on Waterhouse, who had heretofore managed to surmount his opposition, found himself in increasing difficulties. Partly, at least, because of the interest aroused by his lectures, a group of wealthy Bostonians raised a subscription of over 30,000 dollars in 1805 to establish a botanical garden and professorship of natural history at Harvard. Waterhouse—so he later claimed—"did every thing in his power to forward the design," including the publication of a series of popular essays on botany in the Boston *Monthly Anthology* beginning in 1804. The subscribers, however, reserved the right to name the first incumbent. Waterhouse had few friends among them, and at least one, John Adams, was never consulted about the choice. Accordingly, the post went to William Dandridge Peck.

Peck was probably as well if not better qualified for the job than Waterhouse, but the latter, who saw what he had built about to be taken from him, was understandably distressed. In a letter to a member of the Corporation, Judge John Davis, he threatened that, should this professorship interfere with his reputation and interest, he would publish a pamphlet narrating his efforts to promote natural history and then quit his post to lecture and practice in Boston. Peck left Cambridge immediately following his appointment for 3 years of study in Europe. By the time he returned and the possibility of conflict between his lectures and Waterhouse's arose, the latter's position was slipping even faster.[20]

For one thing, Waterhouse further alienated the medical profession in 1806 by a slanderous newspaper attack on the Massachusetts Medical Society and several of Boston's most respected practitioners.[21] Nor were his political views enhancing his popularity. Writing in 1815, he attributed the loss of his position at Harvard primarily to partisan animus:

When Mr. Jefferson came into office, the late Judge Lowell, a leading man of the *Junto*, and a very influential governor of this University, and a warm friend of mine, gave us, of the college to understand, that the church and all our other sacred Institutions were in danger,

---

[20] Waterhouse, *Botanist*, vi–viii; Ford, *op. cit.*, pp. 27–28; Lane, *loc. cit.*, pp. 13–14; Quincy, *op. cit.*, 2: 291–92, 328–30, 542–43; Cohen, *op. cit.*, pp. 103–108.

[21] Blake, *op. cit.*, pp. 55–60.

particularly the University, that therefore it behoved us Professors to ralley with the clergy, and together form *the front-rank* in the Massachusetts *army of federalism*, in opposition to infidelity, Jacobinism and *Jeffersonism*. My associates, and the clergy very generally swallowed and relished this doctrine, while I remained rather silent. I however, at length, said thus much to my esteemed friend Lowell: "as I know not exactly what you mean by *federalism*, I should rather, that we unite and endeavour to form the front rank of knowledge, and virtue, and piety, and leave to the politician the government of the State." "True," said these Junto-men, "but WE *must form these politicians*." It is from this Seminary go all the Lawyers, Divines and Physicians, and *gentlemen*, and here they must imbibe *true* principles, (which were little more than hatred to France, adoration of England, and contempt of their own country). From this time, the exercises and orations of the students were replete with *Essex Junto* doctrines; and soon after the pulpits uttered similar sentiments. I could not entirely conceal my disapprobation of this line of conduct.

When Federalist newspapers ridiculed an alleged mountain of salt described by Jefferson, Waterhouse continued, he upheld the President's science. This "stopped the current of low abuse" against him, "but brought the vengeance of the party on my head. I was stiled 'the flatterer of the Infidel Jefferson.' "[22]

At the time Waterhouse wrote this letter, he was seeking the rewards of past and future political services. Actually, at least until the *Chesapeake* affair in 1807, he was far from being a good Jeffersonian Republican. While Waterhouse did not look upon the election of Jefferson as a national calamity, as did high Federalists like the Warrens, he was, as he wrote Jefferson himself in 1805, "a moderate man, or a lukewarm federalist." He was therefore "excluded from the solemn feasts and *clamorations* of the outrageous party men," but he continued to vote the Federalist party ticket. As late as January, 1807, he could still write in a letter about the

"Democrats" and "their vile party purposes."[23]

Even in 1809 the Boston Republicans by no means regarded Waterhouse as their man. When Jefferson named him physician to the Marine Hospital in Charlestown in November, 1807, as a reward for his efforts to promote vaccination, the *Columbian Centinel*, leading organ of New England Federalism, expressed gratification at the appointment; it was the disappointed local Republicans who complained.[24] Waterhouse took up his duties with vigor. He improved the hospital buildings and grounds, instituted several beneficial changes in the regulations, started an out-patient service, and gave clinical instruction to a number of students. He also appointed his wife directress to the hospital, with the result, so he claimed, that it was managed better than ever before and at less expense.

Unfortunately, not all his actions appeared in quite so favorable a light to the authorities in Washington. After Madison succeeded Jefferson as President in 1809, Waterhouse's enemies—including William Eustis of Boston, a physician, Republican, and more especially Madison's first Secretary of War—returned to the attack. By this time Waterhouse had apparently forsworn Federalism: at least he received a testimonial letter from Massachusetts' leading Republican, Elbridge Gerry, that he was a friend of the administration, as well as other letters from physicians supporting his professional ability. Nevertheless, he was forced to acknowledge some of the charges brought against him. In Madison's opinion, these rendered it "inconsistent with the general principles, proper to be maintained by the Government, to permit him to remain in his present station. . . ." Madison offered Waterhouse an opportunity to resign, but he refused to take it. Thereupon, in July, 1809, he was removed from office. "Without enter-

---

[22] Waterhouse to Dr. James Tilton, Mar. 24, 1815, in Massachusetts Historical Society, *Proceedings* (for 1920–21), **54**:160–61, 1922.

[23] Waterhouse to Jefferson, Apr. 7, 1805, Jefferson Papers, Library of Congress; Waterhouse to Dr. Bartlett; Jan. 30, 1807, MS. in Massachusetts Historical Society; Blake, *op. cit.*, p. 66.

[24] *Columbian Centinel*, Dec. 12, 1807; Feb. 17, 1808.

ing into other details," explained the Secretary of the Treasury, forwarding the President's decision, "I will only state that his having supplied his own family with provisions which have been charged to the Hospital, and his having allowed compensation to his wife under another than her present name, rendered it impracticable to continue him in the public service."[25]

How far this dismissal was due to factional political opposition within the Republican party (it is hard to imagine that Federalist politicians' views could have had much weight with Madison), how far to professional jealousies and animosities stemming from Waterhouse's personality and his efforts at monopoly, and how far to his misdeeds at this post, is impossible at this point to say with assurance. It is certain, however, that it did not raise his standing with the Harvard Corporation. Already distressed by the appointment of Peck as Professor of Natural History in 1805, Waterhouse saw to his dismay the election of Professor Samuel Webber, with whom he had already had at least one run-in,[26] as president of the university in 1806. In 1807 the Corporation appointed Webber and Judge John Davis a committee to investigate the state of the mineralogical cabinet. They professed themselves unable to find many items but received only an indignant reply from the keeper. In April, 1809, after Peck returned from abroad, the Corporation withdrew Waterhouse's authority to present his lectures on natural history. In October, alerted by reports that Waterhouse had been ousted from his Marine Hospital post "on charges said to affect his moral character," the Corporation discharged him from further care of

the mineralogical cabinet and turned the keys over to the librarian. Thereupon, as he had earlier threatened, Waterhouse inaugurated a series of public lectures on natural history in Boston in December, 1810, and the following July he reissued in book form his previously published essays on botany. Public self-justification was undoubtedly his primary purpose.[27]

In *The Botanist* Waterhouse pointed out that natural history comprehended not mere description and classification, but the processes of living organisms. "There appears to be as much difference," he explained, "between the nomenclator of a museum of natural bodies, and a natural historian, . . . as there is between the mere anatomist, or dissector of the human body, and its physiologist."[28] This obvious allusion to John Warren, the professor of anatomy, was both pointed and timely, for their feud was rapidly coming to a head.

The immediate origins of the final break arose from the removal of the medical school from Cambridge to Boston. Since its establishment, the necessity of traveling to Cambridge to give lectures had been a burden to Warren and Dexter, both of whom lived and practiced in Boston. With the appointment of John Warren's son, John Collins Warren, as adjunct Professor of Anatomy in 1808, and of John Gorham as adjunct Professor of Chemistry in 1809, the proportion of professors in Boston rose to four to one. There were, however, more important considerations than personal convenience. Cambridge was a small town completely lacking in the clinical facilities essential for a first-class medical school, even by the lax American standards of that day. As a result, Harvard's medical institution was still small and backward. From 1788, when the first M.B. was granted, through 1810, the university conferred only 51 medical degrees in course, and many of the most promising young men from Boston were going to Philadelphia for

[25] Waterhouse to Benjamin Lincoln, Collector of Customs at Boston, June 29, 1808, Records of the Bureau of Customs, Boston Collector, Letters from the Treasury, Collectors, etc., 1789–1818, 1: no. 20, National Archives, Record Group 36; Gallatin to Henry Dearborn, Collector of Customs at Boston, June 30, 1809, *ibid.*, no. 58; Gallatin to Dearborn, July 18, 1809, *ibid.*, no. 67; Waterhouse to Jefferson, June 21, 1809, Jefferson Papers, Library of Congress; Waterhouse to General Varnum, May 8, 1813, in *Military Surgeon*, 63:68–75, 1928; John W. Trask, *The United States Marine Hospital, Port of Boston* (n.p., 1940), pp. 25–26.

[26] Lane, *loc. cit.*, pp. 9–10.

[27] *Ibid.*, pp. 14–17; Harrington, *op. cit.*, 1:295–96; Pettigrew, *op. cit.*, 2:493; Cohen, *op. cit.*, pp. 105–6; Waterhouse, *Botanist*, v–viii.

[28] *Ibid.*, xiii.

their medical training.[29] Furthermore, it was becoming apparent that unless Harvard moved its school to Boston, others would set up a new institution there.

Influenced by these considerations, Warren and Dexter petitioned the Corporation —whether or not they told Waterhouse in advance is a matter of dispute—to transfer the school to Boston, and in July, 1810, the Corporation agreed. After securing permission to use the Boston almshouse for clinical teaching, the Corporation also appointed an intimate personal and professional friend of the Warrens, James Jackson, Professor of Clinical Medicine, and, despite Waterhouse's protests, the Overseers, after no little debate, concurred. Under considerable pressure Waterhouse reluctantly agreed to lecture in Boston, and the school opened there in December, 1810. The move was little to his liking, but it undoubtedly benefited the institution immeasurably.[30]

Waterhouse's belief that he was being unjustly persecuted soon led him into more active protest. In February, 1811, a group of physicians, including a preponderance of Republicans, petitioned the legislature to incorporate a Massachusetts College of Physicians with powers like those granted similar institutions in other states. Though the petition was somewhat vague, it was generally believed, probably correctly, that the petitioners' object was to set up not only a new medical society but also a new medical school, in rivalry with the existing institutions. Nevertheless, Waterhouse vigorously advocated their cause with his too often abusive pen. In the *New England Palladium* of April 23, 1811, appeared an article, almost surely by him, supporting the proposed College because it would "hold up Medicine to the public, and to posterity, not as a mere money getting trade, but a liberal profession worthy the respect and confidence of the

public . . . ." In the next issue this censure of existing institutions was answered by a writer who recalled the profession's philanthropic activities and then concluded: "All these things will be still more justly estimated when contrasted with the deeds of *agents* for the new College, such as a *liberal dispensation of Cow Pock matter—for a small fee; generous inoculation* of seamen,—when paid for by a merchant; and the *disinterested offer to vaccinate a hundred* individuals in two rich parishes—at the expense of a benevolent unknown."[31]

This struck home. Waterhouse exploded with a thinly veiled lampoon of Warren, accusing him of opposing the College because he feared it would diminish his profits, and of attempting to appropriate for his own profit a legislative grant to the Massachusetts Medical Society. Lest anyone miss the point, Waterhouse, so the story goes, walked down State Street newspaper in hand, pointing out the article to all he met.[32]

Finally, in November, 1811, the Warrens, Aaron Dexter, and James Jackson presented a letter to the President of the University charging that Waterhouse had "been engaged in the support of plans inimical to the interest of the medical Institution," that he had "been guilty of duplicity & want of veracity," and that he had "repeatedly published in the newspapers without his proper signature, suggestions and insinuations injurious to our characters & highly offensive to our feelings, & such as are designed to diminish our usefulness in the University." They could no longer, they concluded, hold further communication with him. The members of the Corporation seem to have considered the quarrel very thoroughly, and they gave Waterhouse every opportunity to speak in his own defense. He showed no signs of contrition or even a desire for accommodation. Rather, as the battle over the proposed College approached its climax, Waterhouse became increasingly abusive. He labeled the medical school "an establishment, which, as it is at present administered,

[29] Harvard University, *Quinquennial Catalogue of the Officers and Graduates 1636–1930* (Cambridge, 1930), pp. 851–52; Leonard K. Eaton, "Medicine in Philadelphia and Boston, 1805–1830," *Pennsylvania Magazine of History and Biography*, 75:66–70, 1951.

[30] Harrington, *op. cit.*, 1:296–305, 357–63; Pettigrew, *op. cit.*, 2:492–93.

[31] *New England Palladium*, Apr. 26, 1811.

[32] *Ibid.*, May 3, 1811; Morison, *op. cit.*, 223.

is one of the most nefarious and powerful engines in erecting a detestable aristocracy, and destroying the vital principles of republicanism," and his accusations against the Warrens became more strident than ever.[33] Charge brought countercharge, and once the argument descended to personalities the younger Warren could outpoint Waterhouse every time. It was hardly an overstatement to decide, as the Corporation did in May, 1812, that harmony and confidence among the medical professors had been destroyed. Finding the charges preferred against Waterhouse true, the Corporation voted that he "be & he hereby is removed" from the Hersey Professorship of the Theory and Practice of Physic.[34]

Setting himself up as the victim of Federalist persecution, Waterhouse now plunged more deeply into political affairs. Beginning in October, 1812, he published a series of some 45 political articles in the *Boston Patriot* over the signature "Independent Whig." Besides giving vent to his feelings, this work also offered more tangible rewards. Waterhouse's income from private practice was never large, and the Republicans valued his ready pen. Soon he was pulling wires to get a new job. At Waterhouse's behest, John Adams, who had also forsworn allegiance to Federalism, late in 1812 wrote Benjamin Rush, the famous Philadelphia physician, asking, "Can nothing be done to save an amiable Family and a Man of first rate Merit from oppression, from becoming a sacrifice to Tory Vengeance, and professional envy?" "I feel for Dr. Waterhouse," Rush replied. ". . . Can nothing be done for him at Washington? He would make an excellent purveyor to a military hospital." Rush also offered to "second and support a recommendation from his friends in and near Boston for a situation in the marine and military hospitals which shall not separate him from his family. The cause of his dismission from office by Mr. Madison must be noticed in his recommendation," he added, "and its falsehood exposed if possible."[35]

Though Waterhouse at first sought only reinstatement at the Marine Hospital, he soon began to look higher. When Rush died on April 19, 1813, Waterhouse hoped to get his position as Treasurer of the United States Mint, but the appointment of James Rush, Benjamin's son, forestalled this possibility. He then put in his bid for a berth as Physician General to the United States Armies, enclosing an endorsement of his "abilities, learning, professional knowledge & integrity . . . and also of his steady attachment to the cause of his country," signed by leading local Republicans.[36] The administration was not willing to go that high, but finally, at the end of June, 1813, awarded Waterhouse a commission as Hospital Surgeon. "Although it falls short," he replied to the Secretary of War, "of the place my friends had flattered me with, I hesitate not to announce to you my acceptance of it."[37]

This being wartime, the number of openings in the military service was relatively large. After the Treaty of Ghent was signed, however, a reduction in force appeared in-

[33] *An Answer to a Letter Addressed to a Republican Member of the House of Representatives of the State of Massachusetts, on the Subject of a Petition for a New Incorporation, to Be Entitled the College of Physicians* (Boston, 1812). The quotation is on pp. 3–4. If not the author, Waterhouse at least aided in the distribution of this pamphlet; see copy in John Jeffries Papers, Houghton Library, Harvard University.

[34] Harrington, *op. cit.*, 1:379–90; Lane, *loc. cit.*, pp. 17–21; Edward Warren, *The Life of John Collins Warren, M.D.* (Boston, 1860), 1:102–7. For J. C. Warren's rejoinders, see *A Letter Addressed to a Republican Member of the House of Representatives of the State of Massachusetts on the Subject of a Petition for a New Incorporation, to Be Entitled "A College of Physicians"* (Boston, 1812, copy in National Library of Medicine); *Reply to a Pamphlet Purporting to Be an Answer to a Letter Addressed to a Republican Member of the House of Representatives on the Subject of a Petition for a New Incorporation, to Be Entitled a College of Physicians* (Boston, 1812, copy in Jeffries Papers, Harvard).

[35] Adams to Rush, Dec. 21, 1812, in *Old Family Letters: Copied from the Originals for Alexander Biddle. Series A* (Philadelphia, 1892), pp. 325–326; Rush to Adams, Jan. 8 and Jan. 22, 1813, in L. H. Butterfield, ed., *Letters of Benjamin Rush* (Princeton, 1951), 2:1175, 1177.

[36] Rush to Adams, Feb. 15, 1813, *ibid.*, 2:1183–84; Rush to Waterhouse, Feb. 15, 1813, in Waterhouse Papers, Harvard Medical School Library; Adams to Waterhouse, May 9, 1813, in Ford, *op. cit.*, pp. 99–100; Waterhouse to General Varnum, May 8, 1813, *Military Surgeon*, 63:68–75, 1928.

[37] Letter dated July 6, 1813, Letters Received, Records of the Adjutant General's Office, U. S. Army, National Archives, Record Group 94 (hereafter cited AGO Records, NA).

evitable. Anxious to be retained, Waterhouse at this juncture sent Dr. James Tilton, the army's Surgeon General, his views on the necessity of maintaining at least part of the medical department built up during the conflict. Young men, he noted, could easily return to practice, but as for himself, "I cannot live out of the public employ. I am completely thrown upon them, like a pauper on the parish, & if they do not retain me, I & mine must perish, for I might beg in vain in the federal town of Boston. . . ."[38] A month later Waterhouse sent Tilton another long letter outlining his career, his contributions as a writer, and his sacrifices to the cause of Republicanism. He asked for a job as medical superintendent of the New England military districts with headquarters at Charlestown. "My wish is to be retained in the service in my old residence," he wrote, "and to be so situated and circumstanced as to be able to serve my country as a medical man, and *with my pen as a literary one*."[39] Powerful friends came to his support. On June 17, 1815, Messrs. Thomas Rowe and Joshua Hooper, Jr., publishers of the Boston *Yankee*, wrote to the Adjutant and Inspector General of the Army urging the retention of Waterhouse at his current location. "Since that formidable champion, 'OLD SOUTH,' retired a conqueror from the political lists," they avowed, "no writer has wielded the pen more forcibly or indefatigably than this gentleman—to whose talents *all* the republican papers in this vicinity are highly and continually indebted."[40] For services rendered, Waterhouse was kept on: "When the army was reduced to the peace establishment, the Board of officers, acting according to certain military principles, left me out; but President Madison took his pen and put me in again." By special direction of the Secretary of War, Waterhouse was permitted to reside at his home in Cambridge. The appointment was purely politi-

cal. Forced to importune again in 1821 at the age of 67 when the army was further reduced, Waterhouse admitted, in a letter endorsed "Confidential," "I expected the board would have acted as they did; for I never was in the actual service of the Army."[41] This time, however, President Monroe let him go.[42]

Since leaving Harvard, so he wrote Adams, Waterhouse had scarcely looked into a medical book.[43] As the years passed by, he devoted himself primarily to literary pursuits. In addition to newspaper articles and a diary filled with acid comments on men and events, he edited *A Journal of a Young Man of Massachusetts* (Boston, 1816), which was originally written by a ship's surgeon captured by the British during the War of 1812. Much more extensive was Waterhouse's 449-page work, *An Essay on Junius and His Letters* (Boston, 1831), a volume of political history and reflections seeking to prove that the author of the famous letters of Junius was the great William Pitt. His final endeavor was again an editorial one: from notes and other information supplied by John B. Wyeth he drew up *Oregon; or a Short History of a Long Journey from the Atlantic Ocean to the Region of the Pacific, by Land* (Cambridge, 1833), a stirring story of western travel despite Waterhouse's moralizing additions. It was, except for possible newspaper items, Waterhouse's last publica-

---

[38] Letter dated Feb. 25, 1815, Letters Received, AGO Records, NA.

[39] Letter dated Mar. 24, 1815, Massachusetts Historical Society, *Proceedings* (for 1920–21), 54:159–65, 1922.

[40] File no. 9705, Letters Received, AGO Records, NA.

[41] Waterhouse to Adams, June 4, 1821, in Ford, *op. cit.*, pp. 158–162; Waterhouse to Surgeon General Joseph Lovell, May 23, 1818, Personal Papers, Medical Officers and Physicians, AGO Records, NA; Waterhouse to Lovell, Oct. 18, 1820, Letters Received, AGO Records, NA; Lovell to Waterhouse, Oct. 26, 1820, Letters and Endorsements Sent, Records of the Surgeon General's Office, U.S. Army, National Archives, Record Group 112 (hereafter cited SGO Records, NA).

[42] Throughout his army career Waterhouse lived at home. He was appointed Hospital Surgeon, 1st Military District, June 29, 1813, and discharged on Apr. 14, 1818, with all other Hospital Surgeons, as a result of a new act of Congress regulating the Medical Department. Four days later he was appointed Post Surgeon and in September received duty as medical officer at Charlestown arsenal, later moved to Watertown. He was honorably discharged June 1, 1821. Register of Medical Officers, and List of Officers in the Medical Department 1775–1892, both in SGO Records, NA. His original commissions are in the Waterhouse Papers, Harvard Medical School Library.

[43] Letter dated June 13, 1821, Ford, *op. cit.*, p. 164.

tion.[44] But he retained an ability to enjoy novelties almost to the last, noting in his journal at the age of 85, "Went to see for the first time the giraffe, and relished the sight of that rare animal not a little."[45] On October 2, 1846, just 2 weeks before the first public demonstration of ether anesthesia in the Massachusetts General Hospital, Benjamin Waterhouse died.

As a medical man, Waterhouse is known chiefly for his role in the introduction of vaccination, and it was here that he showed most clearly not only his virtues but also his faults. For one thing he praised himself far more than his achievements deserved. More important, his efforts to profit from monopolistic control of a medical innovation were hardly in keeping with the ethical concepts of the medical profession, then or now, or with his own pretensions to philanthropy. Moreover, he was in fact a promoter rather than an originator. Waterhouse became a skilled practitioner and a zealous advocate of vaccination, but he contributed nothing new to its techniques. This in general was characteristic of his scientific career.

He did not always lend his support as wisely as in the case of Jenner. On March 30, 1813, for example, he penned a testimonial for John P. Whitwell's "Volatile aromatic Head-ache snuff," which the proprietor happily printed in handbills and newspaper advertisements for years to come.[46] Later he steadily supported Samuel Thomson, founder of the medical sect that bore his name, partly because the Massachusetts Medical Society, which "persecuted" Waterhouse, also "persecuted" Thomson;[47] similarly, Waterhouse aided Dr. John S. Bartlett when the latter became embroiled with the Society in the 1830's.

These events occurred late in Water-

house's career. But in 1783, at a meeting of the American Academy of Arts and Sciences, he had called for works on the history of epidemics,[48] yet he produced little on the subject himself. In an address of 1791 on *The Rise, Progress, and Present State of Medicine* (Boston, 1792), he urged the members of the Middlesex Medical Association to "leave the flowery path of speculation for the more arduous one of experiment."[49] This he did himself, as did many others, when he tested the efficacy of vaccination, but he experimented, in the scientific sense, on little else.

Outside of his writings on smallpox, his only publications of clinical interest were his *Cautions to Young Persons Concerning Health* (Cambridge, 1805), a minor *Circular Letter* (n.p., 1817) on dysentery addressed to the surgeons under his command, and *An Essay Concerning Tussis Convulsiva, or, Whooping-cough* (Boston, 1822), a diffuse work of 152 pages written chiefly, it would appear, because Waterhouse had just had the disease himself. Despite an ample display of book learning the volume shows little sign of original observation beyond the author's own case. As here presented, Waterhouse's own ideas are little more than vague speculation. Very self-revelatory is his prefatory apology: "I have only the apprehension, which is, that in transcribing from lectures composed, and compiled twenty and thirty years ago, I may, sometimes, have used the words of another without being conscious of it."[50]

In his own day, Waterhouse's most popular work was his *Cautions to Young Persons Concerning Health*, which went through at least five editions, including three in Europe. Written at the height of his career, it may be taken as a fair sample of his medical ideas. Chronic diseases, including depraved appetite, nervous disorders, gout, asthma,

[44] Viets, *loc. cit.* (note 5), pp. 605–22.

[45] W. R. Thayer, "Extracts from the Journal of Benjamin Waterhouse," Cambridge Historical Society, *Publications*, 4:33, 1909.

[46] There are several examples in the Waterhouse Papers, Harvard Medical School Library.

[47] Waterhouse, Letters on Samuel Thomson, *Bulletin of the Lloyd Library of Botany, Pharmacy and Materia Medica*, 1909, No. 11 (Reproduction Series, No. 7), pp. 56–63.

[48] Waterhouse, *Of Epidemic Diseases Being a Proposal to Collect the History of All the Epidemics of Our Country in Order, as They Arise, or an Attempt towards Filling Up That Capital Desideratum So. Earnestly Recommended by Sydenham* (Cambridge, 1942).

[49] p. 30.

[50] p. [iv].

palsy, apoplexy, dropsies, and cachexia, were all, he wrote, "owing to *chronic weakness;* the source of which is an imbecility of the digestive organs, occasioning errors in 'the first concoction,' which deranges the whole chain of processes, occurring between chylification and sanguification." The earliest derangement of health, Waterhouse continued, the earliest intimation of chronic disorder, was almost always noted as a sinking feeling in the stomach; first came weakened contractility, and then in order listlessness, paleness, irregular sweats, poor digestion, nausea, torpor, hollowness of the eyes, universal debility and increased irritability, a quickened pulse, labored breath, and finally cough and consumption. A troubled mind caused chronic disease, the author averred, because its first effect was deprivation of the powers of digestion; an indolent life, because without exercise old humors passed off too slowly and the appetite became sluggish; and intemperance, because it involved the application of stimulants and narcotics to the stomach. On this basis Waterhouse inveighed against the greatly increased consumption of wine and spirits at Harvard, in place of old-fashioned cider. But he reserved his strongest words for a counterblast against tobacco worthy of James I: "I have been a Professor in this University twenty three years, and can say, as a physician, that I never observed so many palid faces, and so many marks of declining health; nor ever knew so many hectical habits and con-

sumptive affections, as of late years; and I trace this alarming inroad on your young constitutions principally to the pernicious custom of *smoking* CIGARRS." Thirty years later Waterhouse was still supporting the same dogma.[51]

Similar criticism may also be levied against Waterhouse's work in natural history, which is, after vaccination, his chief claim to fame. Waterhouse's delight, he once indicated to Lettsom, was "transcribing from the great volume of Nature"[52] but his major work in natural history, *The Botanist* (Boston, 1811), shows little evidence that he had. It was largely theoretical speculation and derivative systematizing, written for the general public and designed, as Waterhouse acknowledged apologetically to Lettsom, "to create a taste for that pleasing study, and hence its popular dress and style."[53] At a time when many American botanists were making valuable contributions by describing some of the many new species to be found in this country, Waterhouse added nothing to the fund of scientific botanical knowledge.

At his best, Waterhouse was an active popularizer and promoter, of interest in natural history at Harvard, and of the practice of vaccination throughout the land.

[51] *Cautions* (1805), 8, 27; Waterhouse to Samuel Thomson, Dec. 8, 1835, *loc. cit.* (note 47), 58.

[52] Letter dated Nov. 25, 1794, Pettigrew, *op. cit.*, 2:494.

[53] Letter dated July 19, 1811, *ibid.*, 2:495.

ORATIO INAUGURALIS

George Gifford

ON October 7, 1783, the three recently appointed professors of the medical department of Harvard College were inducted into office in the Cambridge meeting house before the highest civil authorities of the Commonwealth: John Hancock, the governor; the clergy; college professors; and the general public. The inductees were Dr. John Warren, Professor of Anatomy and Surgery, Dr. Benjamin Waterhouse, Professor of the Theory and Practice of Physic, and Dr. Aaron Dexter, Professor of Chemistry. Drs. Warren and Waterhouse were installed together — Professor Dexter was not present. Both Warren and Waterhouse delivered Latin orations. Waterhouse's was not published until 1829 and when it appeared, some commented that it was not in "New England Latin." Waterhouse commented, "The day was brilliant, and the night more so for the college buildings were illuminated, together with several others."

Why should this antiquarian relic of 18th century prose in ornate Latin even be translated and read 187 years later? Certainly, the answers to the many problems confronting medicine and the social turmoil will not be found or even suggested here. History does not determine judgment, it carries no specific instruction, and it is not a testament. It does, however, offer the point of departure from which we may set out on the adventure of judgment. Those interested in history seek in it some illumination of the present and some foresight of the future.

Waterhouse's inaugural oration does not hold the plans for the future of medicine as did *A Discourse upon the Institution of Medical Schools in America*, read by John Morgan, May 30, 31, 1765, at the founding of the first medical school in the United States in Philadelphia. Yet it is strangely relevant to some issues today, such as the need for a scientific study of diseases of the mind and the effects of war on medicine.

In June, when the tents are pitched, the examinations over, and the rhetoric begins, perhaps again,

ORATIO INAUGURALIS

by GEORGE E. GIFFORD, JR., M.A., M.D.

"The day will be brilliant" and these words of Waterhouse will serve as both a solace and a touchstone.

AT this special dignified occasion, as a friend of teaching in this Harvard School of Medicine, now with my other comrades on this same faculty, I am settled in the solemn ceremony, and before we have made a good beginning of our duty, my role is to speak greetings according to the custom and to pay indebted thanks.

Therefore, firstly to you under whose direction not only the Academy (college), but our whole republic of Massachusetts prospers! A most esteemed man, a commander, full of important duties, eminent in excellence most illustrious! You are always to be honored by me, our countrymen, and our descendents, through all of the federated provinces, because of the greatest favors placed in this University, while the war was raging and freedom was endangered!

You, too, exceptional guardians, generous patrons of this School of Cambridge, for whom the reason of our highest respect must be attested by me, because, while it was our responsibility, it seemed to us to enrich the College with our learning, I greet you.

And you, most adorned, most learned protector! Most burdened with duty, O noble brilliance of knowledge! Always to be honored as the light of our College!

You too, most renowned professors, and most dear to the College!

And you, most holy translators of the Divine Word! Most of all to be respected!

And you, most excellent circle of devoted youth! The hope of our country! Our concern and love, greetings!

Finally to all of you, seated in rows and lines, O most human audience, I wish you well.

As soon as the citizens of the Republic of Holland, with the highest excellence and with extreme toil, made a claim upon their own very great power for themselves, they took care right away to equip medical schools; indeed they decided most correctly, scarcely could Holland (with any diligence) bring to its people anything so advantageous or of greater fame than well-established medical arts.

By no means, is it difficult out of concern to understand, when war is interrupted, how a people for these reasons may be driven into war from that first place into the place in which you live. Hence that most prudent state of Holland in our generation, with their affairs completed, thought that medical schools should be established, among other things. Then, indeed, with all their energies to direct a course into literary matters; and when labor was given that Knowledge, excellence, but especially the true reverence of God, might prosper through the whole state, it struggled to bring a great deal of information for the sake of these things; that these longed for benefits, and this hope might come to the aid of the laboring Republic.

If these things and similar things of Holland should be lauded, then in reality we Americans must have attained a greater praise: destitution, the drawn sword, and death itself, the things associated with war, pressing hard into our severe affairs, until now prowled about in this war too; with the enemy without, and the traitor within our wrestling defenses; with alliance relaxed and scarcely unbound; with hope only remaining! And, I say, with so many evils pressing hard upon us, with so many

Man in a Green Coat by Gilbert Stuart

Although the subject of this portrait has never been convincingly identified, Charles M. Mount, in his biography of Stuart, conjectures that it is the artist's close friend, Benjamin Waterhouse. The Metropolitan Museum of Art Bequest of Mary Stillman Harkness, 1950.

shadows, and with gloom gathered around us everywhere, either to turn our attention to matters of this kind or to offer the opportunity of fostering honorable sciences (it is more than could be hoped for) surpasses easily all models. But in the midst of turmoil, with no peace, and no repose, the academies, the societies of learned men, have been established among us! To this end amidst awful disasters some hope of restoring sciences shone on, and the School of Medicine raised its head under your direction.

There is little doubt that these deeds of this age will go handed down to our memory for a long time. Writers cannot but marvel at those men who, just as of old in the time of Nehemia, the Hebrew, with the one hand performed their religious duties and with the other grasped the sword. Thus moved neither by the insults nor the weapons of their enemies, they applied themselves to the task of reviving letters as well as of restoring the Republic.

The Medical School is indeed a very powerful defense against the ravages of all nations; when discord was shaking the foundations of our world, although you did not establish it (the Medical School), you supported it in thought. For who is present, who of these young men especially those in the prime of their lives, to whom our misfortunes do not come into memory? Who was not a participant of these same things? But now no violent charge! The matter is safe! The whole world is enjoying peace! Then, all nations, lift up your applause! Shouting out in rejoicing voice to God; surely it calms wars even to the ends of our earth! Yet the triumphal arch is shattered! The spear is mutilated! That Omnipotent God smashes the tyrranical sceptre! Peace rules! The earth rejoices! Immediately desert places and wilderness grow green

again! The lonely place will become crowded! Not for us — not for us, O esteemed listeners! But to him who shakes the quarters of the summit of Heaven with thunder, must praise be given for this peace, this kind of leisure, and so many benefits, and most precious freedom, for eternity, may it be so! The praise of strength must be given, I say, to Him alone!

It is for our learning to preserve the whole man, to make the weak strong, to restore the dying, if possible, and to lengthen life. As great as is the work, so many are the instruments.

Anatomy, chemistry, the knowledge of herbs, and the investigation of remedies, through every course of searching, tend towards the medical practice, concerning which we act. When therefore it is of such power and covers so great a field, I beg you in the name of common humanity to lend me a willing ear while I discourse briefly on the art of medicine.

That medicine was established in most ancient times by trial alone, reason both teaches and will stand over anything of the art of inquiry; presently the truth concerning the theoretical will be considered, and concerning the reason of remedies, as they say, through conferences and debates. Besides, it cannot be denied but that the first part, the empirical statements, are undoubtedly most certain; for in the same matters, there is the same trial. From this source come the writings of Hippocrates, the books of Galenus and Celsius and related things of other ancient physicians, especially those things embracing practical experience. It is very like the truth that has been conveyed to an enduring posterity.

Nevertheless the diligence of younger men weaves many things around the fabric of the body; until now a great deal lies hidden, and will lie hidden for a long time. Nonetheless, he who wanted to discuss with us the ancients in this art, when our anatomy, chemistry, surgery, botany, and physics are weighted carefully and when our new medicines are weighed, and with many of

13

the ancients cast down, either because of hideousness, or in using torments, we will voluntarily admit that they yield I know not how much.

There is nothing more useful, nothing more necessary to the human body, not so healthy as sick, correctly recognized and clearly set forth, than anatomy. This alone searches out diseases; when the abodes of disease are disclosed, although they may be hidden, it exposes the causes of diseases often into the light; hence the great usefulness of anatomy in the study of matters of the body and of suffering.

Who, I ask, best listeners! would ever have thought about the ruptures of the heart, unless it had been discovered in anatomical facts? who would have discovered the milky vessels, the sensitivity of the heart and other muscles, and the peristaltic movement of the intestines, if the application of anatomical facts had been absent? Hence it always remains, that the principle guidepost of medicine is anatomy.

Botany, too little investigated by the ancients, today is refined, so that there is no plant which cannot be easily recognized from certain characteristic marks, put there by the Creator.

Chemistry has not brought less utility to medicine. For, with its aid, hidden viruses in the body which were unknown before, have been disclosed; indeed most rigorous drugs, unknown to the ancients have fallen into the use of men; the whole pharmaceutical field has increased markedly. Therefore the doctor cannot be without a knowledge of chemistry, if he wants to avoid the most serious errors in administering remedies. They are avoided by this trouble! Since a mistake may be manifold, how frequent are false calculations! But this is not the place for telling them.

Nor assuredly could the motions of living creatures be exposed without the exact knowledge of physics. For who could understand how respiration occurs, if the nature of the air were unknown? How could sight be explained, if light were not un-

derstood or if the laws of its radiating were not examined? How could hearing be explained, if it were not supported first by pneumatics?

Indeed, there are single bodies of animals like machines which they call hydraulic, in which with great speed, different humors move in circles, with perpetual movement, a scarcely believable mass. On that account whatever has to do with mechanics and hydrostatics let it be joined in some way to the science of medicine. Where should we search for the precepts of these sciences with greater result than in this very Academy? In fact, I would like to pursue these to a greater extent; but very little time forbids. At another time, on this very lofty and most esteemed subject, I will willingly digress.

As Cicero said, "Men approach more closely to God in no way than in the giving of health to men." So the father of Roman eloquence spoke with Justice. What is more human, what is more worthy for a Christian man, than to bring aid to the feeble and to those afflicted and tormented by disease?

It is to be grieved indeed that that part of medicine which deals with the controlling of the mind, as far as it pertains to doctors, who are taken by the healing of the mind, up to now has been neglected and deserted so that it is almost wholly lost! Wherefore rise up, scholars! And when our conceptions and tests are collected for the common good, and if anything else is very useful, foster and adorn this medical philosophy! The worthiness of the argument bids, the growth of the art persuades, and finally love of the human race keeps it going, so that we may undertake that work!

And you, first among the first, most lofty perfect! You, O wise guardian, devoted to study! You, generous keepers of this Academy! You holy translators of the Divine Word! May all of you consider (nor do I doubt that you will) nothing more important, nothing nearer and dearer to your hearts and your honor than that this college of ours, from

which all wise men judge that extraordinary usefulness is brought to the whole American nation, and indeed to the state in which it is situated are brought honor, riches, and great good fortune, that this college, I say, may receive notable increase from day to day. To you it is granted, O fathers of your country, my supporters and friends, it is in your power to provide for the sciences. It is a source of glory for you that you have established this study, most necessary of all, indeed hitherto neglected amongst you, namely the study of medicine.

Academy of Cambridge! Now that I have been adopted by you, let me be permitted to address you as mother! Come! Proceed! O image of the rising sun, diffuse your light through the limits of our Republic! Never will it be advised by me but that through the benefit of these and future generations, and through the favor of Heaven, you have escaped so many more things; through your embrace you have lighted up all our lands! It is not the place for doubting your future fortune which you have tied to the Republic with a most strong bond.

O may almighty God in his infinite goodness, I pray, at this time when never before has the nation been beset by more peril, make our beloved country, the college, and our liberty, that unparalleled gift of Heaven and the sole support of the Republic, survive undefiled and inviolate and flourish forever.

The author wishes to express his thanks to Roger Scudder for his help with this translation.

There is a copy of Waterhouse's inaugural address, which the author presented to President Josiah Quincey in 1829, in the Rare Book Room, Countway Library. The address, which had been literally translated by Brooks Otis (A.B. 1929), and set freely into English by Reginald H. Fitz '09, was read at the 150th Anniversary Celebration of the Harvard Medical School, October 7, 1933, by Henry Asbury Christian, Hersey Professor of the Theory and Practice of Physic.

THREE CENTURIES
OF
SCIENCE IN AMERICA

An Arno Press Collection

Adams, John Quincy. **Report of the Secretary of State upon Weights and Measures.** 1821.

Archibald, Raymond Clare. **A Semicentennial History of the American Mathematical Society: 1888-1938** *and* **Semicentennial Addresses of the American Mathematical Society.** 2 vols. 1938.

Bond, William Cranch. **History and Description of the Astronomical Observatory of Harvard College** *and* **Results of Astronomical Observations Made at the Observatory of Harvard College.** 1856.

Bowditch, Henry Pickering. **The Life and Writings of Henry Pickering Bowditch.** 2 vols. 1980.

Bridgman, Percy Williams. **The Logic of Modern Physics.** 1927.

Bridgman, Percy Williams. **Philosophical Writings of Percy Williams Bridgman.** 1980.

Bridgman, Percy Williams. **Reflections of a Physicist.** 1955.

Bush, Vannevar. **Science the Endless Frontier.** 1955.

Cajori, Florian. **The Chequered Career of Ferdinand Rudolph Hassler.** 1929.

Cohen, I. Bernard, editor. **The Career of William Beaumont and the Reception of His Discovery.** 1980.

Cohen, I. Bernard, editor. **Benjamin Peirce: "Father of Pure Mathematics" in America.** 1980.

Cohen, I. Bernard, editor. **Aspects of Astronomy in America in the Nineteenth Century.** 1980.

Cohen, I. Bernard, editor. **Cotton Mather and American Science and Medicine: With Studies and Documents Concerning the Introduction of Inoculation or Variolation.** 2 vols. 1980.

Cohen, I. Bernard, editor. **The Life and Scientific Work of Othniel Charles Marsh.** 1980.

Cohen, I. Bernard, editor. The Life and the Scientific and Medical Career of Benjamin Waterhouse: With Some Account of the Introduction of Vaccination in America. 2 vols. 1980.

Cohen, I. Bernard, editor. Research and Technology. 1980.

Cohen, I. Bernard, editor. Thomas Jefferson and the Sciences. 1980.

Cooper, Thomas. Introductory Lecture and A Discourse on the Connexion Between Chemistry and Medicine. 2 vols. in one. 1812/1818.

Dalton, John Call. John Call Dalton on Experimental Method. 1980.

Darton, Nelson Horatio. Catalogue and Index of Contributions to North American Geology: 1732-1891. 1896.

Donnan, F[rederick] G[eorge] and Arthur Haas, editors. A Commentary on the Scientific Writings of J. Willard Gibbs and Duhem, Pierre. Josiah-Willard Gibbs: A Propos de la Publication de ses Mémoires Scientifiques. 3 vols. in two. 1936/1908.

Dupree, A[nderson] Hunter. Science in the Federal Government: A History of Policies and Activities to 1940. 1957.

Ellicott, Andrew. The Journal of Andrew Ellicott. 1803.

Fulton, John F. Harvey Cushing: A Biography. 1946.

Getman, Frederick H. The Life of Ira Remsen. 1940.

Goode, George Brown. The Smithsonian Institution 1846-1896: The History of its First Half Century. 1897.

Hale, George Ellery. National Academies and the Progress of Research. 1915.

Harding, T. Swann. Two Blades of Grass: A History of Scientific Development in the U.S. Department of Agriculture. 1947.

Hindle, Brooke. David Rittenhouse. 1964.

Hindle, Brooke, editor. The Scientific Writings of David Rittenhouse. 1980.

Holden, Edward S[ingleton]. Memorials of William Cranch Bond, Director of the Harvard College Observatory, 1840-1859, and of his Son, George Phillips Bond, Director of the Harvard College Observatory, 1859-1865. 1897.

Howard, L[eland] O[sslan]. Fighting the Insects: The Story of an Entomologist, Telling the Life and Experiences of the Writer. 1933.

Jaffe, Bernard. Men of Science in America. 1958.

Karpinski, Louis C. Bibliography of Mathematical Works Printed in America through 1850. Reprinted with Supplement and Second Supplement. 1940/1945.

Loomis, Elias. **The Recent Progress of Astronomy: Especially in the United States.** 1851.

Merrill, Elmer D. **Index Rafinesquianus: The Plant Names Published by C.S. Rafinesque with Reductions, and a Consideration of his Methods, Objectives, and Attainments.** 1949.

Millikan, Robert A[ndrews]. **The Autobiography of Robert A. Millikan.** 1950.

Mitchel, O[rmsby] M[acKnight]. **The Planetary and Stellar Worlds: A Popular Exposition of the Great Discoveries and Theories of Modern Astronomy.** 1848.

Organisation for Economic Co-operation and Development. **Reviews of National Science Policy: United States.** 1968.

Packard, Alpheus S. **Lamarck: The Founder of Evolution; His Life and Work.** 1901.

Pupin, Michael. **From Immigrant to Inventor.** 1930.

Rhees, William J. **An Account of the Smithsonian Institution.** 1859.

Rhees, William J. **The Smithsonian Institution: Documents Relative to its History.** 2 vols. 1901.

Rhees, William J. **William J. Rhees on James Smithson.** 2 vols. in one. 1980.

Scott, William Berryman. **Some Memories of a Palaeontologist.** 1939.

Shryock, Richard H. **American Medical Research Past and Present.** 1947.

Shute, Michael, editor. **The Scientific Work of John Winthrop.** 1980.

Silliman, Benjamin. **A Journal of Travels in England, Holland, and Scotland, and of Two Passages over the Atlantic in the Years 1805 and 1806.** 2 vols. 1812.

Silliman, Benjamin. **A Visit to Europe in 1851.** 2 vols. 1856

Silliman, Benjamin, Jr. **First Principles of Chemistry.** 1864.

Smith, David Eugene and Jekuthiel Ginsburg. **A History of Mathematics in America before 1900.** 1934.

Smith, Edgar Fahs. **James Cutbush: An American Chemist.** 1919.

Smith, Edgar Fahs. **James Woodhouse: A Pioneer in Chemistry, 1770-1809.** 1918.

Smith, Edgar Fahs. **The Life of Robert Hare: An American Chemist (1781-1858).** 1917.

Smith, Edgar Fahs. **Priestley in America: 1794-1804.** 1920.

Sopka, Katherine. **Quantum Physics in America: 1920-1935** (Doctoral Dissertation, Harvard University, 1976). 1980.

Steelman, John R[ay]. **Science and Public Policy: A Report to the President.** 1947.

Stewart, Irvin. **Organizing Scientific Research for War: The Administrative History of the Office of Scientifc Research and Development.** 1948.

Stigler, Stephen M., editor. **American Contributions to Mathematical Statistics in the Nineteenth Century.** 2 vols. 1980.

Trowbridge, John. **What is Electricity?** 1899.

True. Alfred. **Alfred True on Agricultural Experimentation and Research.** 1980.

True, F[rederick] W., editor. **The Semi-Centennial Anniversary of the National Academy of Sciences: 1863-1913** *and* **A History of the First Half-Century of the National Academy of Sciences: 1863-1913.** 2 vols. 1913.

Tyndall, John. **Lectures on Light: Delivered in the United States in 1872-73.** 1873.

U.S. House of Representatives. **Annual Report of the Board of Regents of the Smithsonian Institution...A Memorial of George Brown Goode together with a selection of his Papers on Museums and on the History of Science in America.** 1901.

U.S. National Resources Committee. **Research: A National Resource.** 3 vols. in one. 1938-1941.

U.S. Senate. **Testimony Before the Joint Commission to Consider the Present Organizations of the Signal Service, Geological Survey, Coast and Geodetic Survey, and the Hydrographic Office of the Navy Department.** 2 vols. 1866.

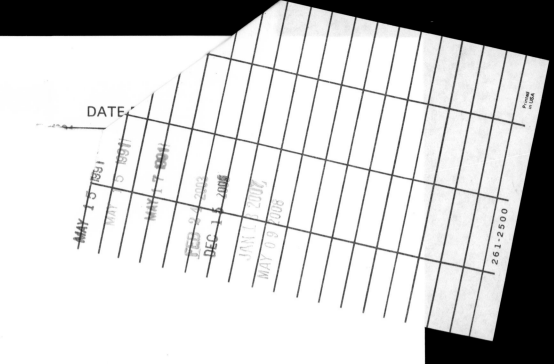